DATE DUE

Jan 18 '68			
Feb 8 '68			
GAYLORD			PRINTED IN U.S.A.

THE
WHITE ROSE
of STUART

The Story *of* 𝔉lora 𝔐acdonald,
Heroine *of* 𝔗he '45

By *LILLIAN DE LA TORRE*

THOMAS NELSON & SONS
Edinburgh   NEW YORK   Toronto

823.912
D37w

LIBRARY OF CONGRESS CATALOG CARD NUMBER: 54-9873
PRINTED IN THE UNITED STATES OF AMERICA

31,800
nov '54

To nine nice nieces

Marilyn
Lillian Barbara
Laura
Suzie
Mary Elena
Martha
Helen Lillian
Chiquita
and
Anna Lillian

Contents

Book One ❦ Young Flora

THE ROYAL ROSE

There is a flower in yon garden
  Smells sweeter than the thyme;
It is a bright and lovely flower,
  And I wish that flower were mine.

Oh! It's sweeter in December bleak
  Than any flower in May,
And it would be a sad pity
  That it should e'er decay.

He is a rose, a royal rose,
  With a blue and rolling eye;
The White Rose of Stuart
  I'll wear until I die.

                          (OLD SONG)

CHAPTER I ❧ *The Girl in the Tower*

THE TRUE STORY of FLORA
MACDONALD, *now imprisoned in the* TOWER *of
London, and soon to answer a Charge of* HIGH
TREASON.

Told by HERSELF without Deceit.

DECEMBER, 1746.

FLORA MACDONALD was born in the Isle of South Uist,
among the Outer Hebrides, the Western Islands of
Scotland. She is of the Family and Clan of MACDONALD
of CLANRANALD, Kin to the Present CHIEF, and to that
CAPTAIN of Clanranald who in the YEAR '15 fell at
Sheriffmuir for our rightful Sovereign, KING JAMES
(now in Exile).

How then could she do less than she did for his gallant Son, our Prince, bonnie PRINCE CHARLIE? . . .

The girl in the Tower put down her pen. This would
never do. It was adding treason to treason. With this
paper alone the minions of the usurping King, George II,
could condemn her.

A smile touched the edge of her mouth, as she pictured
the look on the great ones when they should hear such a

defence: "I did it for the King over the water." Their great woolly periwigs would fly right off their bald heads! Far better to say nothing at all.

Letting her quill pen dangle, she leaned her head against the thick stone wall beside her narrow barred window and gazed outward. Gray December clouds raced low over the city, almost seeming to touch the scowling roofs of the old prison. Below her window on the greensward, full of silly self-importance, stalked a huge, ink-black raven. He seemed to cock a beady eye at the girl in the window, almost like the pert gallants who often came to stare at the prisoners.

The raven, a canty old bird, seemed to enjoy the sight almost as much as the most impudent gallant. Flora Macdonald was slim and straight as a willow wand. Her lilac-flowered muslin gown was looped back from the full quilted petticoat. Above the heavy folds her slim body looked slimmer. She held her little self erect, as became a Highland lass, with pride in the Macdonald tartan plaid she wore, pinned at her shoulder with a round silver brooch. Her red-glinting chestnut hair, falling in curls, was bound with the blue ribbon snood of an unmarried Highland girl. Her violet-blue eyes were luminous and steady. In her smooth cheeks the clear crimson came and went.

"No beauty patch, no plume, no powder, no paint—how odd!" the black beady eye of the citified raven seemed to remark.

Flora cared nothing for the opinion of the raven. She hardly knew he was there. Her eye, fixed on the racing clouds, was looking back through time and space. Once more she saw the resolute young face, worn and bronzed. Once more she looked into the brilliant eyes. Once more the tears welled up, and blotted him from her sight.

Flora blinked back the tears angrily. Tears would not help her now. She must gather her wits to face her accusers.

She took up her pen, and began again:

FLORA MACDONALD *was born in the Isle of South Uist* . . .

CHAPTER 2 ❦ *The Child on the Island*

"Flora, how old are you?"
"Five, if you please, sir."
"Angus?"
"Nine, sir."
Side by side, Flora and her brother Angus stood straight and held their heads high, as they had been taught to do. Their young mother looked at them with approval. Flora was slim and dainty in her close-bodied blue homespun gown, with the blue ribbon snood tying back her bronze curls. Angus wore a full white shirt and a philibeg or little kilt of pleated wool in the green-red-and-black Clanranald tartan. Their slim feet were bare.

"What did you do today, Flora?"

The questioner was a visitor from the neighboring Isle of Skye. Big Hugh Macdonald was the mightiest of the Macdonald clan, now that Flora's grandfather, the Strong Minister, was dead. Flora liked Hugh, even if he had only one eye. With his friendly grin, he just looked as if he were winking at you.

"Please, sir, I spun thread with my distaff."

Proudly Flora showed him how she coaxed the wool fibers off the pointed end of her little spindle. She was too eager. She pulled too hard, and the fibers parted.

"Mend it, Flora," said her mother.

Flora pouted, but there was no escape.

"Never put off what is hard, or dangerous, or disagreeable," said her mother quietly. "Remember this motto: *Do what has to be done.*"

While Flora was trying to splice the parted fibers, it was Angus's turn to tell Hugh:

"I went to the rocks for lichen for my mother to dye the yarn."

"I'll wager that you looked for birds' eggs the while," remarked Hugh.

"Yes, sir, the gulls' eggs lie loose among the rocks. But I could not come at the nest of the sea swallow, for they drove me away."

"I went too. I saw cormorants diving for fish," said Flora, unwilling to be overlooked.

"I saw a whale spouting in the sea."

"I went to the mill, there were dragonflies over the millpond."

"The miller is all dusty like a moth," said Angus.

"That's why they call moths *millers*," explained Hugh.

"I found an eagle feather," said Angus.

He showed Hugh his bonnet, the round tam-shaped headgear that every Highlandman wore. Angus could wear an eagle feather in it, because he was related to the chief.

"Listen, listen, I saw a mother seal and a baby seal lying on the rocks," said Flora.

"Seals are people," said Angus darkly, "people under a weird spell."

"Did you see the Merry Dancers in the sky?" asked Hugh.

"No, sir." The northern lights came oftener in winter.

"Did you see the Blue Men in the sea?"

"Oh, no, sir, I'm afraid of the Blue Men."

"Did you see the green shee, the faery folk?"

"There's a faery hill by the loch, all round and poison-green," said Angus. "Flora better keep away from it."

"Why?"

"Because," said Hugh, "if you aren't careful, the green people will snatch you away into their home under the hill."

He began to tell a story about a girl who was snatched away by the shee. She went out one day alone, just to gather berries and hear the birds sing. Nobody knew what became of her. But one day—

> Late, late in the gloaming, when all was still,
> When the fringe was red on the westling hill,
> The wood was sere, the moon in the wane,
> The reek of the cot hung over the plain

Like a little wee cloud in the world alone;
When the ingle glowed with an eerie flame,
Late, late in the gloaming Kilmeny came home!

Kilmeny, Kilmeny, where have you been?
Long have we sought both holt and den;
By fall, by ford, and greenwood tree,
Yet you are halesome and fair to see,
Where got you that cloak of the lily sheen?
That bonnie snood of the birch so green?
And these roses, the fairest that ever were seen?
Kilmeny, Kilmeny, where have you been?

Kilmeny looked up with a lovely grace,
But no smile was seen on Kilmeny's face;
As still was her look, and as still was her eye,
As the stillness that lay on the emerald lea,
Or the mist that sleeps on a waveless sea.

When a month and a day had come and gone,
Kilmeny sought the greenwood lawn;
There laid her down on the leaves so green,
And Kilmeny on earth was never more seen.
It was not her home, and she could not remain,
She left this world of sorrow and pain—

"Hugh, don't fright the child!" cried her mother as Flora hid her face in the sheltering skirts.

"Well, well, Flora need not fear. The shee are afraid of cold iron—and see, what I brought you!"

It was a long pin to hold her little plaid scarf. She pinned it at her shoulder, and felt safe.

Big Hugh went to the door and looked out. The long gray summer twilight was waning.

"It's a long pull across to Skye. I'll be stepping."

"Why don't you stay here!" said Flora. Immediately she knew from the silence that she had said something important.

"Why don't I, Marian?" said Hugh softly to her mother.

"I've told you over and over, I'll not marry again. I'm Ranald Macdonald's widow. I have his children to care for and his work to see to."

"I could help you. The 'tack,' the lease of Milton, is a burden for one woman and a boy."

Flora's mother stood in the blue peat-fragrance of the fire and shook her head. She was dressed in the old style. Her plaid shawl or arisaid was of white with bright crossing lines, pinned on her bosom with a broad circle of silver and caught at the waist with a belt of silver-linked leather. Her hair hung down. Flora thought she looked beautiful. Big Hugh thought so too. But she would not say yes, and after a while he went away.

Hugh was hard to discourage. He kept coming back. Flora was glad when he came. He always brought her something—a pretty shell to hold her pins, a sweet sugar sucket to eat, a fresh snood—and he always gave her a big smile to go with it.

At last, one day in spring, he came without a smile. He had armed clansmen at his back. He talked angrily to her mother. Flora couldn't quite understand what he meant.

"I'll dangle no longer, Marian," said Hugh. "It is an old custom in these Isles, that he who cannot buy or beg a wife may steal her. So take up your plaid and come with me."

Flora's mother answered proudly; but Hugh's armed men were a strong argument, and she went at last, weeping. Flora thought the world had come to an end. The maids could not console her.

In a week Marian came back, smiling. She had new clothes, and a gold ring on her finger. After that Hugh lived at Milton. Flora approved of the new arrangement.

It was a happy life for a child at Milton. The thatched farmhouse was comfortable. It was made of stone to keep out the weather. The best room had a fireplace and a chimney, with furniture and hangings from the mainland. It was cozy on winter evenings by the fire, watching the bannocks bake on the hearth and smelling the meat roasting on the turning spit. When the wild winds blew, it was cozy in bed in the inner room. Flora's bed was built like a box, and closed up with doors like a little cupboard. In the long dark winter, it was the best place to be.

But Flora liked the summers best. Then you could go outdoors. You could hear the long musical roll of the waves on the beach, and smell the thyme and gorse and clover mingled with the salt tang of the sea. When you stepped out of the door, four lakes met your eye. The mountains rose behind you, tawny or purple with heather. On the downslopes lay the green machars or meadows, and beyond the meadows were the beaches and the sea. The sea was called the Atlantic. It stretched all the way to a new land called America.

If you went over the mountains, you came to more water and more islands, and at last, they told her, to the mainland of Scotland. Some day Flora would go there.

In summer, it was time to drive the cattle to the glens. Flora loved to go along. They would stay in the glen all summer. There were little summer huts called shielings to stay in, made of squares of sod and roofed with heather or bulrushes or fern. It was like camping out. You played by the mountain stream all day, while the goats and the black cattle ate the sweet young grass. The lasses would milk them, and make butter and cheese to eat with the oaten bannocks they baked on hot stones by the fire. Flora wished summer would last forever.

One day in summer, as Flora and Angus were sitting on the rocks above the shieling in the glen called Alisary, a strange boy came over the ridge. As he half-ran, half-slid down the rocky slope, Angus looked him over coolly.

He was a pleasant-looking boy, not much younger than Angus. He was tall and sturdy, with a curly mouth and a clever eye. He was bare-footed, clad only in shirt and phili-beg. A gun was slung over his shoulder.

When he came to rest, Angus spoke. This was his ground.

"What's your name?"

"Neil Maceachen Macdonald of Howbeg on Benbecula," said the newcomer glibly.

"Angus Macdonald of Milton," said Angus as glibly. "That's Flora," he added indifferently. "What are you doing in my glen?"

"I came over from *my* glen. Coradale, under Mount Hecla." He pointed back toward the mountains. "You can come over to Coradale any time you want. I know a secret way. You can come too," he added to Flora.

"Why?"

"Why? My life, but girls are silly! Coradale is the finest glen on Uist. When the day is fair you can look clear across to the Isle of Skye. And the plovers and the red deer—

and the eagle's nest that I know—and I have a secret cave where we can hide from the Norsemen!"

"Come on!" said Angus.

Coradale was the finest glen for hiding in all Uist. The cave was fine and deep and dry, and you could watch the whole countryside without being seen. It was wonderful for playing Scots and Norsemen. Of course Flora always had to be the Norsemen, but she was used to that.

Other times, Neil would come over the mountain to sit with them by the burn at Alisary and just talk about things. Neil had a quick mind and an observant eye. He and Flora found things to laugh about that merely puzzled solemn Angus. Like Flora, Neil was musical. He taught her songs to sing. There was a scary one about the Great Silkie Seal of Skule Skerrie. There was a funny one about an old battle:

> There's some say that we won,
>   Some say that they won,
> Some say that none won at all, man;
> But one thing I'm sure,
>   That at Sheriffmuir,
> A battle there was, which I saw, man!
> And *we* ran, and *they* ran,
> And *they* ran, and *we* ran,
> And *we* ran, and *they* ran away, man!

It was the English that ran away, Neil said. Flora was too young to understand it very well, but when they came to the part where everybody ran away, she laughed very hard indeed.

One day in June, Neil taught her a new fine song with a marching lilt:

The times are ill, but they will mend,
Be sure that sun will follow rain,
That German George's rule will end
And the King shall enjoy his own again.
Let every Scottish Jacobite
Fight for the right with might and main,
We'll put the English Whigs to flight,
And the King shall enjoy his own again!
Fa la la la, fa la la la . . .

"Neil."

"What, Flora?"

"Neil, what is a king?"

"The King is over everybody."

"Is he over Clanranald?"

"Of course he is. Everybody has to do what the King says, because God sent him to rule."

"Who is German George?"

"The King at London," said Angus.

"He's a usurper," said Neil.

"A what?"

"A usurper. He stole the crown and usurped the throne from the man who ought to be King."

"Who ought to be King?"

"James Stuart, God bless him, the King over the water. The English Whigs chased the Stuarts away, and got the German kings to reign instead. But you'll see, one day King James will come back with an army, and the loyal Scots will fight for him, and the King shall enjoy his own again."

"Neil, where is he now?"

"In Italy."

"Has he got any little boys?"

"He has a son called Prince Charles Edward, not very much older than you. After King James he'll be King."

"When I grow up," decided Flora, "I'm going to marry Prince Charles."

"You are *not*," said Angus.

"Why not? Neil, why can't I?"

"Because princes have to marry princesses."

"Oh," said Flora. She wished she were a princess.

"Fa la la la, fa la la la," sang the three children, "The King shall enjoy his own again!"

In the Tower of London, Flora Macdonald put down her quill, shaking her head and smiling. This was no memory to set down for the eyes of the judges of German George. "A rebel since childhood," they would call her, and condemn her all the faster. But the tune still ran in her head:

"The King shall enjoy his own again . . ."

CHAPTER 3 ❧ *The Lass at Nunton*

"FLORA MACDONALD is of the Family and Clan of MACDONALD of CLANRANALD, Kin to the present CHIEF . . ."

The girl sitting at the barred window nibbled her quill. How in the world could she make the whey-faced Whig, the cold-blooded Sassenach, understand what a Highland chief meant to his clan? She wished she could picture for them the first time she had seen Clanranald, for she had never forgotten it.

It was when he became the chief, in 1730. There was a great clan gathering. Angus had to go, young as he was, for even at twelve he was one of the principal men of the clan. Flora was only eight, but her mother took her along too.

At first it was all a confusion. The plain of Benbecula was a shimmer of bright tartans and blue bonnets, and in every blue bonnet was the clan badge, a sprig of heather. Sunlight glanced on weapons, dirk and claymore, gun and metal-studded leather shield. In the distance glittered the sea, and against it lifted the solemn gray ruins of the Castle of Borve. The women in their white and colored arisaids looked like a garden of flowers. The barefooted little boys darted about underfoot. Somewhere they were barbecuing whole oxen over great fires. The crisp smell filled the air. The clan sniffed the aroma and seethed with anticipation.

Then silence fell. The little boys stopped wrestling, and the little girls clung to their mothers' skirts. A trumpet sounded. The line of bagpipers struck up "Clanranald's Gathering." The folk parted, and between them walked their chief.

Ranald Macdonald of Clanranald was not a tall man. He did not have to be. He walked first, alone, and carried his handsome head with such pride that he topped his tallest follower. He was a tawny man, with wise, penetrating eyes and aristocratic fine features. He wore three eagle feathers in his blue bonnet. His belted plaid was of finest Macdonald tartan. The clan badge that held it at his shoulder, the crossbelt that supported the claymore at his side, his badger skin sporran, were all mounted with silver.

As he walked between his people, every blue bonnet came off. There was a great shout, "Gainsay who dare!" and the blue bonnets went flying in a cloud.

At his shoulder, their weapons rattling, came his henchmen, dressed in their best, with bonnet and clan badge, gun and sword and target. First among his followers walked his handsome younger brother, Alexander, looking both lofty and amused, and the red-haired small boy who was Clanranald's heir, striding manfully to keep up with his father and chief.

Behind them Flora saw her uncles and her cousins, and a crowd more of the principal men of Uist and Moidart.

All the while the great war pipes skirled and the people shouted. When the chief stood on a high place before them, they fell silent. An old man stepped forth. He spoke to the chief, and gave him a sword. Clanranald swung the naked sword high above his head, and once more the people shouted:

"God bless the chief, and us to his service!"

Then that part was done, and it was time to dine. Clanranald dined in state under a long pavilion thatched with heather. The clansmen sat down in their order, handing their ladies. The little boys foraged. Flora clung at her mother's skirt. Stepfather Hugh cut her off bites from the fat ribs, and she chewed them shyly.

New impressions crowded in upon the girl from Milton so thick and fast that it was lucky that the festivities lasted a whole week. Every morning the Macintyre pipers, hereditary pipers to Clanranald, paced back and forth before the big house sounding the great war pipes. Every afternoon the chief entertained his clansmen at a feast under the heather shelter. Every evening there was dancing in the pavilion.

The other chieftains of the Isles kept arriving to pay their compliments to the new chief. The plain shimmered with the blue and green of the proud Macneill of Barra, the yellow and black of Macleod of Raasay, the bright red of Macdonell of Keppoch. Sour Macleod of Macleod came from Dunvegan in full panoply, with his "tail" of followers complete, all splendid in their tartans, with the juniper badge of the clan in their bonnets of blue. There were his jest man, his strong man, his messenger, his baggage-bearer, his sword-bearer, his horse-leader, his bard or poet, his shanachie or historian, his pipe-bearer, and his piper. His piper was the greatest piper of the Isles, Donald Ban Macrimmon, of the famous piping family, who had a college of the pipes near Dunvegan.

Flora had never heard such piping. She could remember when as a small child, listening to the piper of the village, she had thought that the bagpipe was an animal. It had a tartan body—the bag, five spraddling legs—the stocs, a long neck with holes in it—the chanter, and a pain in its stomach that made it howl dolefully as the piper squeezed the breath out of it.

Now at Benbecula she heard the great war pipe blown by the masters of its music, Macrimmons of Macleod, Macarthurs of Sleat, Macintyres of Clanranald. All in a line they would pace the sward, backward and forward, their kilts rippling, the long pipe banners flying, to the noble shrill skirling of the pibroch. Flora wanted to march too, to cry, to shout aloud.

At night, in the long twilight, the pipes skirled a livelier measure, and the clansmen danced Highland reels, swinging the lasses and tossing them high in the air. Clanranald and his lady would lead off, somewhat more sedately, and the little boys would jig by themselves around the edges.

Flora had never seen so many little boys all at once. She lost count of her cousins; there seemed to be dozens. Lady Clanranald had a good half-dozen sons herself; the oldest, young Ranald of the red hair, was not much older than Flora. Angus, her brother, was twelve; Neil Maceachen and his brothers ranged from thirteen down. All Nunton seemed to be alive with boys, and more kept coming.

On one of those sparkling days, big Hugh Macdonald took Angus and Flora to the landing place at Rushness to welcome ashore his own chief, Sir Alexander Macdonald of Sleat, chief of all the Macdonalds of Skye. Sir Alexander arrived across the Minch from Skye in a great birlinn or rowing galley, with his clansmen singing at the oars. When the ship grounded on the sand offshore, it was the duty of Sir Alexander's strong men to bring his chief ashore on his shoulders. Even in that odd situation, the young chief looked elegant and dignified. As he shook hands with his clansman at the water's edge, Flora studied him. He was in his first youth, with a pale face, a long nose, and melancholy eyes. Just fresh from his college days at St. Andrews, he had modified his Highland dress with the touches of a young man of fashion. Instead of a kilt, he wore tartan trews, a kind of tight long trouser cut on the bias. On his feet he wore leather shoes, cut snug and buckled with silver. His short coat was trimmed with gold lace. On his head he wore a fashionable wig, with a great many tight curls. At first to Flora it looked real. She was surprised when later, one hot morning, she saw his own close-cropped hair.

When Hugh presented Flora, Sir Alexander lifted her in his arms and hugged her. Flora felt at once that she had a friend in this kinsman.

Other clansmen greeted her. She lost count of them, they were so many. She noticed Donald Roy Macdonald, because he was grown-up, redheaded, tall, and handsome, and because he tossed her high in the air. A boy in the crowd was smiling at her. He was no older than Angus, tall, graceful, and handsomely formed. His eyes were large, dark, and melting, with beautifully arched brows. His jet-black hair was tied with a ribbon at the neck. Flora thought him the handsomest boy she had ever seen. She smiled back. He came to her, took her hand, and deliberately kissed her cheek. The little girl turned red, and put her hands behind her. Thereupon this unaccountable boy bowed calmly and walked on, leaving Flora staring. It was her first meeting with Allan Macdonald.

Flora was finding everything new and wonderful. She was enchanted with Clanranald's mansion at Nunton. There was a great hall for dining, and parlors for withdrawing, and rows of bedrooms upstairs, all with fireplaces and chimneys, and floors and paneling of wood.

The crowd of clansmen had to sleep in the pavilions, wrapped in their plaids, but Flora's mother was a guest at Nunton, and Flora of course stayed with her. It seemed to her bliss enough just to be there and admire the beautiful things—china vases on marquetry tables in the parlors, furniture of mahogany or gilded wood, windows with crown glass in them and French damask draperies hanging before them.

Most of all she admired the great hall. Neil displayed it to her as if he owned it, for Clanranald had taken a great fancy to the clever little boy, and Neil was living at Nunton. Flora stared at the chief's great carved wood chair. It had pictures cut into the back.

"What's that, Neil?"

"That's Clanranald's 'scutcheon," said Neil.

It was a kind of picture in the shape of a shield. On it were many different things. There was a birlinn, with a salmon swimming by it; a wild animal rearing up and shaking its claws, a *lion*, Neil called it; an eagle in a tree; and a hand holding a cross. Above it was a picture of a castle, with a mailed fist holding a sword, and on each side was a big bear shot through with an arrow. The same picture, painted on a board, hung over the great fireplace.

In the parlor was an odd sort of box standing on legs. It had ivory teeth. Flora wondered what it was for. One night she found out. That night, instead of dancing reels in the pavilion, the chiefs gathered at Nunton and danced quite a different sort of dance. A lady sat down at the box, and her fingers flew over the ivories, and a tune tinkled out, a tune slow and stately. Sir Alexander, with an air, stepped up to Lady Clan and bowed very low, offering his hand with a flourish of his fingers. Lady Clan, clad in a low-cut gown of tartan silk, curtsied deep, and set her fingers above his. He led her to the center of the floor, and they stepped a minuet. As they advanced and retreated, bowed and dipped, Flora had a glimpse of a world far away and different from the world of the Isles. The sinuous motions, the clear tinkle of the tune, and the grace with which the young gentleman bent his curly peruke and kissed the lady's fingers as the dance ended, all made Flora feel as if she were in a dream.

In the morning all the gentlemen went off early to see the clansmen compete at Highland sports. Big Hugh Macdonald would throw the stone of strength for a wager. There would be running and wrestling. The little boys in a mob would play shinty, whacking a wooden ball with crooked sticks.

The ladies did not go. They lay abed late after the dancing.

Only Flora was stirring. In the stillness she tied her own snood and stole quietly to the parlor. She went to the box and touched the ivories with her small fingers. It tinkled for her. Fumbling, she found the notes of the piper's tune, then tinkled it again faster, and sang it softly in her sweet true little voice.

"Good morning, Flora," said a voice at her elbow. It was soft-footed Lady Clan. Flora's mother stood beside her. Flora turned red, and curtsied in confusion.

"This is the spinet, my dear," said Lady Clan, smiling. "Her name is *Ceolag*. I can see you have made friends with her already. Would you like to learn how to make such music?"

"Oh, yes, if you please, madam," breathed Flora.

"Then, Marian," said Lady Clan to Flora's mother, "you shall send her to me. She shall learn her notes, and she may at the same time learn her letters from Ranald's tutor."

"She's young," said Flora's mother, drawing the child close. "Let her stay with me until she learns her letters at the village school, and then you shall have her."

So when Flora left Nunton, it was with a promise to go back there soon, and stay.

Then suddenly the years raced. One moment, it seemed, Flora was a little girl sitting in the peaty turf hut that housed the school, staring with bewildered eyes through the thick sheet of yellow transparent horn that protected the hornbook, at the chicken tracks called letters, and chanting "A, B, ab" with the rest. The next moment she was thirteen, almost a lady, living at the Clanranald mansion at Nunton, learning to play the spinet and use the globes, to net purses and sew a straight seam.

Back at Milton, Angus was a grown-up man of seventeen, learning from stepfather Hugh how to run the tack

of Milton. Neil was even farther away. Clanranald had
sent him all the way to France to make a scholar of him.

At Nunton the schoolroom was full. Young Clanranald
was almost fifteen, beloved by his clansmen for his gallant
bearing. He preferred the braes to the study, and spent
much time gazing outward. His brother Donald at Flora's
age was already looking forward to a soldier's life. He was
destined, like so many young Scots, for the French army.
Besides, there was a babble of younger children, including
two little girls still in the nursery.

At Nunton Flora's horizon was widening. She would
trace on the globe of the world the land mass of Europe,
picking out Austria and France and Holland, and the confusion of petty states that were the bits and pieces of Italy
and Germany. She put her finger on Rome:

"Here lives our rightful King, James VIII of Scotland,
and his heir, Prince Charles."

She touched Hanover, far to the north, in Germany.

"From here comes our wrongful King, George II. May
he go back there!"

She traced the British Isles, cross-channel from France.
Off the west coast of Scotland, far to the north, were the
Isles of the Hebrides, and among the outermost was Uist.
She tried to make herself understand how the doings in
Rome and Hanover might come to disturb the peace of
Uist; but she really did not believe it.

She swung the globe a half-turn, and there was the New
World. All to the south belonged to Spain. All to the north
belonged to France. To the west, nobody knew how far,
ranged the red Indians. On the thin edge of the North

American coast, in colonies from Charleston to Boston, the British had stubbornly dug in their toes. Flora did not dream that that could be important to her either.

Until she went to school, Flora knew only one language, the language of the Highlands, called Erse. On a woman's lips, the speech of the Isles was a soft purr. When the shanachie stood forth at Clanranald's table and recited the exploits of the Macdonalds, it had a fine vehement martial ring. Flora loved the language of her childhood, and spoke it all her life. At school she learned also to speak the language of the Sassenach, English. With her fine musical ear, she learned to pronounce the crisp sharp words of her adopted language as if she had been born to it.

When Flora was sixteen, Neil Maceachen came back from school at Douay. At nineteen, he was perfected in Latin and Greek, and spoke French like a native. He brought his violin, and had the skill to make it sing. He brought too a grown-up, quick observation of people and things, and a civilized, easygoing manner. It was too easygoing for some of the rough Highlanders. They thought he lacked courage. One day he was to prove differently.

Neil just suited Clanranald. Clanranald himself was a scholar. He could walk and hunt and shoot as well as the next Highland chief, but he preferred to sit home at Nunton, writing his own legal papers and rent-rolls, or poring over manuscripts in the ancient Erse. He was one of two men in the Highlands who could still read and write the old pointed letters of the Erse tongue.

Flora had no ambition to be a third. It did not become a young lady to show off among scholars. She was glad when Neil became tutor at Nunton, but she did not feel obliged to become his rival by learning Latin and Greek, or even French. It was more pleasant and becoming to play upon the spinet while Neil fiddled a reel.

When Flora was seventeen, it was time for her to leave the Clanranald schoolroom. Some of her companions were leaving too. Young Clan was almost out of his teens. His father decided it was time for him to complete his education by seeing foreign parts. Neil was detailed to go along as tutor, guide, and interpreter. Donald too was off for France, to join the army. Flora said good-bye to them, and to Nunton, with great reluctance.

She understood what the next step was. A proper young lady of seventeen was supposed to marry. Her kinfolk were supposed to arrange it. They would pick a suitable young man. They would give him a sum of money for a dowry. He would sign a paper promising to take care of the young lady. Then the young man would be introduced to the young lady, and immediately he would carry her off to the altar.

Flora Macdonald was a remarkable girl, with a quiet will of her own. She had no use for such a commercial arrangement, and she was in no hurry to be married. She went back to Milton, back to the summer shieling and the winter fireside, happy just to be home again, to hear the Erse spoken and listen to the sound of the sea.

CHAPTER 4 ❦ *In Society*

Miss Flora Macdonald of Milton, seventeen years old and as pretty as a picture, was going a-visiting. The gentlefolk of the Western Islands spent lots of time visiting about. They didn't mind the difficulty of traveling. They were sure of weeks of fun and good company at the end of the journey. The gentlemen could count on good sport, going out with the guns and the gillies for red deer, grouse, muircock, and plover. The ladies could count on a dance at every day's end. Everybody could count on feasts of game and plenty of good French claret.

But this visit in the summer of 1739 was a very particular visit, and had very particular consequences. Sir Alexander Macdonald, chief of the Sleat Macdonalds, had brought home a bride. It became the duty of all his clansmen, and all the neighboring clansmen, to call at his mansion and pay their respects to the new lady of Sleat.

So Flora and her stepfather and her brother Angus and her mother and her half brother James and her half sister Annabella made their way to Monkstadt. With gillies to carry their gear in bundles and little trunks, they walked from Milton, north along the footway by the shore, as far as the arm of the sea that separates the Isle of Uist from the

Isle of Benbecula. There they had to rest and wait a little
while the tide ebbed. When the tide was low, there was a
passage of dry sand, a mile in length, all the way from Uist
to Benbecula. They all walked across. Flora and little Annabella laughed a lot to see the silly flounders flopping in
the shallow pools left by the ebb.

When they came to Nunton, they stayed the night.
Lady Clanranald was ailing, and she could not join them.
Old Clanranald elected to stay at home too. They borrowed a six-oared rowing boat, and six clansmen to man
her. Early the next morning, in fine fair weather, they set
out in the boat for Sir Alexander's home in the Isle of
Skye.

It was a long pull across the Minch, even with a sail set
to help them and a fair following wind to drive them over
the sparkling waves. But before day waned they found
themselves under the bold volcanic cliffs of Skye, and soon
they landed at the beach at Monkstadt. They all got out
and walked up from the beach to the mansion house.

It was a beautiful spot. The last rays of the sun shone on
smiling green fields and meadows of grain, and made ruddy
the mountain peaks of the Quiraing beyond. The spacious
mansion stood on a hill, overlooking a beautiful blue lake
dedicated to the saint of the Isles, Saint Columba.

As the visitors ascended the hill, their host, as the custom was, came out to greet them. Sir Alexander had not
changed much since Flora had met him first on the strand
at Rushness. He still looked pale and melancholy, and he
still had his sweet smile for Flora. He gave a warm welcome to his clansman Hugh and all the family, and walked
with them up the hill back to his grand house. As soon as

they were refreshed from their journey, they went to the drawing room to pay their respects to the new lady of Monkstadt.

Sir Alexander's bride was a Lowland lady, an Earl's daughter. As she rose from the table where she was pouring tea, Flora caught her breath at the sight. Lady Margaret was tall, almost six feet in height, with a high-held head and an air of repose and majesty. She was not many years older than Flora. Her eyes were shining and kind, and her complexion was a perfect rose and white. She wore garb of fashion, a plum-colored petticoat, and a gown of blue shot with plum, looped up over a wide-panniered hoop and falling in a straight panel behind. She had a black apron edged with lace, and a tiny cap of lace on her upswept hair.

To Flora and Annabella she looked like a goddess come to earth, as she glided gracefully toward them with both hands outstretched. Flora dropped her best curtsey; but Lady Margaret took the pretty Highland girl in her arms and kissed her warmly. From that moment the two young women were fast friends.

That night there was a great ball in Lady Margaret's honor. My Lady dressed herself splendidly in green brocaded with gold. Her stomacher was jeweled. She wore a French necklace of topaz and crystal, and topaz buckles on her green satin shoes. Her gown was caught back with ribbon knots to show her petticoat of emerald satin. Jeweled butterflies on wires trembled in her high-swept hair. She carried a fan of ivory and lace.

When she was dressed, she sent her serving-lass to fetch Flora. Flora had completed her simple toilette. She went at once. She caught her breath when she saw the splendor of her hostess, but Lady Margaret only laughed.

"Let me look at you," she said.

Flora dropped a curtsey. She had dressed in her best for the ball. She wore a sheer linen smock, drawn in folds to the throat, its full sleeves pushed back from the arm. She did not need stays, but she wore them, laced tight about her slender waist. Over them was clasped the full flowing gown of tartan silk, with the Clanranald pattern sparkling on a ground of white. A gauze kerchief covered her shoulders. Her tawny hair fell free, and the blue satin snood caught the curls back from her face.

Lady Margaret looked at the bare throat, the ringless hands, the glossy, red-gleaming curls, and wondered why ladies of fashion went to so much trouble to look less lovely.

"What shall I give you," she asked, "to wear for my sake? You are complete as you are. Stay, you must have a fan!"

She opened a box of inlaid ebony on her dressing table, and set forth a file of fans—fans of gauze and sandalwood, adorned with lace and lacquer, or painted with little pictures in the French manner.

"Not gauze or lace," said Lady Margaret, sorting. "They are not for the tartan lass. Here is your fan, my dear."

She extended a French fan of finest chicken skin, delicately painted with white roses among ruddy leaves.

"Here is the fan for the tartan lass," said she, "showing the rose we all love—the white rose that is the emblem of the House of Stuart!"

"I will treasure it," said Flora, "for your sake, and for the sake of our rightful King."

Belowstairs fiddlers were tuning. Charles Macarthur could be heard blowing up the bag of his pipes. The two lasses embraced, and went down together.

They found the great hall ablaze with candles in branching gilded sconces, and Sir Alexander ready to welcome his clansmen and neighbors.

Flora looked at the Sleat chief in surprise. He did not wear the tartans of his clan tonight; he was wearing his wedding clothes. He had been married in white and silver. His full-skirted coat was brocaded, silver on white. His snug stockings were heavy white silk with silver clocks, and his shoes had red heels and jeweled buckles. His white satin breeches were buckled with gems below the knee. There were diamond buttons on his long, silver-embroidered waistcoat, and a froth of lace ruffles at throat and wrist. It was the first time that Flora had seen the full splendor of high fashion in the world beyond the Highlands. She could not quite decide whether it was beautiful or silly.

When Sir Alexander opened the ball by stepping a minuet with his stately wife, to the light melody of spinet and fiddles, their attire, so flashing and flowing, seemed exactly right. When the reels began, Flora wasn't so sure. Then the free ripple of a kilt, the quick flash of muscular knees, seemed better suited to the dance. She watched one dancer in particular. He was a tall lad, graceful and finely formed, with a quiet handsome face. His jet-black hair was tied smoothly back from his broad brow. His dark eyes under arching black eyebrows glowed without smiling.

Flora wondered who he was. It seemed to her she had
seen him before.

She was not to wonder long. He had been dancing with
a rosy, plump girl who never stopped laughing. When the
reel ended, he took her back to a matron as rosy and
plump, and left her there. When the pipes sounded again,
he was before Flora.

"Will you honor me?"

She gave him her hand, and he led her out. The reel
was a merry one; even Flora had no breath to spare. She
footed it laughing, tossing back her glinting curls. Her
partner kept up nimbly. He never took his glowing eyes
from her face, even when at the close he set his hands
about her slender waist and tossed her high in a froth of
petticoats. When the reel was over, Flora was glad to un-
furl the roses of her fan and set them fluttering.

Her partner was an unaccountable young man. One
minute he was beside her, looking down on her with his
glowing eyes. The next minute he was gone.

"Well, my dear," spoke Lady Margaret beside her,
"how do you like Allan Macdonald?"

"What is he?"

"A clansman. His father is Sir Alexander's factor, and
manages the estates. It's a most suitable match, Flora. Will
you have him?"

"Why must I have anybody? I'm happy as I am."

"You need not have anybody till you wish. Probably you
are wise. You should see the world before you choose a
husband."

"I am not likely to see the world," said Flora, smiling,
"from this corner of the Isles."

"Tut," said Lady Margaret, "you'll see the world, I warrant you."

Donald Roy Macdonald was claiming Flora's hand for the new reel. The difference in their ages did not prevent Flora from holding the tall young man in high regard. She stepped out with him with pleasure. Allan Macdonald was nowhere to be seen.

The next morning Flora opened sleepy eyes on a gray day. Pearly clouds hung on the mountaintops. The loch shimmered like dove-colored satin. Behind closed doors the late-dancing guests still slept. Flora was restless. She slipped into a gown of lavender, took up her plaid, and went out.

She walked along the loch's lonely shore. No one was in sight. At the other end of the loch she came to the little church of Kilmuir. On a grassy height lay the quiet burying ground. Here and there a tall Celtic cross or a walled enclosure told where people of consequence were laid. Around them small slabs of stone showed where the simple folk lay. Flora sat on a low wall of stone and looked over the loch. There was a feeling of eternity about the silent place. Flora felt as if she could stay there forever.

Behind her a footstep sounded. Flora shook with an involuntary shudder as she turned.

"Don't be afraid, miss," said a pleasant deep voice. It was Allan Macdonald. He came from an enclosure behind her and sat down at her side.

"I'm not afraid," said Flora, smiling. "You must have walked over my grave."

"My own, more like," said he, "for that's the family burying plot I came from."

"This is your home, then?"

"My people have lived in this island since time forgotten."

Looking out over the loch, Allan began to talk. It was almost as if he was talking to himself.

"No one remembers," he said, "a time when the Macdonalds were not in the Western Isles. We chased the Norsemen back over the sea. Our bones lie under this sod. This ground is ours, because we are a part of it. The chiefs of the Isles fought for it, in every great battle the Scots have known. They led the clan to Bannockburn, to Flodden, to Killiecrankie, to Sheriffmuir. They will lead us again when the time comes."

"And you will follow!"

"I will follow my chief to the death. Sir Alexander is a good man, wise and kind; but I would follow him no matter what he was."

Flora looked at the speaker. His dark eyes were fixed on the cloudy horizon. His arms were crossed on his broad chest, and his long brown hands touched the tartan folds of the Macdonald plaid where it drew down over his shoulders. His blue bonnet was badged with the heather. His face in profile looked lofty and purposeful, with the high brow, the aquiline nose, the mouth and chin firm-set. Only his clear skin flushed with high color showed how young he really was.

"A Highlandman's chief is his king and his father," said Allan, "and it is the clansman's duty to follow without question wherever the chief leads. I should not think myself fit to lie in this ground when I die if I did otherwise."

"I know," said Flora. "I am a Macdonald too."

"So you are." For the first time Allan looked at her. The glow in his eyes became a smile.

"That makes us cousins," he said. He took her hand in his.

"Kissing cousins," he added in the old Scotch phrase, and pulling her to him, before she could draw breath, he had kissed her.

At the touch of his lip to her cheek she knew who he was.

"Why!" she cried, "it was you—at Nunton—years ago—"

He smiled down on her.

"It was I. I have often wondered, since, if you remembered that bold little boy, and if he was the first to—"

"To have the impudence—" supplied Flora.

"To have the impudence—to do this—" With perfect calm the extraordinary young man saluted her again. Flora pulled away laughing.

"If you have wondered—"

"Yes?"

"Then you may continue to wonder!"

Abruptly she was off down the slope. She heard his footsteps running behind her. He was going to catch up, of course. Flora was not sure that she would mind if he did. But before he came up with her, they both sighted a group of people coming along the path by the loch. With one consent they slowed to a walk and paced along sedately side by side.

The ladies approaching were the rosy lass Allan had danced with, and the plump dame he had returned her to. They hung on the arms of a tall, strongly built, merry-

looking gentleman of middle age. From his resemblance
to Allan, Flora guessed that he was Allan's father, Macdonald of Kingsburgh. As the group came toward her,
their laughter rang out over the water.

Flora felt herself drawn to them all. There was a gay,
brave warmth that bound the family, the jolly husband
and wife, the merry sister and her quiet brother. They were
destined to share a strange adventure with Flora. If she
had foreseen it, she could not have taken them all more
quickly to her heart.

She was sorry when in a few days the house party broke
up, and the family from Kingsburgh went back there.
Flora stayed on.

She soon found out what Lady Margaret had meant
when she predicted that Flora would see the world. The
chief's wife proposed to make sure that she did. When she
went to Edinburgh for the winter season, she took Flora
along.

Then a new kind of life opened up to the girl from the
Isles. She had never dreamed of such a city as Edinburgh.
The towering narrow houses seemed to her to scrape the
sky. They had pointed round towers, turnpike stairs that
wound round poles, and crow-step gables. The long High
Street stretched along a spine of rock, rising from Holyrood Palace on the plain to the fortress called Edinburgh
Castle at the top of the ridge. On one side of the ridge lay
the North Loch, on the other smiling fields and country
houses filled the plain.

Sir Alexander's town lodging was modest. It was only a
floor in a tall house that opened onto a court, or close, off
the High Street. The best room's windows looked into the

broad place in the High Street called the Lawnmarket. Flora could watch the lasses at the booths selling linen and lawn. She could see the rusty-red coats and huge Lochaber axes of the men of the Town Guard. She could watch the sedan chairs come by, with some fine lady closed inside the leather half door, and lusty Highlanders between the shafts fore and aft, hurrying uphill at a trot. She could hear the drum roll that summoned the garrison of the Castle, and the basket women calling: "Caller herring!" She could hardly wait to explore this fascinating new world.

"You shall do so," promised Lady Margaret, "and I'll give you a guide who will please you, I'll warrant."

"Who?"

"One who knows the town, a student at the University. You must be ready in the morning betimes."

So Flora was ready. She looked at the sunny sky, and put on her lavender gown, her buckled shoes, her best blue snood. When the lass summoned her, she went to the drawing room to meet her guide.

He was a tall youth in Lowland garb. The knee breeches and white thread stockings, instead of kilt and tartan hose, still looked strange to Flora. The youth bowed low. When he straightened, he smiled at her with a face full of mischief. It was Allan Macdonald.

"You! A student at the University!"

"At your service, Miss Flora. Sir Alexander has brought me hither to get my education. A part of it I've been getting by seeing the town; so today I'm to educate you."

"Let us go."

It was a wonderful new world, and Allan was part of it. They walked on the half-moon of the Castle, and from it looked out across the North Loch toward Leith and the waters of the Firth of Forth. They walked down the Royal Mile to where the Palace of Holyrood stood in the King's Park. Above rose the crags that were topped by the blunt shape of the bluff called Arthur's Seat.

There was no king in residence now that German George sat on his usurped throne in London. They were free to roam the halls and grounds.

The chapel was in ruins. Sunlight coming through the broken roof fell on the neglected graves in the holy aisles. Passing inside the Palace, the pair from the Hebrides wondered at the splendor of carven windows and vaulted ceilings. In the great gallery hung paintings of the royalty of Scotland, from Malcolm Canmore to the last Stuart.

As they came away, Flora was no longer "miss." Allan had found his own name for her—"Flory."

She plucked a white rose by the garden walk.

"Scotland has no King any more," she said, "but I will wear the Stuart rose for the sake of the King over the water."

She put it in her hair. Plucking another, she set it in Allan's hat like a cockade. Then he offered his hand, and led her up the long hill again. Along the way were town houses of great folk, or coaching inns. Near the city gate, the Netherbow Port, was the old house Preacher John Knox used to live in, two hundred years before, with its little windowpanes and its high stone steps. Still going up, they came again to St. Giles' Cathedral under its airy tower like a king's crown. The market cross stood before it. On the other side was the Parliament House, with the lion of Scotland over the door.

Along the inner side of the Cathedral the goldsmiths had built booths, backed up to the Cathedral wall. Each man had a counter, an awning on poles, and a high stool. Before some of the counters, 'prentices in blue aprons were crying their wares.

"See, Flory, the crames!" Allan pulled her in that direction.

On the wooden counters were set out all kinds of goldsmiths' work—rings, lockets, chains, little boxes for snuff or pins. The two young people from the Isles passed up and down the row, looking at the little things as if they were so many crown jewels. Late sunshine made them sparkle.

"Oh, Allan," said Flora, "how beautiful! I shall always remember this day."

"And me?" asked Allan earnestly.

Flora pretended to consider this question seriously.

"And you? We-ell now, how do I know? Happen I might forget *you*."

"You'll not if I can prevent," said Allan, still serious. "Flory, let me buy you a fairing."

"A gift? Oh, no, Allan," said Flora quickly. "There's no need. I'll contrive somehow to hold you in mind." She laughed out loud at his serious face.

"To remind you of this day when we've been so happy together. I'll not be denied." He drew her to the counter.

"What d'ye lack, what d'ye lack!" chanted a red-headed 'prentice. He could see in Allan's eye that a sale was in view. Experience told him when the lover was ready to spend.

"I've pin boxes, snuffboxes, toothpick cases—here's a locket in shape of a heart—here's a fine silver chain, you know how the song goes—" The youth sang solemnly, in a husky voice:

" 'Twas a braw Highland laddie, I heard him exclaim,
I'll bind my love with a silver chain,
With a silver chain and a golden ring,
For I love my sweet lassie above every thing."

Flora blushed rose-red. The unabashed 'prentice rattled on:

"A silver chain, here sir, hold it in your hand, right Spanish silver it is—and a golden ring, here's one, sir, has two hearts intertwined, as you may see, and here's another has one fine heart in filigree, you may take your choice. May I make so bold, sir, is the lady your bride, or only your sweetheart?"

"Why—" stammered Allan, and then blurted, "my bride, if she'll have me."

The impudence of Allan Macdonald, telling this red-headed 'prentice before he told her! Flora put her small nose in the air; but Allan, intent on the ring, never noticed.

"Well then, sir," said the 'prentice, shoving it into his hand, "take this of the two hearts. Take it in your hand, sir, you may read the posy carved within it."

Allan read the posy aloud: *"I am thine, as thou art mine."*

"Pray, Mr. Macdonald," said Flora loftily, "give the lad back his posy, for there's no truth in it."

Belatedly Allan saw his mistake. What odd things girls were, to be sure. Flora must know his heart! But one was always in danger of affrighting the delicate creatures.

"Yes, Flory, if you bid me," he said quickly. "Come, lad, show me what's for a sweetheart."

"This of the one heart, sir, is much admired."

"Has it a posy?" said Flora coldly. "Take care it tell truth."

"A sentiment only," said the brisk 'prentice.

"*Thine forever*," read Allan. "Flory, my sweeting, this one tells truth. Let me put it on your finger."

Flora put her hands behind her. She did not mean to be won so easily.

"Is there not another verse, sir?" She improvised it to the old tune:

> "'Twas the wee Highland lassie, she answered again,
>   I will not be bound with a silver chain,
>   I will not be pledged with a golden ring,
>   For I love my freedom above every thing!"

"There's no such verse, ma'am," said the 'prentice, vexed to see his sale go glimmering.

"Then there ought to be," said Flora.

"Perhaps," said the resourceful 'prentice, "the lady will wear it on a silver chain about her neck; this is the fashion with them that's not pledged."

As he spoke he slipped the ring onto a slender silver chain, and the chain about Flora's neck, before she could protest.

"Do, Flory, wear it for my sake," begged Allan. "You see, 'tis the fashion."

"Absolutely the *ton*, as we say in the French," urged the 'prentice.

"Well—" said Flora, willing to yield, "if 'tis the *ton*—" She gave her hand to Allan, and let the smile come.

"I thank you," she said from her heart, "for your gift, and for your love to me, and I will wear it in token of the good will I bear you."

Allan kissed the hand she gave him.

"No more than good will?" he said.

"Do not ask me!" she cried, blushing crimson. "I will wear it. Let the rest wait."

Allan's grave eyes looked deep into hers, and saw what he wanted to see.

"I am content," he said.

Still holding her hand, he tenderly guided her up the twilit High Street, toward home.

Thus began a winter of gaiety for the Highland girl. She began to move in the best society. Lady Margaret's mother, the Dowager Lady Eglinton, was a famous beauty, and she took Flora everywhere. At Lady Eglinton's house in Jack's Land Flora met Lady Margaret's six tall sisters. They were all beauties. It was an extraordinary sight to see the eight tall ladies alighting from their sedan chairs as they proceeded in state to enter the rooms for the winter Assemblies.

Flora must go to the Assemblies too. Anybody who was anybody went to the Assemblies. But first she must go to a private party in Jack's Land. All the young ladies of the family went, in great suspense, for that night would decide their fate at the Assemblies for the winter. It was then that they drew for partners.

Stately Lady Eglinton presided. She took every girl's fan, and into a gentleman's cocked hat it went. Then she personally handed the hat around to each young gentleman, and he drew out a fan. The owner of it was his partner for the season.

Fortunately each gentleman took good care to be acquainted with the appearance of the right fan. When the hat went round, Flora was a little afraid lest some careless lad draw the fan of the white roses by mistake; but none did. It was left for Allan to fish out on purpose.

Flora's first appearance at the Assembly was a solemn rite. She was gowned in Lowland style, with white roses in her upswept hair and a gown of ice-green satin, cut low, with falling ruffles of lace. About her neck was the slender silver chain; but the ring of the posy was slipped into her bosom.

Allan Macdonald presented himself in the unaccustomed glory of peach-colored brocade. He wore a sword at his side. The ends of his glossy black hair were put into a black silk bag tied on with a ribbon bow.

He handed Flora solemnly into the waiting sedan chair, and walked along beside it down from the High Street to the first angle of the steep West Bow.

The Assembly was a handsome old house with little leaded windowpanes. In the lobby a reduced nobleman was peddling white kid gloves to any forgetful gentleman who needed a pair. Allan had not forgotten his.

They went round and round the dizzy turnpike stair up to the long room on the second floor, wainscoted with

carved oak to the ceiling. The presiding lady was related
to a judge, and she looked it. She bore down like a ship in
full sail. Lady Margaret stepped forward to introduce
Flora.

"Miss Macdonald of—?"

"Of Milton."

So far so good. The young lady was Somebody of
Somewhere. The judge's lady unbent.

Soon Flora and Allan took their turn on the floor,
solemnly stepping to the tune of the fiddles. It was not
much like the Highland reels at Nunton, but Flora enjoyed
it. Allan never said much, but it was sheer joy to dance
with him and feel how motion answered motion almost
by instinct. When the dance ended, it was good manners
for him to bow low and kiss her hand; but Allan's kiss had
more in it than good manners. Too soon it was midnight,
and the sedan chair had to turn home again.

Other times, Flora and Allan strolled by the North Loch
on sunny mornings, or drank tea in the drawing room on
rainy afternoons. They were comfortable together. Flora
was sorry when the season ended.

After that season, Flora's life ranged from the Lowlands
to the Highlands and back again. She spent some time with
Lady Margaret, at Monkstadt or in Edinburgh. She went
to Kingsburgh to see Allan's sister Nannie married. She
was Nannie Macallester now. Flora could not see what
Nannie saw in her serious husband, an exciseman in the
King's Customs. But Nannie was delighted with him.

In the summers Flora loved to be at Milton, or in the
shieling at Alisary, sitting in the sun and watching the
cattle and dreaming dreams. As summer followed sum-

mer, she wished, sometimes, that Uist were nearer to Kingsburgh. Allan's education was done, and he had his work to do as his father's assistant in Skye.

In the winters at Edinburgh there was plenty to do. Lady Margaret saw to it that in between her social duties Flora was constantly learning the accomplishments of a highbred lady. At the school of the prim Misses Henderson, just a step off the High Street, Flora met with the writing master, the music master, the dancing master. A gentlewoman came to teach fine embroidery, and another to communicate that famous light hand at a fancy pastry.

After a while Lady Margaret did not go home to the Isles so often. Sir Alexander was ailing, and his doctor advised him to stay in Edinburgh. It was both more salubrious for his health and more convenient for his medical man. Life became quieter for Flora.

Thus several years slipped away. Flora still wore Allan's fairing around her neck. When she saw him, nothing was changed; but she saw him so seldom. Still, she was not in a hurry to change her way of life.

Nevertheless, great changes were impending. Sir Alexander kept watching events with grave eyes. A war was raging on the Continent. Flora had not even noticed its beginning. It had begun when the Austrian Emperor died, and the other nations had tried to dictate who should succeed him. By 1744 most of Europe was embroiled. It was like a dogfight, Flora sometimes thought, which would begin with two curs snarling at each other over a bone, and end with a streetful of snapping teeth and flying fur. Unfortunately, there was no watchman to separate the combatants by the scruff of the neck, which, in Flora's opinion, was what they needed.

Britain had kept out of it for a while. But the French went too far. They assembled a great fleet, put the renowned Marshal Saxe at the head, and set out to invade England. They took on board with them an adventurous young man, Charles Edward Stuart, heir to the King over the water. They meant to set him on the throne of England.

But once again, as in the time of the Spanish Armada, the luck of the English held. Their friend the sea rose in storm, wrecked the French ships, and drowned the men or drove them back to France. Nobody knew what became of Charles Edward.

Then the English declared war on the French. The newspapers were full of it. They were fighting on the sea, in the West Indies, on the edges of the Colonies. The French were overrunning Flanders. Sir Alexander took in all the papers, and watched the news anxiously.

On April 5, 1745, the papers told him, the young Duke of Cumberland, German George's soldier son, set out from the Court of St. James's to take command of the English and their Allies in Flanders. The French were besieging Tournai. The Duke collected his forces and marched to lift the siege. The French sent an army to meet him.

On May 3rd, King George left England for Hanover. He felt more at home there.

On May 11th, the English and the French fought at Fontenoy. The Highland regiment called the Black Watch fought with glory; but the English were defeated.

When Sir Alexander Macdonald heard that the British were beaten, he hastily began to pack for the return to Skye. He had reason to think that something was going to happen.

Book Two ❧ Charles Edward Stuart

SOUND THE PIBROCH

Sound the pibroch loud on high
From John o' Groats to Isle of Skye
Let all the clans their slogan cry,
And rise and follow Charlie!
　It comes upon me to arise,
　To rise and follow Charlie!

And see a small devoted band
By dark Loch Shiel have ta'en their stand
And proudly vow with heart and hand
To fight for royal Charlie!
　It comes upon me to arise,
　To rise and follow Charlie!

From every hill and every glen
Are gathering fast the loyal men,
They grasp their dirks and shout again
Hurrah! for royal Charlie!
    It comes upon me to arise,
    To rise and follow Charlie!

(MRS. NORMAN MACLEOD, SR.)

CHAPTER 5 ❧ *Sound the Pibroch!*

Flora was glad to be at home. Sitting on the turf bank before the little shieling at Alisary, watching the cows and the goats and flicking the needles through the soft wool or twirling her spindle on her hip, she would look along the shimmering sea to the distant misty shape of the island of St. Kilda and the limitless Atlantic beyond, and drink up the silence and peace of the Outer Isles. The war in Europe seemed very far away.

At Nunton, too, little had changed. Old Clanranald still buried his aristocratic nose in his books and rent-rolls, or translated from the old Irish, his fine clerk's handwriting flowing under the sharpened quill. His hair and beard were more grizzled, perhaps, but his abstracted eye was as sharp as ever. Lady Clanranald had the same still sweetness. She was thinner and whiter, but there was no stoop in her proud bearing. She was very glad to see Flora. So was Neil, recently returned from France. He had left young Clanranald on the mainland of Scotland, and Donald, the soldier, in France.

The piper still played on the terrace before the windows in the morning, and he still marched up and down the great hall while the chief of Clanranald dined. The clansmen still thronged the chief's table to drink his French claret and eat his beef and game and venison.

At Nunton one could read the papers from the mainland. Flora scarcely bothered. The news came from so far away it seemed like fiction. What did she care if the armies of Europe marched and countermarched, or if their ships on the ocean grappled in combat? What did she care if on July 9th a British ship of war had attacked two French privateers? It was nothing to her if the smaller one, by name the *Du Teillay*, outsailed the Britisher and gave her the slip. At least, so Flora supposed.

On August 2nd, the *Du Teillay* cast anchor off South Uist. There was someone of importance aboard, for Clanranald was sent for. He listened to the message, and frowned. He had no mind to go. Young Clanranald was still on the mainland. Alexander of Boisdale went, Clan's brother. He was gone all day, and came back scowling like a thundercloud.

"The young man is mad," he said angrily to his brother. "I begged him to go home. 'I *am* come home,' says he coolly, 'for this is my home, and these are my people, and I will not think of turning around and going back.' Even while I argued, he orders up the anchor and away we sail towards the mainland, with my little boat swinging astern. In the end I gave up, jumped into my boat, and rowed back to Uist. Clan, if you'll be guided by me, you'll keep clear—"

Flora, watching her herd on the southern slope of the isle, saw the *Du Teillay* pass. Armed men were on the deck, the sun glittered on steel. The white sails belled with a fair wind. About the mast circled a great sea eagle. Among the armed men perhaps the sun made a crown around a yellow head held higher than the rest, and lighted a slim form clad all in black; but if it did, Flora's eyes slipped past him uncaring. She was not yet to look upon his face.

One of those days, her stepfather Hugh had gone away to Skye. He was negotiating with his chief, Sir Alexander, for the lease of Armadale, which would fall vacant in November.

It was an afternoon in August when Hugh came back. He brought in his boat a passenger, a clansman from the mainland, Flora's cousin Alexander, the poet of Dalelea.

The two men came into the best room at Milton at dusk. Hugh threw the newspapers on the table. An item that was uppermost caught Flora's eye.

"What is this!" she exclaimed, and read:

By the Lords Justices

A PROCLAMATION

> Ordering a reward of thirty thousand pounds to any person who shall seize and secure Charles Edward Stuart, the eldest son of the Pretender, in case he shall land, or attempt to land, in any of his Majesty King George's dominions.

"Hm," said Angus, "what will the son of the Pretender say to that?"

"He has said it," said Alexander. "The son of King James—for I hold that 'Pretender' is an uncivil way to allude to our rightful King—has made a counteroffer. He offers a suitable reward to him who lays the London usurper by the heels."

"Of thirty thousand pounds?"

"A figure nearer what old George is worth—thirty pounds."

"This is mere repartee," said Angus, "but with such a price on his head, surely Prince Charles Edward will not now dare to appear on these shores."

"He has appeared," said Hugh.

"The Prince has landed!" exclaimed Angus. "With how many men at his back?"

"Seven," said Hugh.

"Seven regiments?"

"Seven men."

"Have no fear," said Cousin Alexander with a smile. "He is himself seven regiments in his own person."

"Have you seen him, then?" cried Flora.

"I have had that honor. No sooner had the *Du Teillay* anchored off the mainland, than our young chief, Clanranald, hastened to go aboard. He took with him his principal followers, of whom I was so lucky as to be one."

"Oh, tell me the whole story!" cried Flora.

"Well, then, when we were carried on board, we found a large tent erected with poles upon the ship's deck, and refreshments set out. An old lord acted as host; but the Prince was not to be seen.

"About half an hour after," Alexander went on, "there entered the tent a tall youth of a most agreeable aspect, dressed in a plain black coat, a shirt without ruffles, a cambric stock with a buckle, a broad hat with a canvas string fixed to a coat button, black stockings, and brass buckles to his shoes. In short, he was dressed like a clergyman. Yet at first sight of him I rose to my feet, and felt my heart swell in my throat, so commanding and handsome was he.

One of the bystanders told me hastily that he was only an English clergyman come to visit the Highlands."

"Go on, go on!" cried Flora. "What did he say?"

"He saluted us politely, and we bowed in return. He singled me out, and desired me to sit with him upon a sea chest. He began to ask me questions, and I answered with perfect freedom. 'Do you not feel cold in that habit?' says he curiously, pointing to my belted plaid and naked knees. 'I believe,' said I, 'that I should only feel cold if I wore a different habit.' At this he laughed heartily.

"After this, he left us, and for a time walked the deck in talk with Clanranald, who listened, thoughtful and in some perplexity. A young cousin of ours stood by. As he caught the drift, his eyes sparkled, he flushed, grasped his sword, and caught his breath to speak. The Prince noticed, turned to him, and called out, 'Will not you assist me?' 'I will, I will!' cried the lad, 'though no other man in the Highlands should draw the sword, I am ready to die for you!' And he threw his bonnet in the air. 'And I,' cried young Clanranald at once. 'And I—and I—and I!' cried all your kinsmen with one voice."

"Oh, brave!" cried Flora.

"Thus the Clanranald Macdonalds of the mainland engaged their honor to their lawful Prince. We will follow him cheerfully and risk our fate with him, though no others should join us."

"It is a rash undertaking," said Angus soberly.

"Be it so. We are committed. When he had our promise, he changed to Highland garb and went ashore."

"And there," said Hugh, "I was the first man to meet him and kiss his hand, walking along the shore towards

Boradale. It is a right royal youth, tall, elegantly formed, fair of complexion, blue of eye, with his own yellow hair combed back and tied with a black ribbon."

"At Boradale," said Alexander, "we formed a guard of honor to him of our own people, fifty picked gentlemen and warriors. The whole neighborhood, men, women, and children, crowded to him to kiss his hand, and we all did our best to give him a right hearty welcome to his own country."

"How could you leave the place where he is?" cried Flora.

"I am sent to raise for his army my kin upon Uist."

"They will not rise," said Hugh. "Old Clanranald has forbidden it. He has more prudence than daring."

"Then let him sit soft by the fire, and read in the papers that his son has restored the crown to his rightful King!"

"And you, Father, what will you do?"

"I will follow my chief, little daughter."

"Where will Sir Alexander lead?"

"I wish I knew. Prince Charles sent over young Clanranald with letters to Sir Alexander and to Macleod of Macleod on Skye. Having my business at Monkstadt, I went along. At first our welcome was hearty. Sir Alexander seemed disposed to raise his clan for the Prince. Then overnight, he gets letters from Macleod, and he turns plaguy cold and shy, and begins to counsel prudence. But it is too late for prudence. Even now the clans are summoned to a rallying point in the Highlands!"

Flora was at Nunton, some three weeks later, when young Clanranald arrived. He had a chill reception from his father, and tears from his mother; but the younger clansmen clustered around him in the great hall to hear the news. The lasses stood on the benches so as to miss nothing. The handsome young man stood below the family coat of arms over the chimney piece, with his ruddy face lifted and a great light in his eyes.

"King James VIII is proclaimed!" he cried. "And Prince Charles is to be his regent and rule in his place until we have won by the sword the right to crown the King!"

He pictured the scene:

"It was in Glenfinnan, at the head of Loch Shiel, where Clanranald land meets the country of Cameron of Lochiel. It is a deep glen surrounded by crags, with the green water of the loch stretching westward away. The Prince was ready at dawn to raise the standard, but when he stepped out on the shore with his honor guard of Clanranalds—there were no other clans gathered at all! I think he was struck to the heart; but he said nothing. As we waited, and wondered what to do, suddenly over the brow of the eastward crag comes from far away the skirling of the great war pipes. In a little while the long banners lift over the crest, and here come the Camerons marching, seven hundred strong—philibegs swinging in time, pipes shrilling, pennons fluttering, and every blue bonnet bearing the white ribbon cockade. In the forefront marches the gallant Lochiel. Oh, then there was a wild Highland yell that ripped open the sky!"

Young Clan's hearers let out a breath. The men fingered their weapons.

"And then," went on the young chief, "we saw that

they brought prisoners! Seventy captured redcoats marched
without arms in their midst.

" 'Now,' says Charles, 'we will raise the standard.' It was
raised by the old lord that had followed his father. Lochiel
stood by the Prince, and I on his other hand, and saw the
red and white silk shake out in the air. If you had but seen
the Prince's face as the banner rose! He was garbed in the
bright red of the Royal Stuart tartan, with ribbon and star
on his breast, and his blue Highland bonnet above his yellow hair, armed like the rest of us with dirk and claymore.
His eyes shot fire. Never have I seen so noble and soldierly
a figure. I will follow him to the death if need be!"

"Aye!" breathed his hearers.

"When the royal banner was snapping in air, the Prince
spoke to the clans. He spoke like a soldier, few words and
simple. 'I am filled with satisfaction,' said he, 'to find myself among the loyal and gallant gentlemen who now sur-
round me. I have come among you, because I am satisfied
that you are all prepared to live or die with me for the
right of your King and the defence of your liberties; and
for my part, I am resolved to conquer or to perish at your
head!'

"Upon this all the Highlanders threw their bonnets in
the air in a flying cloud of blue, and cheered till the narrow glen rang. As they cheered, the Prince turned to the
captive major of the redcoats.

" 'You may go back to your general,' said he. 'Tell him
what you have seen, and say that I am coming to give him
battle!' "

CHAPTER 6 ❧ *To Rise and Follow Charlie*

After her clan took up the sword for Prince Charles, Flora could hardly wait for news. Whenever a boat touched the shore, she ran with the rest to hear what news the boatman would tell.

"Our Prince is in Edinburgh!" cried a Macdonald clansman to the crowd on the shore, one day in September. Eagerly they clustered around to hear his story.

"Lochiel and his Camerons took the Netherbow Port without a drop of blood shed. The Prince marched in at the head of the clans, and now he holds the castle of his ancestors at Holyrood! It was a braw sight to see him come down into the King's Park, in his Highland tartans and his blue bonnet, with his yellow hair tied back and the star of St. Andrew on his breast. The people thronged him all the way, till he was forced to mount and ride. Still they thronged to kiss his hands, his boots, to touch him anyhow. Then at last he dismounted and went into the Palace, and a gentleman with naked sword marshaled him into the house of his forefathers. That night there was a great ball in the gallery. They say he dances as he rides, like a god; and all the ladies are in ecstasy. There is a white rose

in every bosom, and a white cockade in every hat! And
every lassie singing—

> Oh, Charlie, he's my darling,
> My darling, my darling,
> Charlie is my darling,
>   The young Chevalier!"

Soon the wearers of the white cockade had another song
to sing, a mocking song to the frightened English general:

> Hey, Johnnie Cope, are you waking yet?
> Or are you sleeping, I would wit,
> It's a wonder to me when the drums do beat
> That you don't awake in the morning.
>
> Fie now Johnnie, get up and run,
> The Highland bagpipe makes a din,
> It's best to sleep in a whole skin,
> For 'twill be a bloody morning!
>
> For all their bombs and hand grenades,
> 'Twas when they saw the Highland blades
> They ran to the hills like frightened jades
> All pursued by the clans in the morning!
>
> Cope went along to Haddington,
> They asked him where was all his men,
> 'The pox on me if I do ken,
> For I left them all in the morning!'

The ring of listeners rocked with laughter. The singer
was a Clanranald clansman who had seen the English run
at the battle of Prestonpans.

"A rout, a rout!" he cried. "When they heard the pipes,

and saw the cold steel of the claymore, they ran like red deer, as fast and as far, and left us the field and the plunder!"

In November, Hugh Macdonald took up the lease of Armadale. Armadale was a pleasant one-story thatched house of several comfortable rooms, built on the site of a former dwelling that had been burned years before. All that was left was the orchard wall and a walk of fine large ash trees. The house stood on a pleasant knoll rising from a cove on the Sound of Sleat, not very far across the water from Little Mallaig on the mainland. It was pleasant to look across the strait and see the fishermen's houses and the gulls hovering over the Sound, and the high head of Ben Nevis against the sky.

When Hugh Macdonald took his wife and family to Armadale, Flora went along to help her mother get settled. It put her one step nearer the troubles on the mainland; but it put her, also, right at the gateway to the Isles, where all the news came by. She was always eager for news of the cause she held dear.

After the victory of Prestonpans, the rumors flew thick and fast. The French were landed—the French were not landed—the Hessians were landed—the Hessians were not landed. Prince Charles held court every night at Holyrood, wearing fine tartan silk and red velvet breeches. Prince Charles slept with his Highlanders in the field, wrapped only in his plaid. (He did both.)

Prince Charles and his Highlanders had crossed the Esk and marched off for London.

That was no rumor. Even remote Uist thrilled to hear

that the Highland army, with Macdonalds of Clanranald in the van, were marching on London with the Stuart Prince at their head.

The next news left the wearers of the white cockade puzzled and incredulous. At Derby, within 127 miles of London and the crown, the Highland army had turned back. Not an Englishman had joined them, and the usurper's son, the burly Duke of Cumberland, was moving an army behind them to cut them off from home.

He failed. By one of their brilliant fast marches, the Highlanders crossed the Esk ahead of him, and got back to Scottish ground. The Duke pursued. What would happen next?

On a soft day in early spring, Flora was sitting on a turf bank by the old orchard wall at Armadale. The clouds, many and thin and high, trailed quick light shadows over the dancing wavelets of the Sound of Sleat, and her eyes followed them in a dream. She was singing to herself.

> O he's a ranting, roving lad,
> He is a brisk and bonnie lad,
> Betide what may I will be wed
> And follow the boy with the white cockade!
>
> I'll sell my spinning wheel, my tow,
> My good gray mare, my old red cow,
> To buy myself a tartan plaid
> To follow the boy with the white cockade!
>
> Betide what may I will be wed
> And follow the boy with the white cockade . . .

The minor cadence died along the air, and she lost herself in her dreaming.

The man coming along the road saw her before she saw him. He looked at her long. Her close-fitted gown was the young green of the budding leaves in the ash-tree walk. It was cut low, but the full white smock covered her to the silver chain about her creamy throat. On her bosom she wore a knot of ribbon like a white cockade. Her burnished hair was shaken loose.

She was far away in her dream as the man came closer. She never looked up until his shadow fell upon the knitting in her idle hands.

"Allan!"

She gave him her hand, and he kissed it, a ceremony they both performed in the grand Edinburgh manner. A moment he stood looking at her without releasing her hand. Then he pulled her to her feet and into his arms.

When he let her go, she could only stare at him. This was not Edinburgh manners. She knew that as a proper young lady she ought to swoon, or cry out, or slap him, or all three. With breath coming fast, she was considering all three courses, and also a fourth which she had thought up for herself—to throw her arms about his neck—when Allan remembered his manners as a proper young gentleman, and dropped to his knee, pulling off his blue bonnet.

"Forgive me," he said.

Then he rather spoiled the effect by putting his arms about her waist and holding her close.

"I've come to say goodbye. I'm going to the war. Sir Alexander is raising the clan."

"At last!" cried Flora in delight. She raised him to his feet, and took the knot of ribbon from her breast.

"At last I may put the white cockade in your bonnet!"

Allan picked up the bonnet he had dropped, and crushed it in his hand. A chill breath blew over him, and over her at the change in him.

"You mistake, Flora. The clan is to be raised for King George."

He showed his bonnet. It bore a red St. George's cross. The white cockade fell from Flora's hand.

"But you cannot!" she cried. "You cannot take arms against the son of your lawful King!"

"Where my chief leads I follow," said Allan.

"He is wicked and weak," cried Flora, "to lead you against your own Prince and your own people. Why should you have to follow?"

"I know my duty," said Allan stiffly.

"Then I know mine," said Flora as stiffly.

With angry energy she snapped the silver chain around her neck and held out to him chain and ring together.

"Bring it back to me," she said, "when you wear the white cockade!"

Over Skye was more shadow than sunshine as Flora walked slowly back to the house.

She found big Hugh standing by the fire. His blue bonnet was cocked jauntily over his one good eye. He too wore the red George's cross.

"We march tomorrow for the Ferry," said he, "and so on to headquarters at Inverness."

"Father!" she cried. "Why must you go?"

"Sir Alexander gives me no choice," said Hugh calmly. "He himself has little enough appetite for it. But he is egged on by the chief of Macleod. The Macleods are marched already."

"Do you *want* to go?" asked Flora.

"Of course not. As little does Allan of Kingsburgh *want* to go, or many another good fellow of my acquaintance. As little, they tell me, did half the Macleods want to go. They say his piper, the great Macrimmon, marched from Dunvegan with the tears streaming down his cheeks, and playing his own lament on the war pipes, for he foresees that he will never return."

Soon Sir Alexander's men marched away. The next news of Prince Charlie's doings was brought to Skye by the same men. They came streaming back in full flight, red crosses and all. They had been utterly routed by an army of five men! They never stopped running till they had put the Sound between them and the terrible forces of the Prince. The Highland army had entered Inverness without firing a shot.

Allan Macdonald was so ashamed of the whole affair that he never came near Flora. Stepfather Hugh thought it was a great joke. Another Macdonald of the right side had them all laughing as he told the tale at the house door.

"Thus it was," said he. "The wicked Laird of Macleod hears that Prince Charles is not far from Inverness, rallying his men to attack the town. He is housed at Moy Hall. Moy Hall belongs to brave Lady Macintosh, the lass that raised her clan alone when her craven husband ran away to join King George's men. Macleod decides to take the

Prince by stealth. He musters fifteen hundred Macleods and Macdonalds, puts himself at the head, and marches out by night to surprise the Prince.

"Now some say that a loyal old lady of Inverness sent a runner to Moy by a short cut, and some say a tavern lass heard the militia officers planning, and ran all the way to Moy in bare feet. Whichever it was, Lady Macintosh gets warning. She sends out a sturdy blacksmith, one Donald Fraser, and four men with muskets. They are to watch the road and bring her word when the Macleods are near.

"It is nigh dawn. Here come the militia along the road, marching in silence, wicked Norman at their head. Lying in ambush, the stout blacksmith gets an itchy trigger finger. He decides to try whether five men fighting in a just cause cannot give a good account of themselves against fifteen hundred. He posts his men here and there, with very particular orders.

"As the Macleods file into the narrow place where the gallant five lie hid, they hear the bold blacksmith shout in a loud voice: 'We have the dogs now! Advance, Clanranald! Forward, Lochiel! Up and at 'em, Keppoch!' At the same time musketfire rakes them from each side and from different places, for the men of Moy dash back and forth, firing from one crag after another, shouting the different clan slogans as they fire. 'We are trapped!' cry the Macleods. 'We are surrounded!' Back they go on the run, dragging their dead with them."

"Did wicked Norman fall?"

"To my sorrow, not he. It was his piper that fell at his side, the great piper of the Isles, Donald Ban Macrimmon."

The listeners were silent. The joke tasted sour. They

fell to mourning for Donald Ban, the last of the great pipers, who had piped his own lament as he marched, much against his heart, uselessly to his death. Soon all the Isles were singing Macrimmon's lament:

Macleod's wizard flag from the gray castle sallies,
The rowers are seated, unmoored are the galleys;
Gleam war axe and broadsword, clang target and quiver,
As Macrimmon plays Farewell to Dunvegan forever.

Farewell to each cliff, where the breakers are foaming,
Farewell each dark glen in which red deer are roaming,
Farewell lonely Skye, to lake, mountain, and river,
Macleod may return, but Macrimmon shall never.

Farewell the bright clouds that on Cuillin are sleeping;
Farewell the bright eyes in the Fort that are weeping;
To each minstrel delusion farewell! and for ever—
Macrimmon departs to return to you never!

The Banshee's wild voice sings the death dirge before me,
And the pall of the dead for a mantle hangs o'er me;
But my heart shall not fly, and my nerve shall not quiver,
Though devoted I go—to return again never!

Too oft shall the note of Macrimmon bewailing
Be heard when the Gael on their exile are sailing;
Dear land! to the shores whence unwilling we sever,
Return, return, return we shall never!

All too soon the lament was for themselves. In mid-April, suddenly and completely, the hopes of the house of Stuart were wrecked forever. The Highlanders were slaughtered and scattered at Culloden, and their Prince was driven to flight. Word came to Sir Alexander's militia to return to the mainland, for there was nothing more to fear. Hugh Macdonald marched away. Flora, sick and stunned, stayed with her mother.

The next few days were heart-rending. Fleeing Highlanders began to pass through Armadale, making for their homes in Skye and the Outer Isles. They were dazed, wounded, and heartbroken. Flora and her mother fed them, tended them, and passed them on. From them they heard such stories as pierced their hearts and broke their sleep at night.

"We fought half-starving and before our men had all gathered," said one wounded boy. "The redcoats had cannon, and we had none. They stood, and we fell three deep before their fire. The Highland charge was broken. As the wounded lay on the lost field in the cold of night, the redcoats stole everything we had, even to our shirts. In the morning comes a highborn Whig lady in a coach-and-six to see the sights, as if it was a waxwork, and rides over the bodies of the dead for sport. I saw the coachman flick at a dying Highlander with his whip as if he had been a dog in a ditch. Then came the redcoats to finish off the dying. They blew out our brains without mercy. They thought me dead already, or I could not have escaped. I saw the Duke of Cumberland himself ride through the field with his officers and soldiers following him. He draws rein beside a wounded Highlander lying bareheaded on the ground. Seeing no cockade— 'To whom do you belong?' says he. 'To the Prince!' cries the wounded man. 'Colonel Wolfe,' says the Butcher Duke to his aide, 'pray draw your pistol and shoot me this insolent scoundrel!' 'Your Royal Highness,' says the officer, 'I will give you back my commission in the army before I will become your executioner!' Oh," cried the young Highlandman, "Wolfe is one Englishman that I could serve under without shame!"

"Did they save the poor man?"

"No, miss. The Butcher Duke cursed and blustered, and got a common soldier to do the dirty job for him."

"And the Prince?"

"I saw him ride forward rallying the clans. Then the redcoats advanced, and a knot of Irish officers turned his bridle and rode off with him. I do not know what became of him."

CHAPTER 7 ❧ *The Fugitive Prince*

Soon after the defeat of the Prince at Culloden, Angus came to Armadale. He came to fetch Flora back to South Uist. Now that he was in charge of Milton, he said, he needed his housekeeper. Flora was glad to go.

On the way back they stopped on Benbecula. Nunton was still peaceful. When they sat down to dine the next afternoon, to the skirling of the pipes, it hardly seemed as if anything had changed. There was old Clanranald at the head of the table, and Lady Clanranald at the foot, and the long table between filled with clansmen and guests.

Neil Maceachen was there. So was Captain Donald Macdonald, Flora's old playmate at Nunton, whom she had not seen since he went away to join the French army. He had come back to fight for the Prince, escaped safe from Culloden, and hoped to remain undisturbed at home until things simmered down. Young Clanranald, he said, was in hiding on the mainland.

At the table, also, Flora was surprised to see Master Macaulay, the minister of South Uist. Being a strong Hanoverian, he could hardly be expected to sympathize with the kind of talk he would hear over the table at Nunton.

There could be but one topic: Where was Prince Charlie?

"The young man will soon be captured," said Macaulay positively. "It is known that he has taken his flight into the Isles. General Campbell with a strong force is gone after him to St. Kilda. Any day we shall see the sails returning off Uist, and know that they have taken the Young Pretender."

As they were drinking their French claret, a herdsman rushed into the room. He brought with him a whiff of the byre, and he was winded and disordered from running; but he was admitted at once to his chief.

He brought such news that his wits were addled. He shouted it, without a thought.

"Armed men! Armed men have landed—dressed like officers—and their leader is taller by a head than any, and yellow-haired, and carries himself like a king. They came upon shore at Rushness—we are invaded, the war has come upon us!"

Clanranald signed to the piper, and the tune broke off. The same name was in every head, but nobody spoke it.

In the bustle, Macaulay sent for his servant, whispered in his ear, and ordered him off. Meanwhile old Clanranald sent his son Donald to see what this landing might mean.

The minister's servant was the first to return. His shoulders were wet; wind and rain were lashing the isle. Flora watched master and man confer by the door. The minister was licking his lips in suppressed excitement. He scrawled a line on a leaf of his pocket notebook, folded it, handed it to his man, and gave him a mighty shove to hasten his departure. Then he turned to the company, flicked his eye over their faces, bowed, and went away smiling. Flora watched him go with great uneasiness.

Then Donald returned.

"It is the Prince! He is lodged in a hut by the shore, with no other cover against the rain but the boat sail!"

"In a hut!" exclaimed Lady Clanranald. "The son of my King in a hut! Clan, you must go at once!"

Old Clanranald sighed deeply. He had done all he could to stay out of the affair; but now the affair had come to him. He had no other honorable course, but to go to his Prince, and serve him.

"I will go," he said. "You, Neil, since you can speak the French, you shall accompany me."

Neil donned his bonnet with delight at being chosen. Old Clanranald sighed again, wrapped his plaid about him, and went out into the storm.

It was morning when Flora saw Neil again.

"Well, miss," said he saucily, "what will you pay me for a kiss of my mouth, for I have kissed the hand of our bonnie Prince since last we met?"

"Not a half-penny," said Flora, "for I don't purchase secondhand goods."

"You'd say different, could you but see him! He sits upon turf in that miserable hut, with the rain leaking upon him through the chinks and only an old sail to protect him, and still he bears himself like a king on his throne."

"What is he like to look at?"

"He's tall and handsomely shaped. His eyes are sad, but he laughs much, and keeps up his heart. He is dressed in a shabby tartan kilt and an old servant's coat. His hair is yellow, and the look on his face is noble. Not a man there but would die for him."

"Who is in his company?"

"His pilot, and a pair of Irish captains, and his servant, one Ned Burke."

"Neil, is he safe? What will become of him?"

"He is safe, and takes ship from Stornoway. They will sail east-around for France. Thence he will come again with troops."

"I pray that he may."

"Flora!"

It was Angus, disapproving.

"Come, Flora, we must be stepping to Milton."

"Wait, Angus, there is so much I want to know from Neil!"

"Flora, in such times as these, it were better for you to know nothing!"

So Flora went back to Milton, and knew nothing. She was very busy redding up the farmhouse. She sometimes thought Angus must have been stirring up his gear with a stick.

When all was set to rights at Milton, it was time to drive the cattle up the glen to Alisary. This was always the happiest time of the year for Flora. She loved the quiet mountain corrie, the glass-clear burn murmuring over the pebbles, the bright grass, the sun on the gray rocks, the distant sight of the sea. She even loved the little black cattle and the wicked-faced goats. There was a look about them that reminded her of the look on Master Macaulay's face when he left the hall at Nunton.

At this picture Flora, watching the herd on a sunny afternoon, set down her spindle to laugh. The sun danced on her bright hair.

"What, pretty cousin!" said a voice behind her, "are you not afraid of the headache, that you sit so boldly in the sun?"

It was Neil Maceachen. He came striding, half running, down the slope to her side.

"Why should I fear the sun?"

"You should not; for I may tell you that the high and mighty most illustrious Prince Charles does not fear it, but believes it does him all the good in the world; and when the officious Captain O'Neille would have him move into the shade, he bids him to pack about his business!"

"What nonsense is this? What do you know of Prince Charles? Is he not off for France by this time?"

"Far from it. He is on Uist."

Flora could only stare.

"When he approached Stornoway to embark, he was mobbed by two hundred men in arms, who had somehow been warned of his coming."

"The goat!" cried Flora. Then at Neil's puzzled look

she amended: "Macaulay. His father dwells in those parts. Sure Macaulay was quicker than we, and sent a warning to the Prince's enemies. But two hundred men! How did he come off safe?"

"He resolved to sell his life dear. But they did not thirst for his blood, only for his absence. They refused him a ship, and bade him turn back, which he had no other resource but to do. So back they all come. They are chased by the King's ships, and forced to hide upon a desert island and live upon drying fish and oatmeal mixed with seawater. But at last they win back to Benbecula, and send for Clanranald. I thought the old man would weep. But off we go, he and I again, with gun and lead-belt and powder horn pretending to go a-hunting, and come to the Prince.

"We found him in a little hovel by the shore, thin and weatherworn with his hardships, but in perfect good spirits. 'I have escaped many perils on sea and land,' says he, 'and I am now satisfied that I shall never die by water or the sword. Providence,' says he to Clanranald, 'has sent me back under your protection, where I hope to be sheltered. I throw myself into your hands. Dispose of me as you see fit.'

" 'You have nothing to fear,' says old Clanranald. 'I will find you a place to hide, where none but your friends shall come near you.'

"I conducted him then to Bareness, where there is a little hut for a refuge. It did not prove very convenient. The door was so low, that to go in and out, being so tall, he must kneel and creep in. It was too much for even his incomparable patience. He begged Clanranald to send him to some Christian place where he could have more room,

'For,' said he, 'I think that this monstrous hole was deserted by the Devil himself because he had not room to turn around in it!' "

"His Royal Highness is pleased to be merry!"

"He is always pleased to be merry. He will dance Highland reels by the hour, with no more accompaniment than his own singing and the knacking of his thumbs. He and Ned Burke are forever at their flyting game of 'Devil speed the liars,' and Ned lost the bout and took the buffet by the Prince's lie about the Devil leaving the hut."

"Well, but did the poor Prince leave the hut?"

"He did. 'Neil,' says Clan, 'we'll hide him in your forest house in Coradale. No one comes there. There is a cave with a prospect over sea and heather'—you remember the cave, Flora. 'The Prince may be safe there as long as he chooses.' He swore that the forest house was a palace to the hole he had left. We made him a seat of green turf. He sat and looked over the glen, and ate oat bread with cheese, and goat's milk with it. I washed his poor travel-galled feet as he smoked a pipe of tobacco, and then upon a bed of heather and rushes he slept the sun around the sky."

"How shall a Prince of gentle rearing pass his time in such a wilderness?"

"I tell you, merrily. He strolls with his gun, for he is a perfect marksman, and will bring you down muirfowl on the wing. He has the art of whistling the plover out of the air to him, that it is a wonder to see him surrounded by their wings. He runs like the deer, and I have seen him bring down a buck shooting on the run."

"And why," asked Flora, "have you left your charge to come to this side of the island?"

"To see my good cousin, and offer that kiss before its price goes up."

"Hoot, toot," said Flora.

"And to look to the west, and see if the cursed Campbell should be coming from St. Kilda with the King's ships."

"Never a sail," said Flora.

"Then I'll go back over the mountain; for I don't think Angus will care to hear my news at all."

Sun and shower, twilight and dawn, went over the shieling. It was on a day of mist that Flora, walking along the glen where the cows were grazing, met a stranger. She stopped still. What was he, what did his presence mean?

The stranger came on toward her along the margin of the stream. He was a slim, wiry young fellow with a lean dark face, ink-black hair tied behind with a bit of ribbon, and dramatic dark bristling eyebrows. He wore the tattered remains of a white uniform from which the gold lace was fraying. His white breeches had a flapping tear on one thigh. He pulled off a large three-cornered hat and held it over his heart as he came near. He halted, advanced a wayworn boot, flourished the hat three times, and bowed to the ground.

"Goddess," he cried, "divine Flora, I kiss your feet!"

He bowed again, low enough to do so, if he really intended to.

"You know my name?" said Flora.

"No, madam," said this puzzling person, "I have not that honor, to my regret."

"Yet you call me by my name, Flora."

"Flora was a goddess. *Per baccho*, the gods were at your christening!"

Flora had no idea what to make of him. The smack of his tongue was Irish, yet not Irish. The look of his long upper lip was Irish, yet his liquid dark eyes and olive skin were certainly of the South.

"Flora," he cried, "goddess of flowers, accept the homage of your humble servant who lays himself at your feet—Captain Felix O'Neille, yours to command!"

He executed another bow which, Flora thought, would certainly lay him at her feet in earnest; but he recovered himself nimbly, and kissed her hand with an air.

"Captain O'Neille," she said, enlightened. "You are welcome to Alisary. How have you left our royal master?"

"Ssh!" cried the Captain, rolling his dark eyes at the cows. "Rocks have ears!" He advanced his mouth within an inch of her snood, and uttered: "He is well!"

"And yourself, sir?"

"My sufferings are as nothing," said O'Neille earnestly, "if my royal master is saved."

"Amen," said Flora. She began to like him better.

"I come to spy if the coast is clear," said the Irishman, "or if the King's ships are come from St. Kilda."

"The coast is still clear," said Flora.

After that first meeting O'Neille came often to Alisary to see if the coast was clear. When he put aside his play-acting, Flora found him an earnest, devoted, pleasant young man. Whenever he came, Flora patched his tattered French uniform and gave him good things to eat.

Sitting beside her in the glen, watching her small fingers ply the needle, O'Neille told her his history:

"My father was an Irishman of Tyrone, ruined in the exile of the Stuarts. I was born in Italy, and served in the armies of Spain. Then I joined a regiment of wild-goose Irishmen—"

"What are wild-goose Irishmen?"

"Those that flew away in a flock after the battle of the Boyne, and joined the service of the King of France. I joined Dillon's, and they made me learn English."

"You have learned it well."

"I thank you, miss. Good faith, I was glad of it when they sent me to follow Prince Charles. I fought at Culloden—brought the Prince off the field of defeat—and have followed his fortunes ever since. I will follow him to France, or die in these Isles defending him."

"God bless you for it," said Flora, snapping her thread.

The young Irishman kissed the hand that handed him his mended coat. Flora smiled at him, and in return for his story told about her family in the Isle of Skye. O'Neille listened thoughtfully.

After he had left her for the mountains, Flora turned to go back to the shieling. Halfway, she paused to look at the sun on the sea. As she shaded her eyes with her hand, she stiffened. Far away, like drifting petals, she saw sails at the edge of the sea. The redcoat fleet was coming back from St. Kilda! Quickly she sent a herdboy running over the mountain after O'Neille.

The next morning, full of disquiet, she took up her plaid and set out for Benbecula.

Clanranald and his lady were from home. Their daughter Peggy made Flora welcome.

"Only think, Flora," cried the young miss, "my mother has gone to see the Prince, and she would not take me along."

"You are too young."

"I am not! I'll make my way to him yet, you'll see!"

"You will not know how to behave."

"I shall know very well how to behave. I'll curtsey very low, thus—" Miss Peggy showed how she would spread her draperies, wave her fingers, and bend her head with a fetching upward glance of the eye. "Then he will extend his fingers *so*—" Miss Peggy bestowed a stiff hand with a haughty air. "—and I will kiss them *so*—" She kissed her own hand loudly.

Flora began to laugh.

"Forget these monkey tricks. They say he's kind and full of laughter. He cannot sit on a bank of turf and expect the fallals of the French court. If you reverence him for his birth, and love him for his own worth, you will know how to show it."

"La, miss, you're a cool one!"

These daydreams were interrupted by the entrance of old Clanranald and his lady.

"Dear Flora," said Lady Clanranald, kissing her absentmindedly. "I have seen the Prince. Poor lad, he is thin and worn. His mother that's dead would weep to see him. But he's stout of heart for all his troubles. He made much of me, and kissed me twice at parting, and I'm sure I wish him safe with all my heart! But come, Flora, you must be sharp-set for your dinner!"

The pipes were shrilling in the hall. Flora went in, and found at her side Felix O'Neille, who had escorted the Clanranalds from Coradale. His face lighted up at sight of her. During the meal he devoted himself to her. Over the wine he asked her a question:

"What would you give for a sight of your Prince?"

Flora looked at him quickly to see if he was fooling. His face was perfectly grave.

"As I had not that happiness to see him before," she said carefully, "so I do not look for it now. But," she added in a burst from her heart, "a mere sight of him would make me happy, though I was on one hill and he on another!"

O'Neille nodded and said nothing. Flora decided that he was just talking. She went back to Alisary rejoicing to know that the Prince was safe and in health still.

Within a very few days, Flora had to give up all hope of ever seeing her Prince, and almost all hope of his ever escaping alive. The redcoats suddenly began to converge on the island from all quarters. First arrived Hugh Macdonald of Armadale and his men of the militia. Campbell's sails were crowding in from the west. To the east the Minch was thronged with ships. Sloops and schooners were scouring every loch and inlet.

As Flora looked down from Alisary on a sea dotted with sails, once more a man came over the edge of the hill. It was neither Neil nor Felix. It was Flora's cousin, John Macdonald. John had been a lieutenant in the Prince's service, and now, Flora knew, he was in that service still.

"Cousin John, what news?"

"As bad as can be, not to be the worst. I do not see how the Prince can escape capture. He is pressed very hard.

He has been obliged to leave the glen, for no place is safe very long. For nights he has slept in the open, in a little boat lurking in some sea loch, or under the sky in the heather, in rain and mist, with only his plaid to cover him. Food has been hard to find, and safety there is none. He sent me to the south for news, and I return with the worst of tidings. Campbell comes from the west. The soldiers come from the east, from the Minch. The Macleods are on Harris, and will march from the north. More redcoats are on Barra, and this day they will cross to Uist from the south. They will come from all sides, searching every nook and cranny, and march till they meet. How can he escape them? Not a fox can take to his burrow but they will find it. Not a bird of the air can leave this island without their consent. We are all dead men!"

The boy pulled his plaid over his eyes and wept the tears of long exhaustion. After a while he ate the oaten bannocks and milk that Flora gave him, and went away over the mountain, back to die by the side of his Prince. Flora watched him go with a desperate prayer in her heart.

Book Three ✤ Flora and Charles

On hills that are his own by right,
  He roams a lonely stranger,
On every hand he's pressed by want,
  On every side by danger.
Last night I met him in the glen,
  My heart near bursted fairly,
For sadly changed indeed was he.
  Oh! Woe's me for Prince Charlie!

Dark night came on, the tempest howled,
  Out o'er the hills and valleys;
And where was it that your Prince lay down,
  Whose home should be a palace?
He rolled him in a Highland plaid,
  Which covered him but sparely,
And slept beneath a bush of broom.
  Oh! Woe's me for Prince Charlie!

(OLD SONG)

CHAPTER 8 🌿 *At Alisary*

Flora Macdonald stood in the doorway of the shieling at Alisary and watched the long twilight die along the sea. The smooth swells gleamed in the last light like the billowing of a fine gown of changeable taffeta, gray-green shot with copper. Over the hill the great full moon of summer was rising, brightening the green glen beneath her to the unearthly color of a faery hill, and silvering the edge of the rocks above. On the sea to the west and south moon-silver touched with magic a host of sails. But Flora could not feel the spell. King George's ships were converged upon the island, and his redcoats were closing in, two thousand strong, to earn the price of blood—to destroy one brave young man, the son of her King, for a price of thirty thousand pounds.

Flora shuddered. Where was he tonight, under what rock, friendless in the heather? How long could he escape his pursuers? Her heart ached with pity for him. She was suddenly cold. She drew her plaid about her shoulders.

"Do what has to be done," she reminded herself.

She threw a last glance along the glen where lay her brother's cows that she had come to keep. She smiled affectionately at the quiet little creatures, patient and motionless in the moonlight. Then she lifted the little wooden pails that she had just filled with milk, and carried them into the shieling.

The long summer twilight was fading, and the round moon was growing brighter on the darkening sky. Flora stowed away the buckets and prepared herself to sleep. Her bed was only a bank of turf made soft and fragrant with heather. She put off her close-bodiced gown, purple-green like the heather. She freed her bright hair from the snood and shook it loose. In white smock and petticoat, she wrapped herself in her plaid and lay down on her springy couch, inhaling its fragrance deeply. As she drifted into sleep, the last thought of her heart was a prayer for the fugitive lad on the mountain. . . .

She did not know what woke her. The moon had moved higher, and swung south. Moonlight streamed along the floor from the open door. Flora's eyes followed it, still half in sleep. Suddenly she sat up. The flesh of her arms prickled. A man was standing in the doorway. A redcoat? A clansman? Who?

Flora was not accustomed to be afraid. She challenged sharply:

"Who are you?"

"God bless all here," said an easy voice. O'Neille!

"Is this the way of it in foreign parts," said Flora lightly, half vexed, "to call upon a lady at dead of night?"

"Don't be afraid," said the exasperating Irishman.

"I'm not afraid," said Flora.

"Then tell me something quickly. It's your own father has come onto Uist leading the militia, bad success to 'em. Will they pass this way tonight?"

"No," said Flora, "not till tomorrow night. You are still safe in these hills for a few hours longer. But then what will you do?"

"Since you ask, I'll tell you. I've the fine headpiece on my shoulders, miss, and I've contrived a plan. We'll snatch the lad you know of out of their very claws, and that by the help of—"

"Who?"

"Miss Flora Macdonald."

Flora gasped.

"I couldn't! How could I?"

"Now pray don't waste time arguing, miss," said this outrageous Irishman coolly, "for I've brought a friend to see you."

"Oh! Is it—?"

"It is one you won't deny, though you deny me, when you see him face to face."

"Don't think, sir," said Flora grandly, "that I am quite so fainthearted as what that comes to!"

O'Neille merely smiled. Going to the open door, he whistled softly.

"Oh! Wait, wait! I'm not fit to be seen!"

O'Neille looked at the excited girl as she leaped to her feet. The moonlight silvered the full folds of her snowy shift and white petticoat, and gilded the ripples of her loosened hair. Privately he thought her very fit to be seen by any king's son in Christendom, but he restrained an impulse to say so. Outside a plover fluted, and the Irishman fluted in reply.

Flora snatched up her gown and belted it about her.

Barely was she girded, when another shadow fell across
the door, and Charles Edward Stuart, heir to three kingdoms, entered the bothy.

He trod the clay as if it had been the polished floor of
Holyrood, bearing his tall form as proudly as if he still
wore gold lace on his broad shoulders, ribbon and star on
his deep chest. It was to the pride of his bearing that Flora
sank low in a deep curtsey. Instantly, pulling off his
threadbare blue bonnet, the Prince took her hand in his and
raised her, bending to her from his height with a gracious-
ness as inborn as his pride.

Flora was hardly conscious what words he spoke. His
voice was musical. To her surprise he spoke English
purely.

The Prince took the seat of honor—the heather couch
—and O'Neille mounted guard at the door. It was good
manners to offer some refreshment. With perfect simplicity Flora offered all she had—a wooden pail of milk.
It might have been fine wine in a goblet of crystal, so
graciously did the Prince accept. He drank with relish.
Flora saw with a pang that he was hungry.

While O'Neille was finishing off the milk, Flora seated
herself on the ground at the Prince's feet. She had heard
much of his surpassing beauty, his eyes of brilliant blue, his
lips like Cupid's, his form like Apollo's, his bearing like
Mars'—and like a sensible girl she had shrugged it off as
poetry. Now the reality was before her. How different—
and yet how handsome—the real man was.

He wore a threadbare philibeg and plaid of Clanranald
tartan. Upon his feet were rough hairy Highland brogues,
and his tartan hose was scorched the length of his shin. His

muscular knees were bare, and spattered with mud from the streams he had crossed. His rough light curls were bleached, and his face and hands were bronzed by two months under the sky. He looked strong, resolute, and unafraid.

It was fact, not poetry, the beautiful proud curve of the lip, the brilliance of the heavy-lidded eye; but the celebrated classic oval of his face was pared to the bone now with hardship, grief, and suffering.

O'Neille set down the pail and said something to the Prince in a foreign tongue. The Prince nodded, and turned to Flora with a smile that made his haggard face radiant. He took her hand in his.

"You see, Miss Macdonald," he said, "that I am in distress, and very near the end of my resources. I throw myself upon your protection. Will you not take me out of this trap and over the sea to Skye?"

"How can I?" cried Flora, her heart rent. "How can I? Sir Alexander Macdonald has been like a father to me. He is sworn in the service of the redcoats. How can I take you over to his land of Skye and bring ruin on his head?"

"Sir Alexander is not on Skye," put in O'Neille. "He's at Inverness, fawning on the bloody butcher Cumberland. So how can he be ruined whatever may happen on Skye?"

"I cannot," said Flora, and hid her face in her hands.

"You're thinking of the scandal," cried O'Neille, snapping his fingers like one making a discovery, "if you should go careering off to Skye in company with a pair of brave sparks like me and my yellow-haired friend here!"

"I am not indeed!" protested Flora, but O'Neille swept on unheeding.

"Sure the fair fame of Miss Flora Macdonald stands too high to take any harm by such a deed. By it you will gain immortal fame. But if that's in your mind, there's a remedy. If you like, I'll marry you directly!"

"What!" cried Flora.

"Here and now, by this hand!" vowed the Irishman. "We may exchange an oath, by the old Scotch form, and become man and wife forever. Our Prince shall stand witness. What do you say?"

He was in deepest earnest.

"I thank you from my heart," said Flora sincerely, "but there needs no such desperate remedy—"

"Why, as to that, 'tis a pleasure—"

"My friend speaks truth," put in the Prince, his eyes a-twinkle, "for I assure you, Miss Macdonald, you have stolen his heart quite away!"

"I thank your Royal Highness for your interest, and him for his offer; but my heart, I thank fortune, is still my own."

"Then will you go with me to Skye?"

Flora looked into the commanding eyes, and slowly, still, she shook her head.

"I beg you to believe me, it is impossible. They would take you on the shore. How could I prevent?"

"If you cannot prevent, then no one can," said O'Neille "It is your own father that commands the militia. Surely he will consent to send you to visit your mother on Skye!"

Flora wrung her fingers till the knuckles whitened

"I cannot—I cannot—do not ask me. They would take you before my face."

The Prince rose to his full height. His thin face was grim.

"They will never take me. Do you think I would fall alive into their hands? I will make my way to Skye, or I will die upon your beach."

Flora came to her knees. "Oh, no!"

"Then will you not go with me to Skye?"

Flora rested her brow against the bronzed hand he held out to her, and yielded.

"I will go with your Royal Highness through the vast world," she said, "if in that way I can do the least thing for your safety."

"I will always be grateful," he said, and raised her to her feet.

Now it was "Do what has to be done" with a vengeance!

"You may pass me off," proposed the Prince, "for your servingman. It will be a role to be fond of, eh, O'Neille?"

Flora looked at the regal blond head, the aristocratic nose, the fiery eye, and her heart failed her. Who in his senses would take this high-blooded creature for a gillie? What disguise would avail? Such a stranger, whatever his garb, would be stopped on sight. Only an old man, or a cripple, or a child could hope to pass the patrols.

Or a woman.

Flora looked sidewise at the Prince, and a laugh tugged at her lip.

"I shall pass off your Royal Highness," she said solemnly, "as my serving-*woman!*"

The laugh came. It brought the Prince's ready laughter. After a shocked moment, O'Neille joined in, and the moonlit glen rang with their merriment.

"It is a rawboned colleen," remarked O'Neille, still laughing as he impudently scanned his royal master.

"It is not a neat shape," conceded the Prince, looking down his muscular length ruefully. "I doubt I can pass for a woman at all."

"Well now," said O'Neille, "I don't know. I've seen such a long lantern-headed trollop before this. They breed the like in County Tyrone."

"You have hit it!" cried Flora. "If his Royal Highness is overlank for a woman (pray forgive my plain speaking, sir), and if he cannot speak the Erse, all is explained if he's an Irishwoman—"

"Well spoken, Miss Flora, a true Irish bull!"

"And moreover, he may be clad in the Irish style, in a great cap with flaps and an Irish cape with a hood, so that his face may be hid."

"Oh," said O'Neille, "it will be a pretty wench indeed. Your servant, fair Mistress O'Neille!"

"The Old Scratch fly away with *O'Neille*," said the Prince, laughing. "I'll not do the O'Neilles so much honor. I'll be Mistress Burke, after my faithful servant, Ned Burke; and you, my mistress, may call me Betty."

"Well then, Miss Betty Burke," smiled Flora, "thus I take you into my service, and I'll see to your fitting out without delay."

"Now where will you find a gown that will cover those shins?" wondered O'Neille. "You see they're longer by half an ell than any lady's shins that's on this island!"

"How come you so familiar with the ladies' shins, pray, Captain O'Neille?" said the Prince reprovingly. "That matter may be left to Miss Flora."

"And I," said Flora, "shall leave it to Lady Clanranald. I'll go to Benbecula as soon as day breaks."

In that northern isle, summer nights were short. Barely had her midnight visitors left her, before Flora saw the light beginning to return. She rose, in her close-bodied heather gown still, drank a mouthful of milk, took her plaid, and descended the corrie.

As she walked down the glen, she lifted her eyes often and wishfully to the heights, wondering where her Prince had found refuge when he left her, and dropped them again to the beach fearful every moment to see it splashed with the red of the soldiers' coats—or with blood.

But nothing stirred on the shore, and Flora ran lightly down the rocky path until she came to the way that led along the strand to the ford of Benbecula.

She had a long walk before her. On her left hand glittered the sea. On her right hand lifted the hills of Uist, rosy with early bell heather. Plovers whistled, cuckoos called. Tern skimmed the water, and gulls wheeled lazily with an eye cocked for the herring-fry. Flora's loneliness seemed complete.

Yet as she passed under a rocky point, two pairs of eyes, a black pair and a blue, looked down on the little figure in the shadow-purple gown.

"God send every serving-lass such a mistress as Betty Burke's!" said the taller of the two young men.

"Amen," said he of the black eyes.

Flora walked on briskly. Never a redcoat was to be seen. When she came to the ford, the tide was at the ebb. Without losing a moment she crossed over the sands. Once across, she had but a step to go. She was rejoicing at her progress when suddenly she found herself surrounded by armed men. They wore Skye tartans, and the red crosses of the militia. They were all strangers.

They were courteous but firm. Flora had no pass? Then she must wait. When the officer came, he would examine her. If her business was honest, no doubt he would pass her along. In the meanwhile she must wait in the guardhouse.

The guardhouse was nothing but a miserable little turf hut on the shore. In it Flora waited in uneasy suspense. She waited all night. She tossed on the turf couch fretting. Where was Charles? What would become of him now?

In the morning the summons came. Flora went with her heart in her mouth. The officer was at breakfast. He looked up from his broiled collops of mutton, and blinked his one good eye.

"Flora!" It was Hugh Macdonald.

"Father—I was looking for you."

"You have found me, my dear. What can I do for you?"

"I've a mind to go home to Skye."

"That's well thought on," said her father, "for your mother's not over well, and the times are troubled. She'll be fair glad to see you."

"Will you give me a pass?"

"That I will."

"Put in Neil Maceachen to take care of me."

"I will gladly." Hugh reached for quill and inkhorn. "Then the pass is for two."

"No, father. For three. There's my waiting woman."

"You had never a waiting woman before," said Hugh thoughtfully, and put down the quill.

"I have one now." Flora straightened her shoulders and plunged. "It is a poor hungry Irish body that has claimed my protection, and as she spins very well, I thought my mother would be glad of her services, though she's shy and wild, poor creature, and do, please, Father, let me carry her with me to Skye, for she's hungry and weary, and—and I pity her sore . . ."

Flora's breath ran out, and she looked at her father, the Hanoverian captain, in dumb appeal.

"These are ill times," said he, "for a young lass to be going about with strangers . . ." He sat frowning. Flora risked her last cast.

"Do you remember, Father, walking on the shore at Boradale, you saw a boat land?"

"Aye, what then?"

"And from it came a company of gentlemen, and among them one whose hand you kissed, the first to do so upon his landing?"

"Aye, God protect him wherever he may be."

"Then pray, Father, give me a pass for Betty Burke."

Her father slowly raised his head and looked into her eyes. For a held breath there was stillness. Then big Hugh lifted his chin.

"With all my heart," he said. He scribbled a line. "But stay, it will go the better if I pass my own word for Miss Burke."

He drew another sheet and wrote:

MY DEAR WIFE:

I have sent your daughter from this country lest she should be in any way frightened with the troops lying here. She has got one Betty Burke, an Irish girl, who, as she tells me, is a good spinster. If her spinning pleases you, you may keep her till she spin all your lint, or if you have any wool to spin, you may employ her. I have sent Neil Maceachen along with your daughter and Betty Burke to take care of them.

I am your dutiful husband,
HUGH MACDONALD

JUNE 22ND, 1746

He handed the papers to Flora.

"God speed you, my dear," he said, "and God bless you for your kindness to poor, homeless, hungering, wandering—Miss Burke!"

CHAPTER 9   *On Benbecula*

"Oh, Flora!" cried Lady Clanranald as soon as she saw her. "What will become of us! Brother Alexander is taken up by the redcoats and carried off to prison for helping the Prince. His womenfolk are

tied neck and heels until they confess where Charles is hid.
I thank fortune they do not know!"

"Where is Clan?"

"Gone off to the mainland. Peggy and I are alone."

Flora's heart sank. What help could she find here?

But she underrated valiant little Lady Clan. The chief's
wife was stout of heart. She was not held back by what the
redcoats might do to her. She entered into the scheme at
once.

The redcoats from the north were advancing on Benbecula. There was little time left. Too much of it had to
be spent at the needle. There was not a stitch of a garment
at Nunton that would come halfway down Betty Burke's
long shanks. Flora, Lady Clanranald, and Peggy fell to.
No court gown, no wedding dress was ever stitched with
such eager good will.

The next day the good weather broke, and the rain came
down. Sitting snug at her needle by a good peat fire, Flora
shivered for the bonnie laddie lying in the heather.

"Why," said a voice over her shoulder, "that's vastly
pretty, Miss Macdonald. For some great belle, no doubt?"

Flora looked up into the sparkling dark eyes of O'Neille.

"For Betty Burke," she replied calmly, her eye on the
waiting lass putting peats on the fire. "That lady is well, I
trust?"

"Pure well."

The lass withdrew.

"Oh, Captain O'Neille, how does he fare?"

"So badly it could scarce be worse. What he has suf-
fered since you saw him last tongue cannot tell. By missing

of a messenger we have been thirty-four hours without food, forced to wander from place to place, often within gunshot of the militia seeking him, blinded with rain, slipping and falling in mud; at other times lying hid in the heather soaked to the bone, or pent under a rock swarming with biting midges—"

"Alack, how does he bear it?"

"Like a man, nay, like a hero. He never loses heart, and he heartens every man in his company. 'O'Neille,' said he to me as I lay among the heather in an agony of despair, 'O'Neille, is this all the faith and trust you have in God? Let us only trust His providence and there is no fear for us at all. Pull up your spirits, man. Never despair!' "

"So we all must for his sake."

"From my heart I believe it, Miss Flora, there is not such another man in all the world as my Prince."

"I believe it too." Flora set down her needle and hastened to send off some refreshment to the Prince's lurking-place.

At last the gear of Betty Burke was all in order. The boat was ready, and six sturdy boatmen stood by to take them on board in a secluded cove at Rushness. O'Neille was sent to give the Prince the rendezvous. He was reluctant to leave Flora, but he went.

. Flora dressed herself warmly for the adventure. First the full white smock and cambric petticoat; then petticoats of quilted muslin, one above another; and finally over all the purple-green heather gown with its snug bodice. She tied the blue snood around her bright curls, put a silk kerchief about her throat, and pulled the long plaid over her head.

Lady Clanranald was cloaked to the heels in blue camlet. This time fire would not keep Miss Peggy from going along. She wore her best velvet capuchin hood—and a fig for the rain! Two gentlemen escorted them. Angus had plucked up heart and come over from Milton to see his sister launched safe upon the sea. Neil Maceachen had been sent by the Prince to guide them. He carried the bundles, the gear of Betty Burke, and a supply of food from the Clanranald kitchen.

They entered a little skiff at the waterside. Soon they had made their way around the shore to the landing at Rushness. As they pulled in to shore, they saw what they longed to see, the erect figure of Prince Charles holding out his hands to them. When the skiff shot into the cove, he tenderly helped Lady Clanranald to alight. O'Neille at his elbow held out his hand to Flora. Angus tossed Miss Peggy ashore bodily. Neil brought the bundles. Thus they entered the smoky little hut in a stately manner, two by two, better befitting Holyrood Palace.

Their ceremonious progress was rather marred when, as they entered, the smell of burning meat assaulted their nostrils, and the Prince dropped all ceremony to save his cookery. When the boat had been sighted, he had been busy roasting mutton giblets on a spit. He showed them the spit, a makeshift wooden affair.

Lady Clanranald looked at the pitiful peasant's meal, the scorched hose, the soot upon his shirt, then into his weather-worn, thin face, and burst into tears.

"Woe's me, woe's me," she cried, "to see the son of my King in this condition!"

"Come, look up," said he, "and never weep for me.

Don't you know that the wretched of today can be the happy of tomorrow? And let me tell you, well would it be for every son of a king to pass through such an ordeal as mine, for he would certainly be the better for it!"

So saying, he handed them to their places for the feast. They sat on bundles of heather about a rude table of turf and stone. To Flora's amazement, when she laid her hand on his he led her to the place of honor at his right hand, which was certainly not properly hers in the presence of Lady Clanranald. But nobody said anything, and once seated, the heir to three kingdoms devoted himself with exquisite courtesy to playing the host to all his guests equally. He carried in his stocking, along with his dirk, a gentleman's case of French table silver, with which he was very attentive in serving the ladies.

The giblets, barring a scorched edge or two, were delicious. The Prince had been doing something strangely tasty to them.

"I would have you know," said he, "that I have a notable knack in this way of cookery, and though I lose a kingdom I'll still rule in the kitchen!"

It was impossible to be out of spirits. The party grew merry. The Prince's quips and his droll tales of high life in foreign parts had carefree Miss Peggy doubled with laughter, and even Flora, anxious as she was, could not keep a straight face.

In the midst of the merriment a gillie came panting to the door and spoke quickly in Erse.

"They've come!" cried Flora to the Prince. "They are not three miles off, General Campbell and Captain Ferguson and all; they are landing on Benbecula with fifteen hundred men!"

"Not fifteen million redcoats," said the Prince coolly, "shall rob me of a meal half-eaten!"

So saying, he seized a half-emptied platter and made for the boat. His guests, taking their cue, grabbed up bundles and plates and pelted after, and so the victor of Prestonpans retreated in good order, followed by his forces and carrying his supplies with him.

In the dark they coasted round Benbecula, hugging the shore, until they came to another of Clanranald's shielings, set in an inlet. There they continued the feast, and the Prince, undaunted, made them as merry as they had been at Rushness.

Flora had never seen such a man. His beauty and distinction, his courage and gaiety, his sensitive sympathy and consideration, amazed her heart and filled it with—she knew not what. Happy would that princess be who got him for a husband!

What she did not know, and was too humble to guess, was that the Prince, laughing at her over a glass, watching her steady eyes when he seemed to look elsewhere, was feeding a starved heart with her quiet sweetness. He knew as well as she, what she had learned so long ago, that in that calculating world from which he came, "princes have to marry princesses." But in this world of the Highlands, which perhaps he might never leave, there was neither prince nor princess, and—just for a day—the young Stuart clansman might love, honor, and delight in Flora Macdonald. What he must never do, live or die, was tell her so.

The sun was up, and the feast was done, when the gillie brought the news that broke up the merry meeting. The redcoats were at Nunton in force. Captain Ferguson had slept in Lady Clan's bed. General Campbell had asked repeatedly where she was, and Ferguson swore if she delayed much longer he would burn the house to the ground. Upon hearing this the ladies Clanranald went off in haste.

Now it was time to think of departing. The land party must first go off.

"How, the land party?" asked O'Neille suspiciously.

"Yourself and Angus."

"I? I won't leave my Prince. You cannot expect it."

"I cannot take you. I have no pass for you," said Flora.

"What will he do without me? He cannot travel unattended. You must take me, and leave Maceachen behind."

"What can you do for the Prince? You cannot speak Erse. You look like an outlander. You would betray us all in an hour."

The tears ran down the excitable Irishman's face. He fell on his knees.

"Your Royal Highness," he implored, "do not cast me off! Miss Flora, I beg of you, let me come with you to Skye!"

"Nay, Miss Macdonald, let him come," said the Prince. There was a positive ring in the silky tones. But Flora could be as positive.

"He stays."

"Then I'll stay," offered the Prince, touched beyond good sense by his friend's distress.

That brought O'Neille to his feet.

"Before you do that," he said, "I will instantly go about

my business! I am indifferent what becomes of me, provided you are safe."

"I know it," said Charles, and let him go.

The two young soldiers embraced with grief and tenderness. They had been together in unheard-of dangers and difficulties for ten weeks. O'Neille swore that he would make his way to Skye and rejoin his master; but he was not to be so lucky.

When O'Neille had taken his reluctant departure with Angus, there was only one more detail. Flora looked at the Prince, and kept her face straight.

"Are you ready, Mistress Burke?" said she.

"I am in your hands, my bonnie mistress," replied the Prince.

Neil Maceachen undid the bundle, and the Prince regarded its contents with warm interest. Betty Burke's wardrobe was nothing so dainty, she being but an Irish serving-wench. There was a light-colored quilted petticoat, a calico gown sprigged in purple, a white apron, a great toy of a cap, and an even bigger cape of dun camlet with a full hood to go over the head.

The Prince struggled into the coarse full smock and the voluminous heavy petticoats. Whatever he muttered about them, it was smothered in folds of muslin. Before assuming the gown, he coolly took from his discarded man's gear a brace of pistols, and proceeded to belt them on under his petticoats.

"Oh, no, sir, I beg of you, no firearms!" cried Flora.

"Why not?"

"Suppose they should search you! It would lead to certain discovery!"

"Indeed, miss," said the Prince drily, "if they go so narrowly to work to search me, they will find me out at any rate."

But Flora would not hear of it. She was haunted by the picture the Prince had painted when he declared his resolution to sell his life dearly. Finally the Prince smiled down on this small maiden who dared defy his royal will, and gave up his firearms. One weapon he would not give up, an ugly gnarled short club.

"I'll keep my crabstick," said he positively. "With it I'll make shift to knock down anyone that may attack me."

He belted it about him, and proceeded with the toilette of Betty Burke. He struggled into the flowered gown, and Flora cinched it tight about the slim royal waist with the apron strings. The muscular calves were well disguised with shapeless Highland stockings. Lady Clan and Flora had forgotten to put in any garters. The Prince had to don his own. They were the last of his fine wardrobe from Paris, of blue velvet lined with white satin and buckled with silver. Kneeling to buckle the pretty things, Flora admired them greatly.

The Prince then tied at his girdle the large pouch an Irishwoman would wear instead of a pocket.

"It is empty," said he sadly, peering within.

"It must not be," said Flora instantly, "for who knows, Betty Burke may find herself in a pinch for money!"

She slipped some silver into the pouch.

"Oh, miss, what in the world can this be?" demanded the Prince, dangling a huge handful of muslin.

It was the flapping mutch or woman's cap.

"Bend down your head," said Flora, "—if your Royal Highness please!"

On the curly yellow head for which a crown was meant she set the blowsy thing, and pulled the lappets down beside the bronzed cheeks. At this crowning indignity the Prince went off into peals of laughter. Flora looked at her handiwork ruefully. It was said afterward that try as he might, the bonnie Stuart Prince could never conceal himself in any disguise, for he could never alter the stately grace of his bearing and the majesty of his air. But Betty Burke came close to succeeding.

The Prince was donning his camlet cape. Flora took up her plaid.

"Let us go, my mistress dear," said he.

He held out his hand with his courtly air. Flora set her small hand upon it, and so, in his bulky, grotesque garments, like some gold-laced courtier he handed her down the rough path in the rain to the waterside. Neil shouldered Flora's box, picked up the provisions, and followed.

At the waterside the six boatmen waited. Flora's Cousin John was their leader. He knew the Prince perfectly well, and the other five either knew or suspected the truth about the "ban Erinish mor," the big Irishwoman. But they knew better than to treat him like the Prince. They did not know who might be watching. They set about launching the boat.

Meanwhile Neil built a fire among the rocks to dry their dripping garments a little. Just as Flora's hands were warming over the flame, one of the boatmen gave a shout, and pointed.

Four wherries full of armed men were offshore, rowing swiftly in their direction. The Prince seized Flora's hand, and together they ran between the rocks. At last he pulled her down among the heather. Flora lay there in indescribable terror, waiting for the heavy footsteps or the musket blasts that would end the adventure forever.

They did not come. After an eternity in which the Prince and the Highland girl lay rigid, side by side, in the damp heather, Charles ventured to raise his head and spy below.

The wherries were gone. The boatmen had managed to kick out the telltale fire, and the militia had blundered aside.

The declining sun was breaking through the rain clouds as Charles assisted Flora down to the beach again. The boatmen handed them aboard, Neil shipped the baggage, and in a glory of gold flooding the water from the western edge of the sea they set sail for the Isle of Skye.

CHAPTER 10 🌱 *Over the Sea to Skye*

At first it was like a party of pleasure. The boat was stout and seaworthy, having a sail and a twenty-four-foot keel. With a moderate breeze the sail helped the rowers, sitting three on a side at the oars. In the middle there was plenty of room for the three passengers to be comfortable. Flora, wrapped in her plaid, reclined in the center, facing Neil, and supported against the Prince's shoulder, like a lady boating with her gallant. They might have been going picnicking. There was milk to drink. The Prince handed the stone bottle about from lip to lip, "Jock-fellow-like," said the rowers approvingly. They rather wished for a taste of Lady Clanranald's wine, but the Prince said No. There was only a half bottle, and he was saving it for Flora.

The late sun glittered on the water, and gilded the sails that dotted the Minch. To Flora, every sail spoke a threat of death and destruction; but no sail came near, and they moved steadily northward, under the shadow of North Uist, away from their foes. The Prince made bold to put off mutch and hood, letting the freshening breeze rumple his blond curls. As the late twilight fell, enchanted by the long swell of the green water, the nearness of the Prince, and the rhythmic song of the boatmen, Flora felt as if she were in some happy dream. She longed for the moment to last forever.

The rowers were chanting an old Erse boat song. Flora knew the tune, but they were altering the words:

> Speed, bonnie boat, like a bird on the wing,
>   Onward! the sailors cry,
> Carry the lad that's born to be King
>   Over the sea to Skye . . .

It was dark when they left the sheltering shores of North Uist and struck out into the open Minch. By that time the long swells were not so smooth. They were getting higher, and there was a savage toss and jerk to their

motion. Flora, looking at ragged black clouds gathering
overhead, smelled trouble on the rising wind, and snuggled
down in the folds of her plaid. Charles pulled up Betty
Burke's hood. It was ugly, but it was warm.

All too soon the storm struck. It came howling out of
the sky. Waves piled up like mountains, tossing the boat
from crest to crest, and pouring over the gunwale in the
trough. Rain lashed on the gusts. Lightning cracked from
cloud to cloud. The boatmen pulled grimly with all their
strength. The boating song died for lack of breath.

For a moment the only sound was the howl of the wind,
the crack of the thunder, the creak of the oars, the grunt of
the toiling oarsmen. Then a new song began. The voice
was sweet and true and strong, with a manly marching lilt.
The singer was the Prince. Flora looked up at him. He sat
erect, facing into the rain. His hood was pushed back. The
drenching squalls wetted his lean bronzed cheek and kinked
his curls. He was laughing as he sang. His eyes sparkled in
the lightning-flash. He was singing a song that Flora knew:

> Like brothers then we'll face our foes,
> Brave lads shall never fight in vain,
> We'll conquer for the Stuart rose,
> And the King shall enjoy his own again.
> Then throw the Dutch usurper down
> And chase him back across the main,
> The Stuart line shall wear the crown,
> And the King shall enjoy his own again!
> Fa la la la, fa la la la . . .

The Prince was enjoying himself heartily. The rowers,
laughing, picked up the beat, and the boat sped through

the stormy water. Song followed song. As Flora lay wrapped in her plaid, the swing of the music, the pitch of the boat, above all the courage of the Prince, soothed and lulled her, and her eyelids fluttered down.

The Prince, watching her, saw her bosom begin to rise and fall in the long rhythm of sleep. The tune changed to a little island lullaby. The haunting refrain was in Flora's ears as she drifted into sleep.

> Lullay, lullay, my little one,
> Sleep and rest, the day is done,
> Darkness is falling over the water,
> Sleep, sleep, my little daughter.

> Lullay, lullay, done is the day,
> Sleep we and rest while sleep we may,
> Darkness falls on the face of the deep,
> Sleep, little daughter, sleep . . . sleep . . .

She woke with a start. Her lids lifted suddenly, and she looked directly into the eyes of the Prince. Charles, reclining beside her, was bending over her, protecting her body with his own, and her face with his hands on either side.

"Oh, what is it?"

"Don't be alarmed, miss," said Charles softly, with a smile. "It is only the boatman busy about the sail. I feared he might stumble in passing you, or trample upon you in the dark."

Flora found no words to thank him.

"Sleep, Miss Macdonald," said the Prince gently. "No harm shall come to you, for it is but just that I should guard my guardian from harm."

Leaning on his elbow, he struck up once more the sweet drowsy strain of the little island lullaby. Flora was resolved to look her fill upon the beautiful, haggard face so close to her own; but in her exhaustion her lids fluttered down once more, and she drifted again into sleep. The Prince, smiling, drew her plaid closer on her cheek, and the boat sailed on through the stormy night.

Flora awoke with the light. The dawn was calm and misty. At her side the Prince lay sleeping, wrapped in his camlet cloak. Neil was stretched at his feet, so close he could have pillowed his cheek on his master's brogues. The oarsmen swung easily at the oars. The wind was fitfully contrary. In the mist rose the headlands of Skye.

As the sun went higher, the wind chopped about, and blew so strong in their teeth that the rowers were at their last gasp. The Prince set off his camlet cape.

"Come, lads, give me an oar," said he. "I'll relieve him that's most fatigued, so let that man make place."

Six heads shook stubbornly. Six oars continued to propel the boat forward through the ragged swirls of mist.

The mist was almost their ruin. At the last moment it parted, and they saw with a shock that they were running straight in against the point of Waternish. At the same instant they saw the patrol of militiamen on the shore, so close that they could see the red crosses in the blue bonnets.

"Put in!" shouted the sentry.

"Sheer off!" cried the steersman, and the exhausted rowers pulled for dear life.

The sentry raised his musket and ran down the sand.

"Put in!" he shouted, and fired. The bullet whizzed high.

From the guardhouse sallied out a crowd of men under arms.

"Pull!" cried the Prince. "Pull, and don't fear the villains!"

"We have no fear for ourselves," said John, the steersman, "if Providence will but save your Royal Highness."

"I never doubt it," said the Prince, "so never fear for me."

On the shore the soldiers were swarming to their beached boats. Flora looked at the resolute thin face of the Prince, and her heart smote her.

"Forgive me," she said in a low voice. "I have brought you to ruin, for surely now they will take us."

"Don't be afraid, miss," said the Prince calmly. "We shall not be taken. You see it is low water. Before they can launch their boats over that rough shore, we will get in below these high rocks ahead, and they will lose sight of us."

The cool campaigner was right. As they swept around the point, not a boat had been launched; and as it turned out, not one was ever launched, for the oars were all carefully stowed away in the guardhouse under lock and key.

The steersman ran the boat into a cleft in the rocky shore. The whole party coolly began to picnic. Their breakfast was bread and butter, washed down with the water that fell from the head of the rock. When they had eaten, they rowed on in a calm sea.

"Thank fortune," muttered John Macdonald, "that here we leave the country of the Macleods behind; for though Sir Alexander Macdonald did not join his Royal Highness's standard, we are sure to meet with greater favor from the worst of his men than among the cold Macleods!"

"Amen!" said the Prince.

He was putting his trust in the Macdonalds indeed, for they were steering straight for Monkstadt.

It was nearing noon on that summer Sunday when they put in at the beach at Kilbride, a bare gunshot's length from the garden of the big house. Providence was still watching over the Prince. The beach was deserted. The village folk were at church. In the absence of their lieutenant, the soldiers were treating themselves to a long Sunday morning nap.

Flora did not know about the soldiers. They had only recently been stationed there, to prevent the Young Pretender from landing on Skye. If she had known her luck, she never would have tempted fate by leaving the Prince on the beach. But leave him she did, a grotesque, forlorn figure of a wild Irishwoman, perched on her little trunk at the edge of the sand.

"Be sure," said she to the boatmen, "not to stir till we return or send word—"

"And," said Neil, "in case any nosy person comes along, and wants to know who the woman is, then you must answer, Miss Macdonald's maid, and curse her for a lazy jade—what is she good for if she does not go with her mistress?"

The boatmen promised, if necessary, to curse their Prince for a lazy jade. Flora and Neil walked up the path to the big house. There they parted. Neil went to the kitchen to pump the servants. Flora went to Lady Margaret in the small parlor.

My Lady was entertaining company. Flora was glad to see Allan's father, jovial old Alexander of Kingsburgh. A friend from North Uist was there too, Mrs. Macdonald of Kirkibost, whose husband was Allan's captain in the militia. As she greeted them, she saw with a shock of dismay that there was a militiaman present. He was a solemn young Whiggish Macleod. He bowed stiffly, and cross-examined her at once.

"Miss Flora Macdonald? From South Uist with a pass for Armadale? Servants? My men will examine the servants."

It seemed as if Flora's heart would choke her, but she forced herself to lift her eyes to the Macleod lieutenant and say demurely:

"You keep good watch, Lieutenant."

"Indifferent good," admitted the lieutenant, softening slightly. "The Young Pretender will needs be invisible to get past my men."

"That is certainly true," said Kirkibost's lady wryly, "for when I landed, I assure you I had much ado to make the fellows keep their hands off. They seemed disposed to try whether I was a woman or no."

"Pray excuse their zeal," said young Macleod politely. "The Young Pretender may disguise himself. We cannot let him slip through, and lose thirty thousand pounds. A man may do much with thirty thousand pounds!"

"Especially," said Flora, letting her eyes widen at him, "if he's a man of taste!"

"Ma'am," said the lieutenant, softened entirely, "you are vastly polite!"

"Sir," said Flora, "I deal but plainly."

"Pray, my dear," Lady Margaret came to her rescue, "will you not step to my dressing room and refresh after your journey? It will soon be time to dine, and you must take a bite with us."

"Do, ma'am," said the lieutenant.

Flora let her eyes flick up to his and down again.

"Does Lieutenant Macleod dine?"

"He so honors us."

"Then so will I. I will go at once, and make myself more fit for this company. Cousin Kingsburgh, will you walk along with me? I have had no news of Allan these two months past . . ."

The kind old man led her through the door, and closed it behind her.

"Allan is safe and well. He is with Sir Alexander at Inverness, where I thank fortune he can do no harm."

Flora seized his arm.

"Never mind Allan," she said hurriedly, in a low voice. "I must tell you that I have brought over with me for a waiting-maid one—one whom we pray for. He—she is below by the boat. You must tell my lady, and send Neil from the kitchen to get him to safety before this unchancy lieutenant sends to examine him. I'll have to keep the lieutenant thinking of other things. Pray, for all our sakes, make haste!"

The old man put his arm about her slim shoulders.

"Have no more care in this, but go back to your Macleod."

"He's not my Macleod," said Flora disdainfully.

"He would like to be," said Kingsburgh, and left her.

With trembling fingers Flora righted her hair and retied her snood. Then she sped back to the drawing room. She breathed easier to see the lieutenant still lounging in the best chair. He was all hers. By turns he bored her with compliments, infuriated her with Whiggery, and horrified her with threats against the rebels, while she listened wide-eyed and smiling. These topics lasted him through dinner and brought them back into the drawing room again. This time Flora had him to herself.

"Mark you, Miss Macdonald, our illustrious Duke of Cumberland is in the right, whoever shelters a rebel is a rebel; and over the ears of such, says the Duke, let their houses burn!"

From the window Flora could see Lady Margaret and old Kingsburgh in the garden, pacing back and forth in earnest talk.

"And as to the Young Pretender, he'll have a short shrift and a long rope if once he comes into Ferguson's hands; for Ferguson says the beheading block is too good for that young son of a warming pan!"

Betty Burke was nowhere to be seen. In the garden the walkers were joined by a tall, handsome redheaded man who limped. Flora recognized Donald Roy Macdonald. He had got his limp fighting for the Prince at Culloden.

"But Ferguson shan't have him. Depend upon it, he'll make for Skye; and why should not I take him as well as any man? And then with the thirty thousand pounds . . ."

The lieutenant began spending it, so lavishly that the topic held until the conference in the garden broke up and the men departed. Just then in came the lady of Kirkibost, and Flora escaped to the garden.

"It is all arranged," said Lady Margaret hurriedly. "You go on by road to Kingsburgh, where Betty Burke may rest. Kingsburgh has already gone ahead with Miss Burke. Thence you will guide him to Portree. There Donald Roy will be waiting to receive you, and guide your charge on the next step of his way. I will give you a horse to ride. Neil is waiting to lead you."

Listening, Flora plucked a white rose and put it in her bosom, for the benefit of anyone who might be watching from a window. On second thought, she added a red rose. Then she kissed Lady Margaret. For a second they clung, exchanging courage for the risks ahead. Then Flora hastened back to the drawing room.

"Now as I was telling Mrs. Macdonald here—a man may live like a prince on thirty thousand pounds!"

"If he has good taste," said Flora.

Kirkibost's lady, behind the lieutenant's ear, rolled up her eyes in a very uncivil manner.

Flora's red rose was adorning the lieutenant's bonnet, and Flora's patience was hanging by a thread, when Lady Margaret swept back to her guests.

"Dear Lady Margaret, I must be jogging on."

"No such thing!" cried Lady Margaret.

The two young women enacted a little comedy for the benefit of the lieutenant. Flora must stay the night. She had no pressing reason to go forward. True. But Flora's mother was alone at Armadale. Flora wanted to be with her. Upon this Lady Margaret pretended to yield.

"If you must go, you must."

"I'll ride with you," said Mrs. Macdonald of Kirkibost.

Plague the woman! thought Flora. Next thing it will be the lieutenant.

"Pray don't trouble yourself," she said aloud.

"No trouble," said Mrs. Macdonald, "for I ride your way, and we shall be company for each other."

There was no stopping her. Somehow she had picked up a shrewd notion that Flora's maid would be worth looking at, and she meant to have a look at her.

The lieutenant was not troublesome. He handed Flora gallantly to her horse. Neil, at the horse's head, was made the occasion for a display of the lieutenant's vigilance; but since he answered Macleod's stern questions in fluent Erse, he soon demonstrated that he was not the Young Pretender. There was a complete silence about Betty Burke; the lieutenant remained unaware of her existence.

Then the little party was ready to be off. Neil's clasped hands helped Flora to mount. She flung her knee over the saddle horn and let her skirts hang down. The lady of Kirkibost had a manservant and a maidservant to walk beside her. They all set out along the rough bridle path at a brisk trot.

Meanwhile Charles and old Kingsburgh were striking out on foot. In spite of his petticoats the Prince was setting a spanking pace. He could outwalk any Highlander born, and the Highlanders could outwalk anybody else. The handsome young man looked ridiculous with the petticoats slapping about his shins and the lappets on his cap bobbing.

On the way they met the country people coming home from church. The folk stared to see their respected factor in such company. They were surprised at the unbecoming boldness of the strange lanky woman he escorted. They goggled at her extraordinary height, her high-held head, her reckless marching gait. They thought she ought to be more humble toward the quality. They nudged one another and snickered.

"What a bold, untidy, sloppy slattern!"

"Look at the height of her!"

"And the stride on her!"

"And the impudent way she stares you in the eye!"

"It's a woman of the giants!"

"Mind your manners!" said Kingsburgh sharply to the sniggerers as he hurried his uncouth charge along.

Luckily Charles, understanding very little Erse, was neither moved to laughter nor provoked to anger at their comments. He continued to stride along in perfect good spirits.

Shortly after, the party on horseback began to come up with them. As Flora saw the tall form in the distance, her heart lightened. She sent Neil forward to join them.

As Neil caught up, they were just about to ford a swollen stream. Charles grabbed his petticoats in both hands and hoisted them to his hips, and so skipped over with dry ruffles and exposed muscular shanks. He was feeling pleased with himself, when Neil punctured his pride:

"For God's sake, sir, take care what you are doing, for you will certainly give yourself away at this rate!"

"Why, I thank you kindly," said the Prince as well as he could for laughing, "for your great concern for the honor of Miss Betty Burke, and I'll do better hereafter."

At the next burn he did better, as he thought—he splashed through without lifting his skirts at all, and woefully bedraggled himself.

"They call you a Pretender," said Kingsburgh, disgusted. "All I can say is, you are the worst 'pretender' that ever I beheld!"

The Prince to this made no reply, for by this time Flora and her friend were right behind them, and Mrs. Macdonald was making a determined effort to get a look at Betty's face. This made the disguised Prince uneasy, and he took care to keep his lappets between himself and the nosy stranger.

To add to the situation, Mrs. Macdonald's maid, a saucy piece, huffed perhaps by professional jealousy, was freely expressing her opinion of Kingsburgh's companion.

"I think I never saw such an impudent-looking woman," she said loudly. "I dare say she is either an Irishwoman or a man in woman's clothes!"

"She is an Irishwoman," said Flora.

"Bless me! What long strides the jade takes! And how awkwardly she manages her petticoats!"

Flora bit her lip.

"Pray, Mrs. Macdonald," she said, "let us ride faster, for twilight is falling."

With a thump to the ribs she inspired her pony to set the pace. Mrs. Macdonald's pony followed. The saucy maid was obliged to save her breath to keep up with her mistress.

As Flora rode past Miss Betty Burke, she had a merry ogle from the fine eyes, but she managed to keep her face straight, and soon they had left the walkers behind in the gathering dusk. When the Kirkibost party turned off the road, leaving her to go on with Neil, she began to breathe freely again.

CHAPTER 11   ❧   *At Kingsburgh*

Old Kingsburgh had had enough of the main road. Betty Burke was attracting far too much attention. As soon as Flora rode on with the Kirkibost party, Kingsburgh made the Prince take to the hills. Charles had six miles of dragging his petticoats past high undergrowth and over boulders, through pebbly hill streams and over rocky cliffs. He learned to sympathize with girls who had to wear skirts, and resolved never to wear them again himself.

He also learned that his new host, more than any man he had met in his travels, shared his own sense of fun. They were laughing together over some amusing plot as they came down from the hills and joined Neil and Flora on the highroad near Kingsburgh. The last of the long twilight was waning, for it was nearly eleven at night.

At the farmhouse, old Mrs. Macdonald, the canty old body, had concluded that Lady Margaret was keeping her husband at Monkstadt for the night. She was on her way to bed, when up came the maid to her bedside.

"Master has come home, and brought some company with him."

"What company?" said Mrs. Macdonald, yawning.

"Milton's daughter," said the maid, "and some company with her."

"Milton's daughter," said Mrs. Macdonald, yawning again, "is very welcome to come here with any company she pleases to bring. You'll give my service to her, and tell her to make free with anything in the house; but I'm very sleepy, and cannot see her this night."

So saying, she crammed her great flannel nightcap over her grizzled head, climbed into the fourposter, and pulled the tartan curtains.

Downstairs they got rid of the maid. The next role in the comedy was to be played by Allan's sister, jolly Nannie Macallester. She enjoyed every minute of it. It had the more spice for her because her sobersided husband, the King's exciseman, was calmly asleep upstairs. Flora, tired out, sat in the ingle by the fragrant peat fire and watched the game.

Old Mrs. Macdonald had barely closed her eyes when her daughter ran to her bedside.

"Oh, Mother!" she cried, overplaying her part with gusto, "my father has brought in a very odd, large, ill-shaken-up woman as ever I saw! I never saw the like of her, and he has gone into the hall with her!"

On her heels came the old gentleman himself.

"Pray, my dear," said he, "get up and fasten on your bucklings again, and come get some supper for me and the company I have brought with me."

"Pray, goodman, what company is this that you have brought with you?"

"Why, goodwife, that you shall know in due time. Only make haste and get some supper in the meantime."

"Very well," said she, pulling off her nightcap again. "Nannie, do you go into the hall and fetch the keys to the larder, for everything is locked up."

She was still busy with the bucklings of her ample stays when Nannie came running back in a pretended fright.

"Oh, Mother," she gasped, "I cannot go in for the keys, for the muckle woman is walking up and down in the hall, and I am so frightened at the sight of her that I have not the courage to go in."

"Then I will," said her mother, putting on more boldness than she felt.

Down she went. Her courage lasted as far as the door of the great room. There was the odd trollop, sure enough, mud-spattered and soiled, ill-shaken-up with striding through bogs and briars, making long wide steps to and fro in the hall—and Flora Macdonald watching in silence from the corner. The old woman could not bring herself to go in.

"Psst, goodman!" A jerk of the head brought her husband to the door.

"I beg you'll tell me, what is this long, odd hussy you have brought into the house? For I am so frighted at the sight of her that I can't for my life go past her to fetch my keys."

"Did you never see a woman before, goodwife?" says Kingsburgh, keeping his face straight. "What frights you at seeing a woman? Pray, make haste, and get us some supper."

"Fetch me my keys, I beg of you."

Kingsburgh shook his head. He would not spoil his climax. The old lady looked at his determined face, plucked up her courage, and walked into the room.

The long odd hussy was by this time seated near Miss Flora, but immediately rose, came with long strides to the old lady, took her by the hand, and kissed her on the cheek. Old Mrs. Macdonald felt the soft scratch of an unshaven jaw, and started back in dismay. Without saying one word she snatched her keys from the hook and darted out at the door trembling. She still did not guess whose lips had kissed her.

Outside the door old Kingsburgh was hugely enjoying the joke.

"I beg you, goodman, tell me who this person is! I am sure by the beard on his chin that it is some distressed gentleman of the Prince's party."

"Why, my dear," said the old gentleman, no longer able to conceal his pride and joy, "it is the Prince himself. You have the honor to have the Prince in your house!"

"The Prince!" she cried, shocked out of her wits. "Oh Lord, we are all ruined and undone forever! We shall all be hanged now!"

"Hoot, goodwife," said the honest old soul, "we shall die but once; and if we are hanged for this, I am sure we shall die in a good cause. Pray, make no delay. Go get some supper. Fetch what is readiest. You have eggs and butter and cheese in the house, get them as quickly as possible!"

"Eggs and butter and cheese!" cried the housewife. "What a supper is that for a Prince?"

"Oh, goodwife," said the old gentleman, "little do you know how this good Prince has been living for some time past! These, I can assure you, will be a feast to him. Besides, it would be unwise to be dressing a formal supper, because this would serve to raise the curiosity of the servants, and they would be making remarks. The less ceremony and work the better. And see that *you* come to supper."

"*I* come to supper!" she cried in new dismay. "How can I come to supper? I know not how to behave before Majesty."

"You must come," said Kingsburgh, "for I know he will not eat a bit till he see the lady of the house at table. You will find it no difficult matter to behave before him, so charming and easy is he in his conversation."

So old Mrs. Macdonald unlocked the larder and fetched out eggs and bread, butter and cheese. She found some collops of meat, and roasted the eggs. Soon Betty Burke was handing the ladies to their places at the table. Once again he set Flora at his right hand. Mrs. Macdonald noticed the deep regard with which he treated her. He set his hostess on his other hand. Nannie waited on table. This did not suit the Prince. He kept begging her to sit down and eat with them.

"Never a whit," said her mother, "for the servants must not come into this room as long as you are in the house."

The Prince stretched out his long legs under a table covered with a linen cloth, and Nannie brought him bread and butter, eggs and collops. He ate with a hearty appetite.

"And, Nannie," said good Mrs. Macdonald, "the de'il a

drop shall he want of small beer. God do him good of it, for well I wot he has my blessing to go down with it!"

Over his meal the Prince could not resist teasing Flora.

"Miss Flora," said he, "you were much afraid this day when they were firing upon us from the point."

"I am not free of fear yet," she said. "They may come after us here."

"O fie, Miss Flora!" said the Prince. "You'll never see a Macleod dare to search a Macdonald house! And what though they do? Don't you know that my crabstick that lies in the corner there has a charm, that no enemy dare attack me while I have my crabstick?"

"I wish it may be so," said she, "for you may be in yet greater danger than you have been this day."

The Prince only laughed. He proposed a toast:

"To the happiness and prosperity of my landlord and landlady here, and better days to us all!"

Flora drank the toast with all her heart.

Then, having eaten a plentiful supper, Miss Betty Burke produced an old cracked, broken off stump of a clay pipe, ill mended with thread.

"Pray, Mr. Macdonald, can you furnish me with some tobacco? For I have been taught to smoke in my wanderings!"

Kingsburgh hastened to fetch a new clay pipe and plenty of tobacco. The Prince gratefully filled it. His host held a blazing splinter to the bowl, the Prince drew on the long slender churchwarden stem and sat there comfortably smoking before the fire. He looked strange enough, still in Betty's flapping mutch, with one muscular leg cocked over the other.

Seeing the Prince so comfortable and happy at her fireside, old Mrs. Macdonald began to be very free and easy
indeed. She ceased to see a piece of majesty to whom a
person would have to be always curtseying, and began to
see a thin, tired young man, just about the age of her own
son. She grew anxious about his welfare. She looked with
concern on the deep weather burn of his hands and face.
She had heard an unkind report among his enemies, that he
was covered with scabs to the eyebrows. So concerned was
she that without thinking whether or not it was etiquette
she leaned toward him as he sat by the fire, and pushed
back the sleeve from his wrist. Under the coarse shirt sleeve
was a bonnie clean white skin; no lady in the land could
boast a finer one.

At this gesture of simple good will the Prince gave the
honest old woman an affectionate smile. He was amazed
at his own happiness. It was as if he had found in the Western Islands not only Flora, but an affectionate mother, a
sturdy old father, and, yes, a gay young sister, for Nannie
Macallester sat laughing nearby. He had come to them a
hunted man from the cold and wet, and he must go from
them soon; but that only made this evening the happier. He
spoke his gratitude to fatherly old Kingsburgh, affectionately touching the old man's knee.

"It is a lucky thing," said Kingsburgh, "that I happened
by chance to go to Monkstadt, for I had no design of being
there today. What would you have done, sir, if I had not
been at Monkstadt?"

"Why," said the Prince confidently, "you could not
avoid being at Monkstadt today; for Providence ordered
you to be there upon my account!"

The flapping lappets of Betty Burke's cap were in the way. The old man wanted to look upon the Prince's face. In a merry moment he reached out his hand and tipped the foolish headdress off. This met with Charles's approval, for he was heartily sick of Betty Burke and all her pomps. He preferred to sit by the fire with his blond head bare. But Mrs. Macdonald disapproved. It was neither good manners nor good for the health, in those days of drafty houses and gentlemen's wigs, to sit about with the head uncovered. Old Mrs. Macdonald held up her hands in horror, and ran off to fetch a clean nightcap.

Meanwhile old Kingsburgh brought out the blue-and-white china punch bowl, and set about brewing a festive punch. His recipe was famous, involving hot water, lemons, and sugar. The brew was steaming in the bowl when Mrs. Macdonald came trotting back with the nightcap.

This was the sign for the ladies to withdraw, with a "By your leave, your Royal Highness—" The Prince took Flora's hand in his, and led her tenderly to the door. Their eyes said good night.

As Flora mounted the stair, she heard old Kingsburgh tuning up a song. He only knew one, but it was loyal and appropriate:

> Green sleeves and pudding pies,
> Tell me where my mistress lies
> And I'll be with her before she rise,
> Fiddle and all together!
>
> May our affairs abroad succeed,
> And may our king come home with speed
> And all pretenders shake for dread,
> And let *his* health go round.

To all our injured friends in need,
This side and beyond the Tweed!
Let all pretenders shake for dread,
And let *his* health go round.

> Green sleeves and pudding pies,
> Tell me where my mistress lies
> And I'll be with her before she rise,
> Fiddle and all together!

Nannie Macallester tiptoed to her own chamber. Her lord and master, the King's exciseman, turned over and opened his eyes. He listened to her excited story of their distinguished and dangerous guest without saying one word. When she was done, he calmly got up, put on his second-best suit of Highland clothes, took his bonnet and plaid, and jumped quietly out of the window. No one was going to get him mixed up in the escape of the Young Pretender! Fortunately he left his best suit behind him.

In her little room Flora sank deep into the featherbed. It was the first time she had slept in a bed for three nights. As she fell asleep, it seemed as if somewhere deep in her heart someone was singing a haunting little island lullaby.

It was full day when Flora awoke. The sun was shining. Old Mrs. Macdonald was at her bedside. Flora started up.

"The Prince—?"

"Sleeping still, may God do him good of it. He sat late with the goodman, and they were very merry. I have not the heart to wake him."

"But we must go."

"Have patience, my dear, let the poor laddie sleep. And meantime, will you not tell me of your adventures in coming this length?"

Lying snug against her pillows and watching the sunbeam on the floor, Flora relived the eventful forty-eight hours she had spent with the Prince. The old woman heard her to the end. When the story was done she asked a terribly important question:

"What became of the boat crew?"

"They were Uist hands. They returned directly to Uist."

"I wish," said Mrs. Macdonald shrewdly, "that you had sunk the boat and kept the boatmen in Skye. They could have been concealed among us. Then we could have known better what to have done with the Prince, because his ene-

mies by this means would have lost scent of him. But now
the military will seize the rowers and deal harshly with
them. You know what Captain Ferguson is. He does not
spare to torture, burn, and kill if thereby he can gain his
ends. He will wring the story out of the boatmen. All will
be wrong by their returning to South Uist."

Flora felt a sickening shock of dismay. She had brought
the Prince so far in safety. Was she to lose him in the end?

"I hope not," said Flora, terrified, "for we took care to
take their oaths before they parted from us."

"Alas," replied Mrs. Macdonald, "an oath will not signify a farthing. For if once the military get hold of them,
they will terrify them out of their senses and make them
forget their oath."

Flora knew it was too true. The terror the Isles felt for
ferocious Captain Ferguson was a reasonable terror, based
on many acts of savage cruelty. Flora felt the sickening
fear of the hunted. As quickly as she could she donned her
violet gown and tied the blue ribbon about her copper
curls.

She ran to old Kingsburgh, and begged him to waken
the Prince. He was far from wishing to do any such thing.
But Flora begged so hard that finally he went softly to the
Prince's bedroom, tiptoed to the bedside, and drew the
tartan curtains. The hunted Prince lay peacefully on his
side, with his hand under his thin cheek, sleeping as sweetly
as a child. The old man looked with pity on the worn face,
and drew the curtains close. He could not bear to break
that sleep.

As noon passed, Flora could bear it no longer. Once
more she persuaded the old man to go to the bedside. This

time he hardened his heart, and wakened the sleeping Prince. He came awake clear-eyed and smiling.

"How have you rested, sir?"

"Never better in my life," said the Prince, "for I have not slept in a bed for a long time before this."

Old Mrs. Macdonald could hardly wait till her royal guest had broken his fast before she captured Flora in the passage. She wanted a favor of the Prince, and she was sure no one could win his consent so certainly as Flora.

"I must have a lock of his hair, the bonnie laddie. You must go in at once and beg it of him."

"At once! I cannot!"

"What for can you not?"

"He is not yet risen from his bed!"

"What then?" said sensible old Mrs. Macdonald. "No harm will happen to you. He is too good to harm you or any person. You must instantly go in and get me the lock!"

"Oh, no, no!"

Mrs. Macdonald cut the argument short by seizing Flora's wrist with one hand and knocking at the Prince's door with the other.

"Who is there?" called the warm voice from inside.

Flora pulled the length of her arm in a panic.

"Sir, it is I," replied Mrs. Macdonald, holding the girl's slight wrist firmly as she opened the door. "I am begging Flora to come in and get a lock of your hair for me, and she refuses to do it."

The Prince was sitting up against his pillows, dressed in a clean shirt as white as the bed linen.

"Pray desire Miss Macdonald to come in," he said gently. "What should make her afraid to come where I am?"

Mrs. Macdonald pushed Flora forward.

"I cannot rise to you, Miss Flora," said the Prince, smiling, "as I ought in courtesy to do, but will you not come and sit by me here, and you shall have your wish?"

He indicated the chair that stood by his bed head. There was nothing so formidable about the young man as he held out his hand to her, the full white sleeve falling from his bronzed wrist. Her embarrassment fell away. She went to him and put her hand into his in as full confidence and trust as if he had been Angus. As she sat down beside him, dropping her hand he put both his arms about her slim waist and laid his head in her lap. She felt a rush of love and pity for him as if he had been a child. Touching the bright hair, she was startled when Mrs. Macdonald put the scissors in her hand.

"Cut as much as you will," said Charles, "and keep it in token of much more that I will do for you when I can."

So Flora ran her fingers through the yellow hair, and snipped out a curl, and gave half to Mrs. Macdonald, and tied the other half in her kerchief and put it in her bosom. That much of him she had to keep for the rest of her life.

Then as the Prince sat back smiling at her, happy and at his ease, all her fear for him came back, and she begged him to dress and set off for Portree. Now he was willing.

"But not as Betty Burke," said he positively. "I will not consent to woman's clothes again on any account, let the consequence be what it will!"

"The consequence of what?" inquired old Kingsburgh, entering.

"He will not disguise himself again," said Flora. "Pray,

pray, Cousin Kingsburgh, persuade his Royal Highness to change his mind!"

"Why, Kingsburgh," protested the Prince, "it is you has mocked me out of humor with my disguise, laughing at my lusty gait and manlike airs. And now will you have more of this same odd muckle slattern, Betty Burke?"

"The less the better," granted Kingsburgh. "But look you, sir, we cannot have a woman come into the house in the evening and a man go out in the morning. The servants will talk. If you will consent, sir, to but another hour of Miss Burke, she may go out as she came in, and I myself will meet you in the wood above the house with man's attire and a good broadsword, and then adieu Miss Burke! For I'm persuaded that your Royal Highness is too much a man to pass muster in any other dress."

"What do you say, Miss Flora?"

"I say that he is right, sir, and I beg you'll comply."

"Then comply I must."

At once he set about it. Soon there was a summons through the house for women's help.

"Flora! Nannie! You must come away to the Prince and dress him, for de'il a pin can he put in for himself!"

They found the Prince helpless with laughter, entangled in petticoats. He was in sparkling high spirits. He might have been dressing for a masquerade or a practical joke, instead of disguising to escape capture and death. Every item of dress was cause for a new sally of mockery and merriment.

Nannie and Flora righted the petticoats somehow, cinched on the gown, buckled the garters. The Prince, doubling with laughter, was no help at all, but somehow they got the apron tied and the pouch hung at the waist.

"A lusty wench this is!" cried Charles, swishing his petticoats wildly.

"Your cap, if you please, your Royal Highness!" said Flora.

Charles held his head high and laughed at her. Reach as she would, he was too far above her. Upon this the determined lass went to fetch the chair. On the instant he bent his head between her hands, and once again she set the cap on his curls. Suddenly their laughter was all spent.

Now Kingsburgh came in with his contribution. The Prince's old brogues were in shreds. Kingsburgh brought a new pair. They were Allan's, Flora concluded from the size. Would he be glad when he knew that, although he could not be present, he too was doing something for the Prince?

Kneeling, the old man tied the thongs of the new brogues. Then he picked up the old ones.

"These I will faithfully keep," he said to the Prince, "till once you are safely settled at the Court of St. James. Then I will introduce myself at court by shaking them at you, to put you in mind of your night under my roof!"

The Prince, imagining the courtiers' faces at this ceremony, found the picture extremely funny.

"Be as good as your word," said he, laughing.

Now the happy time was over. The Prince must once more take up his wanderings. He dared not walk the road, for fear of the redcoats. He was to skulk along the byways, with a little herd-boy to guide him. Flora would ride on the road, to keep a lookout and warn him if necessary. Neil would carry messages between them. Flora would not see the Prince again till they met in Portree.

The wet Highland rain had begun to fall as the Prince took his leave. Once more he embraced and kissed his kind old hostess. This time the salute was not so prickly. The Prince had at last found time and opportunity to tidy up. This time, too, he got a hearty hug, as good as he gave. He would not say good-bye to Flora. He would not let himself think that he might be captured before they could meet again. He saluted Mistress Nannie, and turned to the door.

"Can none of you," he begged from the doorway, "give me a snuff?"

Mrs. Macdonald produced her best snuffbox.

"Your Royal Highness will honor us," said Kingsburgh, "by accepting it as a gift."

The Prince put it into Betty Burke's big pouch, along with his new churchwarden pipe and the tobacco. It was a pretty silver snuffbox with two clasped hands upon the lid. When the Prince understood that the clasped hands stood for firm and strong friendship, he said:

"For that very same cause I shall try to keep it all my life."

Now he had to go. Flora watched him swinging his long legs through the rainy wood till his skirts were lost among the trees.

In the meantime Kingsburgh was coolly helping himself to the best garments of his son-in-law, the usurping King's exciseman. He selected a tartan short coat, an elegant waistcoat with a gold thread button, and a large warm plaid, all in the dazzling Macallester tartan. He added his best claymore, and his son-in-law's best wig and bonnet. Then in his turn he set off for the wood.

At the top of the wood the Prince thankfully threw off his petticoats and put on man's clothes once more. When he had his plaid about him, the pleats of the kilt cinched tight and his bonnet on, and took the broadsword in his hand, then, thought Kingsburgh, he was a soldierlike man indeed.

They might have been father and son as the Prince took the old man in his arms, bidding him a long and happy adieu, most affectionately thanking him for all his services, and swearing that he would never forget him.

"Alas, Kingsburgh!" he said. "I am afraid I shall not meet with another Macdonald in my difficulties!"

Through tears the old man saw the Prince march away in the rain, his kilt rippling behind him in time to his long easy stride. He saw him join the little boy guide on the ridge, and then the tall form was lost in the gathering rain.

CHAPTER 13 ❦ *Farewell to the Lad . . .*

Kingsburgh was a pleasant spot. The old two-storied house faced west across the loch. It stood halfway up a height, with a wood above and meadows sloping down to the loch below. In the distance the blue mountains of the Isle of Lewis shimmered in a haze of rain.

But Flora did not spare the old place a backward glance as she left it for Portree. She had taken care to utter no word to the Prince of her forebodings over the fate of the boatmen. But now, as she rode forward in the rain, her anxiety was cruel. She dared not look over her shoulder for fear of seeing behind her the redcoats Ferguson would surely send in pursuit. She watched the hills half hoping, half fearing to see the Prince striding along on the upper path among the heather and the gorse. But she never saw him, and at last in the rainy dark she came to Portree.

The harbor shone like a dark mirror where smoky lights blinked from the half circle of the shore. There were no soldiers to be seen. She gave over her little horse to the servant, and went into the inn.

As she stood doubtfully in the low door, for it was quite outside of her experience to travel alone, a man arose from the fireside bench. His height and his broad shoulders made her heart lift for a moment; but he was thick-set, and when he walked toward her he limped. It was Donald Roy Macdonald.

Without a word he held out his hand to her, and Flora set her icy fingers above his.

"Landlord," said he, "a private room for the lady."

The landlord was a civil innkeeper. He escorted them without remark to an inner chamber, stirred up the peats on the hearth, and left them with a single candle on the table. Flora spread out her dripping plaid and sat huddled over the glowing peats feeling the warmth course slowly through her body.

"Where is the Prince?"

"I will take a turn outside, and see."

In twenty minutes Donald Roy was back. The rain was streaming from his plaid in torrents, and he was limping worse than ever. He had not seen anyone stirring. His eyes met Flora's with foreboding.

"There's a little boy outside," said landlord Macnab, appearing at the door, "and he's asking for Captain Macdonald."

Donald Roy went hastily. It was no night for boy or man to wait outside in the rain.

When he came back, the Prince was with him. Flora rose to her feet. Neil Maceachen, following, set down the baggage: four clean shirts, a cold hen, and a bottle.

The Prince was a sorry sight. Through plaid and all he was soaked to the bone. The exciseman's best clothes were a sodden mass, and the full shirt had never been wetter in the washing tub.

"Alack, sir, it grieves me that you have got such a stormy night for your journey," said Donald Roy.

"I am more sorry," said Charles, "that our lady here is all abused with the rain."

He took her cold hands in his. Wet as he was, his hands were warm. His smile was undimmed. Flora smiled back as he seated her gently in her chair by the fire.

"Now, sir," said Donald Roy, "you must shift out of these streaming garments and put on a dry shirt."

"Shift!" said the Prince. "I'll do no such thing. I'll eat. Desire the landlord to send us in what he has in the house."

"When you have shifted your wet garments," said Neil firmly, undoing the bundle of shirts and warming one before the fire. "This is no time to stand on ceremony, sir."

The Macallester tartans were steaming before the fire, the Macallester wig was hanging by the chimney, and Charles was snug in clean linen, when there was a knock at the door, and honest Macnab entered with a platter of fragrant roasted fish, accompanied by bread, butter, and cheese. In his shirt as he was, the Prince held out his hand to Flora, and side by side they sat down to their last meal together. Neil and Donald Roy took places on the bench opposite, and they all pitched in. Flora was surprised to find that she was hungry.

When they had eaten their fill, the Prince called the landlord.

"Is there something to drink can be had?"

"Sir," said the landlord, "you may drink whiskey, or you may drink water, for there's neither ale nor beer in the Isle of Skye except in the gentlemen's houses."

"Have you no milk?" asked Charles.

"There is none in the house, sir."

"There's no help for it," said Donald Roy, "you will have to drink water."

He held out the water cog. It was an ugly battered old thing. They had been bailing boats with it. For once the gently reared young man was set aback. He gave Donald Roy a comically horrified glance. The landlord picked up his tray.

"For God's sake, sir," whispered Donald Roy urgently in the Prince's ear, "do not make dainty, but take your drink without ceremony. The cog is clean, though it looks ill, and if you show too much nicety, it may serve to raise a suspicion here."

"You are right," said the Prince instantly. He took a hearty pull from the ugly thing. The landlord went away.

Then, the Macallester tartans being dry enough by this time, the Prince rose and belted them on. Soon he stood before Flora, the complete figure of a gallant Highlandman. The broad leather belt cinched his slim waist. The clustering tartan pleats rippled behind as he moved, and the fold was flat across the front, where hung the goatskin sporran. Over tartan vest and short coat the broad leather baldrick supported the heavy claymore. His tartan short hose were bound at the knee with long Highland garters. Into one of them was thrust his dirk, with the long flat leather case containing his silver eating utensils. The tartan plaid hung from his shoulders. His yellow curls were brushed back to his nape. Just so had he looked when he marched on foot at the head of the clans deep into the heart of England. Donald Roy saw once more in him the unbeatable leader he loved.

Flora looked up at her Prince. The glow of the fire glittered on his eyes and threw his shadow above him on the wall. To her he looked larger than life, like some legendary chieftain on a stone in the King's Island of Iona.

"Let us go, your Royal Highness," said Donald Roy.

The Prince turned to Flora. A moment he looked at her, and then he sat down again.

"I think," he said, "that I will stay the night."

"It is not safe," cried Donald Roy in alarm. "This is a public house. Anyone may begin to ask who you are, and the result might be dangerous."

"He is right," said Flora, much against her heart.

"Are you in haste to be rid of me?" he reproached her.

Flora could only shake her head.

"Well, then," said Charles, "I will smoke one pipe before I go. Pray, Captain Macdonald, call for some tobacco."

At Donald Roy's bidding the landlord fetched a quarter of a pound—"which is fourpence halfpenny, sir."

"Here is sixpence," said the Prince, waving him off.

"And bring the odd halfpence change," called Donald Roy after him.

"You are very exact," said the liberal-handed Prince, smiling. "Would you have me be at the pain of taking three halfpence change?"

"You must take them," said Donald Roy. "In your present situation you will find halfpennies very useful. I'll warrant your sporran has a different partition for the bawbees."

He made bold to open it, and found a niche. The landlord brought the halfpence, and Donald Roy pouched them for the Prince.

"Now, Captain," said the Prince, drawing up his chair and putting his head close, "I must beg you a favor, which is that you will not leave me here, but go along with me."

He did not say where, and Flora did not want to know.

"Indeed, Kingsburgh assured me that you would go with me," he urged. Donald Roy shook his head.

"With this open wound in my left foot," said he sadly, "I could never be useful to you. I would only be a burden."

"I have always found myself safe in the hands of the Macdonalds," said the Prince stubbornly, "and so long as I can have a Macdonald with me I shall think myself safe enough. I cannot think of parting with you at all."

"It is impossible," said Donald Roy. The tears stood in his eyes.

Now the pipe was out and the fire was dying. The Prince sighed, and called for the reckoning. He had a hoarded piece of gold to pay it with. He took the change, and then asked the landlord to change a second gold piece. There were not twenty silver shillings in the house. The landlord scraped around, and found eleven.

"That will have to do," said Charles to Donald Roy, "for I have more need of silver than gold."

"Great heavens, sir, this is worse than the halfpennies! By this you present the man with ten shillings clear. This is the liberality of a Prince, and the landlord may begin to suspect that it is such in fact. I'll make shift to change your gold myself."

With the silver in his hand the Prince turned to Flora.

"Madam, I am in your debt. I believe I owe you a crown?"

"Sir, I hope it may be so."

The Prince laughed.

"You crack a jest with me," he said, "and you name a debt I can never fully pay. I mean a debt that I *can* pay, a crown piece, five shillings of borrowed money."

"It was only half a crown," said Flora.

"Then there you have it, and my hearty thanks with it."

Flora stood looking at the silver in her palm. The Prince pouched the rest. Then he folded her slim fingers over the coins she held, and held the hand in his.

"For the rest, no gift of mine can ever repay you. But what can I give you to remember me by?"

"I shall never forget you," said Flora.

"I know it."

"And what more do I need, to keep for your sake, than the lock of hair you gave me in the upper room at Kingsburgh?"

They were silent for the space of a held breath.

"Well, but," said the Prince lightly, "there's Betty Burke. Betty Burke does not mean to be forgotten. You must have a souvenir of Betty Burke."

"Alas, sir, you left Betty Burke behind on the hill at Kingsburgh."

"Not quite. Miss Burke's possessions were poor and plain, but she had one bit of finery worth the giving. I kept it for you when I left the muckle hag behind me."

"What was it then?"

"The lady's garters!" Triumphantly the Prince brought forth the dainty French things, blue velvet and white sarsanet, buckled with silver.

"See, Flora, Betty Burke lays these trifles at your feet, and begs you to keep them to remember the odd muckle trollop that was proud to be your servant."

"I will treasure them, and remember her," said Flora in a low voice.

Now the Prince turned to Neil, who had been his guide in fair weather and foul for more than a month of hardship and danger. With a handclasp and an embrace they took leave of one another. Donald Roy stood in the doorway, on fire to be off.

The Prince lingered. He turned once more to Flora, looking down into her lifted face in the rosy firelight. He took both her hands in his. She was the Macdonald he most wanted to have in his company, but he could ask no more of her. He looked long into the little pointed face lifted to his, till the tears blurred his vision. Once and again he kissed the lifted cheek. Her tears were salt on his lips.

Resolutely he turned. From the table he took wig and bonnet, the bundle of shirts, the cold hen. He tied the baggage at his belt, for now he was to go without a gillie. He covered his head and walked to the door. In spite of the miscellaneous baggage and the borrowed gear, to Flora he had never looked more royal. His last words were the words of a king.

"For all that has happened, I hope, madam," said he, "that we shall meet in St. James's yet."

Then he was gone.

With one consent Flora and Neil ran to the outer door and watched the tall graceful figure till the mist and the rain took it. They were still there when Donald Roy came back.

"Oh, Donald Roy, is he safe?"

"He has got off unseen and unsuspected."

"In what direction?"

"Better not know. These were his parting words: 'Tell no one,' said he, 'no, not our lady, which way I am gone, for it is right that my course should not be known.' "

"He is right. I should not have asked."

"I fear, Miss Flora, that I have deprived you of his parting gift," observed Donald Roy with a smile.

"He has given me gifts enough."

"Yet he wished to give one more."

"What was it?"

"A loaf of sugar! There was a loaf of sugar in his bundle. 'Pray, Macdonald,' says he to me, 'take this piece of sugar to our lady, for I am afraid she will get no sugar where she is going.'"

"He needed it worse than I," said Flora between a smile and a tear.

"So we told him; but he could not be persuaded to take it again. He was determined that you should have it. In the end I slipped it into his guide's pocket for the Prince's use. So he parted, going off in a little boat with three men only."

"God grant him a happy landfall!"

"Hist!" said Donald Roy. Flora and Neil looked quickly around. The landlord was coming down the passage. He was inquisitive.

"The other gentleman's gone?"

"I parted with him but now," said Donald Roy curtly.

"Hereabouts? Who was he, then?"

"Well, Macnab, I'll tell you," said Donald Roy with a show of frankness, "he's only a brother rebel of mine, do you see, one Sir James Macdonald, an Irish gentleman. Wearying of Skye, he has gone off for the mainland to skulk among his kinfolk there."

"Oh," said the landlord. "Do you know, he had something about him that looked so very noble, I had taken a strong notion that it might be the Prince in disguise!"

𝕭𝖔𝖔𝖐 𝕵𝖔𝖚𝖗 ✤ Flora Alone

FLORA'S LAMENT

Far over yon hills of the heather so green,
    And down by the corrie that sings to the sea,
The bonnie young Flora sat sighing alone
    The dew on her plaid, and the tear in her eye.
She looked at a boat in the breezes that swung,
    Away on the wave, like a bird of the main,
And aye as it lessened she sighed and she sung—
    Farewell to the lad I shall ne'er see again!
Farewell to my hero, the gallant and young,
    Farewell to the lad I shall ne'er see again.

The muircock that crows on the brow of Ben Connal,
    He kens of his bed in a sweet mossy home,
The eagle that soars o'er the cliffs of Clanranald,
    Unawed and undaunted his eyrie can claim.
The solan can sleep on the shelve of the shore,
    The cormorant roost on his rock of the sea.

But ah! there is one whose sad fate I deplore,
  Nor house, hall, nor home in his country has he—
The conflict is past, and our name is no more—
  There's naught left but sorrow for Scotland and me!

The target is torn from the arm of the just,
  The helmet is cleft on the brow of the brave—
The claymore forever in darkness must rust,
  But red is the sword of the stranger and slave.
The hoof of the horse and the foot of the proud
  Have trod o'er the plumes on the bonnet of blue;
Why slept the red bolt in the breast of the cloud,
  While tyranny revelled in blood of the true?
Farewell to my hero, the gallant and good,
  The crown of thy fathers is torn from thy brow!

(JAMES HOGG)

CHAPTER 14   *Arrested!*

Flora Macdonald was walking under the ash trees at Armadale. She could see the high head of Ben Nevis rising above the blue water of the Sound of Sleat. On the surface of the strait the curlews were skimming their slaty-blue wings. The sun sparkled on the little summer waves, and turned the brown sails bronze.

Life seemed frozen, breathless, like the calm between two storms. It had seemed so since the day, barely a week before, when on her little horse, led by Neil, drained and exhausted, she had come from Portree to Armadale. Since then she had moved about the house like a sleepwalker, waiting for she knew not what. She would lie awake at night listening to the rain on the thatch, and wondering whether any roof covered the fugitive Prince. She would walk the shore by day and watch the shipping in the Sound, tight with fear that in some one of the King's ships he might at that moment lie a prisoner, or worse still, a lifeless corpse.

Now as she walked under the ash trees with her eyes on the water, she was shocked alert by the sound of a horse's hoofs approaching on the road. They jogged easily toward her as she ran to meet them. Soon the little Highland horse came in sight. The rider was Captain Donald Roy Macdonald.

He drew bridle when he saw Flora.

"Oh, Donald Roy, is he safe?"

"Let us go on to the house, and I will tell you what I know."

"No, Donald Roy, tell me now, for I have not let my mother know a word of what we have done. She would be beside herself with fear for me."

"And are you not afraid for yourself?"

"A little," admitted Flora, "useless though it is. But I am not sorry at all."

"Brave lass! Well, let us sit in the shade."

Donald Roy dismounted and slung the reins from a branch. They sat on the grassy bank, the tall ruddy man and the small girl in flowered muslin, and Donald Roy told her what he knew.

"When we parted in Portree, I went straight off to Kingsburgh, and from thence to Monkstadt. All was quiet. At Monkstadt I met with young Lieutenant Macleod, who is your very humble servant indeed, Miss Flora. Macleod had never a suspicion. The redcoats believe that the Prince is still upon Uist. So you see, Miss Flora, we have brought him off safe."

"I thank fortune!"

"And see, Miss Flora, I have something for you."

"Oh, what?"

It was a trifle of linen—the apron of Miss Betty Burke.

"After the Prince had parted," explained Donald Roy, "Old Kingsburgh took up the clothes he had hidden, and was for destroying them. But Mistress Nannie was bound to keep the dress; and by one consent the apron was adjudged to your share. They have a great regard for you in that house, my dear."

"And I for them," said Flora.

She held the apron to her bosom, and then flushed to her ears as she saw Donald Roy smiling at her.

"Let us go along to the house," she said hastily. "You take a weight from my mind, to think that we are all in safety."

"Do not be too sure," said Donald Roy. "Ferguson is ruthless. He may yet find us out."

Barely a day later Flora received an invitation. It was a courteous message from a friend of her father's. He invited her to come to his house at Castleton, a few miles off.

"Don't go," said Donald Roy, "for it is a trap."

"How, a trap?" said old Mrs. Macdonald.

Upon this they had to tell her. The old lady held up her hands in horror.

"We are all undone! Flora, do not go!"

"Shall I wait till they come for me? Do you want to be taken up also?"

"Then I will go with you," said Donald Roy.

"And have the trap close on two of us? No," said Flora positively. "I will go alone. And I will go now, before my father comes home and they take him up with me. This is the best way. I am a gentlewoman. They will not dare hurt me."

Privately Donald Roy was not so sure; but he saw the force of her argument.

"Very well, then," he said. "But before you go, have you Betty Burke's pass about you?"

Flora gave it to him.

"Now, Miss Flora," said Donald Roy, "be sure you admit nothing when questioned. You must say merely, that there was a great lusty woman came to the boatside as you were leaving Uist, and begged to go along, saying she was a soldier's wife. Landing in Skye, she thanked you and went her way."

"I am a very poor liar," said Flora doubtfully.

"You are a good enough deceiver," said Donald Roy with a smile, "to have Lieutenant Macleod sighing over the loyal Miss Flora Macdonald. And remember, to protect our Prince, you must try to be believed."

"I will try," said Flora.

There was no use dawdling. Far better to do what had to be done. Flora put her plaid over her flowered muslin dress, kissed her mother, and gave her hand to Donald Roy. The sunburnt captain kissed it with deep respect. Then she set out alone, on foot, to her friend's house.

As she walked steadily down the road, she met a militiaman. It was her father, and he was on his way home. When he heard her errand, like Donald Roy he wanted to go with her. Again she refused.

"What good will it do, if you are taken up with me? For depend upon it, if they have found out about me, they have found out about the pass. No, Father, go home and comfort my mother. I will go on to Castleton."

At last he yielded, kissed her, and hastened on to Armadale. There he took the pass from Donald Roy and destroyed it. Then he armed himself, and went skulking. Donald Roy thought it the part of prudence to do likewise. Donald Roy was popular, brave, and cautious. Hugh of Armadale was huge, resolute, and well armed. Nobody ever cared to capture either one. But there were others who were not so fortunate.

When her father left her in the road, Flora went on, bracing herself to face her enemies. She faced them sooner than she expected. As she walked along, suddenly she came face to face with a squad of militia. She saw by their tartans that they were Macleods. She drew aside to let them pass.

They did not pass. It was the trap. They were coming in search of her, and they made her a prisoner at once. Before she could think, they had formed a square around her, and were hustling her along ever farther from her father's house.

"Where are you taking me?"

"Government orders, miss. We're to put you aboard *The Furnace.*"

"*The Furnace!*" Ferguson! Flora's heart fainted.

Off they marched her in the dust of the road. Flora was used to long walks, but she never in her life, before or after, had such a walk as that one to the harbor. The Macleods were not abusive, but they were not friendly either, and they were in a hurry. Flora toiled desperately to keep up. She held her head high, but in her heart she was bidding a long good-bye to the hills of home, to the gorse and the heather, the glens and the sea.

At last they came to the bay of Kilmory.

"Where's the Captain? We've caught the rebel kitten!"

Folk gathered around her. Some looked at her with secret friendliness. A few scowled upon her. None raised a hand against her. The ship's lieutenant looked at her coolly.

"Captain's refreshing. He has just exhausted himself with a whipping bout—some scoundrel that presumed to help the Young Pretender to escape."

Flora looked where he pointed, and shuddered. There was blood at the waterside.

"Kill him?" asked the leading Macleod with interest.

The lieutenant spat.

"Half. Rebels ain't so easy killed."

"What'll we do with this one?"

"Take her to Ferguson!"

Ferguson was taking his ease in a thatched hut a stone's throw from the strand. The terrified goodwife was setting a meal before him as Flora was led in. Ferguson looked at Flora as she stood before him, tore the meat from a thigh bone of muirfowl, crunched it, gulped it, and coolly picked his teeth, all without taking his eyes from her. When he was good and ready, he spoke in a heavy voice:

"Where's the Young Pretender?"

"I do not know."

"Don't know? When you have been stravaging about the country with him? When you have smuggled him out of our hands in the guise of Miss Betty Burke?"

"I will tell you all I know of Betty Burke."

Keeping her face straight and her voice even, Flora told him the invention of the soldier's wife.

Ferguson laughed with raucous coarseness.

"She left you at the landing? Indeed? Then who slept in the best bed at Kingsburgh? Who wore the lavender-flowered gown setting out for Portree? Think again, Miss Macdonald. We have ways of getting the truth out of people!"

The Black Captain ripped the other leg from the muirfowl with sudden violence and eyed Flora as he sank his
teeth in it.

"I have no more to say."

"You'll say more before I've done with you!" snarled
Ferguson. "But you'll keep. I've others to attend to. Take
her on board!"

They put her into the ship's boat. Soon they reached the
side of *The Furnace*, swaying at anchor in the bay. They
helped her up the rope ladder and over the side.

She stood on the deck and looked about her. This was
The Furnace, the floating hell that was the dread of every
rebel. It was a seaworthy ship. The thwarts were of oak.
The cabins and the captain's bridge were curiously carved
and painted. The deck was scoured white. Overhead the
masts soared in a tangle of spars and rigging. The sails were
furled. Over all flew the crimson banner of England.

"This way, miss. Have a seat. Captain will be aboard
shortly."

Flora sat on an oak bench that ran under the little arched
windows of an outer cabin. She sat and tasted the bitter-
ness of death. Only one ray of light heartened her. They
were still looking for the Prince. As long as he was safe,
what did it matter what happened to her?

Nevertheless, when heavy feet tramped along the deck
and came her way, instinctively she shrank small in the
window corner.

She need not have bothered. It was Captain Ferguson,
but he had other fish to fry. She caught only a glimpse of
the lowering countenance under the gold-laced cocked
hat as he stamped through. After him two tars in loose-

falling sea pantaloons were hustling a man in Highland costume. Flora knew the man. It was John Mackinnon, of Skye, a kinsman of the old chief of Mackinnon. He came along steadily, with a contemptuous curl to his lip, in spite of Ferguson's threats.

"You'll tell us where the Young Pretender is hid," Ferguson was bawling, "or you'll get a taste of the cat o' nine tails yourself—and if you're as stubborn as nine-tenths of the infernal brimstone rebels, I'll put you into Barrisdale's machine!"

Flora had heard of Barrisdale's machine. Barrisdale was a freebooter, and his extortions were backed with threat of racking in this hideous device, in which they said a man would die in an hour's time. Flora bit her palm to keep from crying out.

Ferguson threw open the door of the inner cabin and stamped through. Mackinnon followed with his head held high.

"Captain Ferguson," said a quiet voice from the inner cabin, "I beg you'll conduct your examination of rebels in a more gentlemanly manner."

"General Campbell!"

Campbell, the commander himself! Flora had no reason to love a Campbell. She did not know whether his presence made things better or worse.

"Welcome aboard, General Campbell," whined Ferguson. "This is Mackinnon, a captain in the mob that followed the Young Pretender. We have reason to think that after the Pretender was smuggled over to Skye by the rebel hellcat, Flora Macdonald, this Mackinnon took him over to the mainland."

"Is that what you learned by torturing my men?" asked Mackinnon contemptuously.

"That's how I deal with rebels, and that's how I'll deal with you, Mackinnon!"

"I'll deal with Captain Mackinnon myself," said the general's voice suavely. "Pray be seated, Captain Mackinnon."

"Captain!" growled Ferguson, and added some words Flora had never heard before.

"Now, sir," went on the general smoothly, "pray do not give us trouble, but say at once, where is the Young Pretender?"

"I do not know."

"How, not know?"

"Sir, I will not attempt to deceive you with a false story. I put his Royal Highness ashore—" (Ferguson was heard to choke on a profane word describing his Royal Highness.) "I conducted him not a gunshot inland, found him a little Highland lad to be his guide, and so left him and returned to Skye."

"I must say, sir," observed General Campbell, "you let slip a notable opportunity of enriching yourself. You must have known the reward for giving him up. Thirty thousand pounds is a fortune. Think likewise how much trouble and fatigue you would have spared the soldiers of King George by delivering him up."

"It never was in my power, sir, to deliver him up. Your Excellency very well knows that I am a man of no influence. I could not command help in such an enterprise. As little durst I attempt it by myself, for he is able to tie two of me, neck and heel, at any time!"

"Tie two of you, Mr. Mackinnon!" exclaimed the general, half mocking. "Why, he must be a dreadful young fellow! He must be remarkably strong indeed!"

"Truly," replied the undaunted Highlandman, "I can assure your Excellency that he is as strong and nimble a young man as any one in all the Highlands of Scotland!"

"I sympathize with your plight," said the general, "being thus unable to secure the fugitive and gain thirty thousand pounds!"

"What a base, unworthy action would it have been!" burst out the Highlander. "I had been in his service, I had received his pay and broke his bread! In his greatest extremity he came to me and threw himself into my arms, desiring me to do with him as I pleased! Should I have given him up? I would not have done it for the whole world! And if I had done it, I dare say you would have looked upon me as a monster of a wretch!"

There was silence in the cabin.

"Gentlemen," said General Campbell at last, "let us lay to heart what Captain Mackinnon says. Let us determine from honor and conscience, and then surely we must applaud his conduct. I hope in his place we would all have behaved the same!"

At this there was a murmur of assent from the hitherto-silent subordinates. Flora could hear Ferguson snorting.

"Pray, Captain Ferguson," said the general, "fill up a glass for me to drink to the health of Captain Mackinnon, and fill up another for him!"

Ferguson's chair gave a protesting squeak as he pushed it back, but then came the gurgle of something coming out of a bottle, and then the voices of the two generous enemies as they pledged one another.

"And, Captain Ferguson," added the general, "be sure to give Captain Mackinnon a good bed!"

Mackinnon was smiling as he followed the two tars out of the cabin and made for his good bed. After him came Ferguson, scowling, and after Ferguson came General Campbell. The general was one of the handsomest men of his time, tall, high-colored, aristocratic of feature, imposing in scarlet and gold lace. He halted as he saw Flora.

"Who is this?"

Ferguson turned.

"The female rebel! How came you here?"

"Is this Miss Macdonald?"

Flora curtsied politely.

"Your servant, your Excellency."

"Yours, Miss Macdonald. You must be fatigued with your journey from Armadale. Pray, Captain Ferguson, desire your men to conduct Miss Macdonald to her cabin."

"Her cabin!" snorted the Black Captain. "No cabin for her! Rebels lodge between decks!"

"No lady lodges between decks while I have the command. Let her be assigned a cabin."

"Mine, perhaps?" asked Ferguson with a sneer.

"A lieutenant's cabin will do. She is to be treated with the utmost respect. Let her comfort be seen to at once."

"Will you not examine her? I warn you she lies abominably."

"She is weary," said the general. "She will not lie when she is rested."

The Black Captain shrugged, and snapped his fingers for the cabin boy.

The cabin was small, but it was not uncomfortable. The bed was a box, decently hung with linen curtains and furnished with blankets. Flora lay down in her clothes. She felt miserably alone, and the future was dark and uncertain; but at least for the present she need not fear mistreatment by the Black Captain. As the vessel swung gently at anchor she drifted into sleep.

She woke at midnight to the sound of running feet, creaking ropes, rattling spars, shouted commands. They were sailing with the tide.

They did not sail far. The next day they cast anchor in Applecross Bay, on the mainland of Scotland. Flora recognized the cool gray hills sloping to the bay, and the pebbly strand edged with wreaths of seaweed. She realized with a sick shock why they were there. They now knew that the Prince had escaped to the mainland.

Well, at least that spared her the distasteful duty of lying to General Campbell. Nothing she knew could make any difference now. When she was summoned, she set her bronze curls to rights, tied her snood, and went to him in the cabin. There she told her whole story.

"How could I let him perish?" she said. "It was mere humanity to help him."

General Campbell listened politely. A subordinate wrote it down, and Flora signed it.

"Now can I return to my mother?"

"I am afraid not, Miss Macdonald. We have orders to send you to the Tower of London."

CHAPTER 15 ❧ *On Shipboard*

The Furnace was rolling gently at anchor in Lochnanuagh, the very place where a short year before the bonnie Stuart Prince had landed with such high hopes. Flora stood at the rail. John Mackinnon stood beside her. He stared in moody silence toward the high cliffs of Boradale. He seemed to be saying farewell to his native Highlands.

What Flora did not know was that he was staring directly at the hiding place of the Prince, within easy shooting distance of the ships. In a crack in the cliff, so cleverly constructed as to be quite unseen unless you knew where to look for it, was a little bothy or hut. They had made it of turf, with the grass side outside, so that it looked exactly like a harmless green brae. It was so close to the King's vessels that a man with a musket might have put a bullet into a bird that alighted on the roof—or into a single head that showed itself at the concealed opening. But no head showed itself. John Mackinnon kept his mouth closed and averted his eyes. By and by the ships weighed anchor and sailed off.

Flora soon found that she was not going to the Tower in such a hurry. *The Furnace* sailed about from the Isles to the mainland and back again. Her heart sank as she realized what they were waiting for—the capture of the Prince. Every time they anchored, she waited in suspense to see the slim form and the bronzed face hustled aboard, ragged and perhaps marked with blood. But time and again they lifted anchor without him.

Many another captive was put aboard. At Applecross Bay, Flora was sorry to see among the captives handsome Malcolm Macleod from Raasay. They put him under hatches with the rest of the common prisoners. Those unhappy captives had no such liberty to walk the deck as was accorded to Flora and a few others. Flora saw them sometimes in the morning herded on the quarter-deck, crowded in with the smelly sheep that were aboard to furnish mutton for the captain's table. The redcoats guarding them seemed to be kinder to the sheep. It wrung Flora's heart to see how day by day the Highlandmen grew more ragged and more gaunt. She knew they lay cold and went hungry. But beyond greeting them at a distance during their short hour on deck, there was nothing she could do.

One day they anchored once more off Benbecula. Flora stood at the rail and watched the bare island where so much had happened, and tears stood in her eyes. As she looked, at first unseeing, there was a bustle on shore, and a drama unfolded itself before her. From the distance she watched it all. The actors looked as small as puppets, and their words were lost in the distance, but the story was plain.

It began when Ferguson, in evil glee over some good news, went ashore. When he stepped onto the land, they dragged before him a captive. The man was no taller than Ferguson. Flora had no need to fear that it might be the

Prince. They exchanged words. The captive shook his head. Ferguson up with his stick and slashed his victim across the face. It took three sailors to hold the man back.

Then Ferguson gave orders. It soon became plain what they were. In a trice the man was stripped and bound to a triangle of muskets. A soldier stood ready with the nine-lashed cat in his hand. Flora gripped the rail and set her teeth. She wanted to turn away, but could not. As she looked, an officer stepped between the executioner and his victim, and confronted Ferguson. Ferguson said something. The officer's answer was to draw his sword. His men massed at his back. For a moment he and Ferguson stood toe to toe and jaw to jaw. Then Ferguson gave way. The man at the muskets was unbound. Ferguson turned on his heel and made off. Flora, feeling a little sick, went below.

The next morning when Flora stepped on deck for a breath of air, there was a new captive aboard. He was not confined with the sheep. He stood pensively at the ship's rail with folded arms, looking off toward the mountain Hecla. Something about him looked familiar. Flora looked at the neat, erect form, the raven-black hair tied behind, the tattered French-cut regimental coat, and recognized him with a pang. It was Felix O'Neille.

Impulsively she went to him. Her heart was full. As she reached him, she faltered. What could she say to him? When he turned to her, she took refuge in jest. She tapped the thin dark cheek lightly, saying:

"To that dark face do I owe all my misfortune!"

O'Neille seized her hand eagerly and kissed it.

"Why, madam," said he, "what you call your misfortune is truly your greatest honor. And if you be careful to act always as nobly, you will in the outcome find it to be your happiness!"

Flora clung to the hand that held hers. For two weeks she had been entirely alone among her enemies, with no one to cling to, no one to confide her fears to. Now she could speak.

"Oh, Captain, what will become of me? They design to carry me to London, which I must think of with the greatest uneasiness, not knowing what may be the end of it."

O'Neille took both the slim white hands in his strong dark ones.

"I will take upon me to foretell what will happen to you," he said with a confident smile. "If you are carried to London, it will be for your happiness. Instead of being afraid, you ought to wish for it. There you will meet with much respect and many good friends for what you have done. Only be careful to make your conduct all of a piece. Never once pretend, through caution, to repent or be ashamed of what you have done, and I dare take upon me to answer for the rest."

"I will do as you say," said Flora.

"I do not think," added he, "that the government can be so very barbarous and cruel as to bring you to trial for your life, and therefore I hope that you have nothing to fear, and that things will happen to you as I have said."

Flora wished she could be as sure of that.

"But what of you, Captain? How came you to be taken? What will become of you?"

"As for what will become of me," said the Irishman, "I have nothing to fear now that I am come aboard where

General Campbell is. I am an officer of France, and in time they will exchange me according to the rules of war. They dare not mistreat me, as the Black Captain has just been taught."

"How came you to fall into Ferguson's hands?"

"Thanks to my colleague, Captain O'Sullivan," said O'Neille bitterly. "When you left me behind—for which I forgive you—I joined him lurking on South Uist. Four days later a French cutter put in. O'Sullivan was wearied out. He went aboard at once. I got a boat and followed after the Prince, meaning to bring him back to safety. I traced him from Skye to Raasay, from Raasay back to Skye, from Skye to the mainland; and there all track was lost. In eight days I came back to Uist. The accursed traitor had not waited!"

"Not for his Prince!"

"For neither of us, bad success to him!"

"What did you do?"

"I lurked in Benbecula, in a rock above a loch; and there they found me out and took me."

"I am sorry."

"No matter. It is as good as starving on the mountain, as long as our Prince is safe."

"Amen," said Flora.

They clasped hands in silence. The same thought was in each mind: where was Prince Charlie?

Day followed day. Still the Prince remained uncaptured. Still the ship lurked about the Isles in hope of his capture.

One day, as the ship lay off Armadale, General Campbell sent Flora ashore under guard. While a maid packed a few belongings for her, Flora said good-bye to her mother.

It was a hard parting, for each woman silently feared that they might never meet again.

"But you cannot go alone!" cried her mother, embracing her wildly.

"I cannot ask anyone to go with me," said Flora.

"I will go," said the maid. She spoke her own language. The soldiers of the guard scowled at her.

"I cannot speak Erse now," said Flora to her mother in English, "but tell Kate that if she goes with me she must go to the great prison of the English, many days journey from here; and who knows if I will ever come back again?"

Flora's mother sobbed, and translated.

"I will go," said Kate.

"Come then," said Flora, and held out her hand.

Hand in hand, like friends, the Highland lady and the peasant girl walked down to the ship's boat and set out for an unknown fate.

At last, one day, they transferred the two girls and their gear into a southbound vessel. When the ship came to anchor off Edinburgh, Flora's head began to spin. She found she was famous. It seemed as if O'Neille was right. Everybody wanted to visit her, to bring her presents, to hear her story. Every day it was like a tea party in the ship's cabin. Sometimes her admiring callers pushed back the tea table and took a trip of dancing. Flora declined to join in.

"My dancing days are done. I shall not dance again until I know that my Prince is safe."

Where was he? Rumors were flying. He was captured; he was hiding in Edinburgh; he was dead. It seemed to Flora, sometimes, that she would go willingly to the gallows that awaited her, if she could only know that he was in safety. Meanwhile there was nothing to do but hold her head high, and wait.

At last the ship sailed for London. Crowds stood cheering on the shore. At first Flora thought they were cheering the King's ship; but then she caught her name, and she knew they were cheering for her.

CHAPTER 16   *The Tower of London*

More than once Flora Macdonald was forced to ask herself, in dizzy wonder, whether, having fallen asleep at Alisary at the magical time of midsummer, she was not still sleeping, and dreaming as she slept. She had lain down that night a simple Highland girl, content on her remote island with the wind and the rain, the sea and the shieling. Was it all a dream, the Prince, the flight from Uist, her capture, long days on the restless ship, and now this breath-taking moment? Would she awake, at the instant perhaps when they set the rope around her neck, and find herself back on her bed of heather in the early summer dawn?

Sometimes, alone among strangers, she ardently hoped so. Sometimes, as now, the world she confronted was so strange and wonderful that she hoped as ardently that it was real, let come what must.

It was December 6th. Her voyaging was almost done. She was afloat on the lower reaches of the River Thames, and approaching the great City of London as fast as six brawny oarsmen could pull the ship's boat against the flow of the tide. Beside her poor Kate Macdonald gaped in wonder.

They had seen shipping in the Isles, but never had Flora seen such a forest of masts, such an archipelago of hulls, as danced upon the waters of the Pool.

The day was fine and frosty. Sun sparkled on the brown water. Every kind of craft crowded the roadstead. Here a great India ship with carven prow towered like a floating palace. There a fast sloop with furled sails idled its slim length. About the tall ships darted and drifted and bumped the little sculls and skiffs. Bumboatmen ferried their loads of trifles and knickknacks from ship to ship. Watermen in bright breeches and white coats shot along in their light rowboats, delivering passengers or seeking them. To the music of oboes and horns and kettledrums, pleasure barges swept along, while the merrymakers sat under striped canvas, singing and flirting and staring about.

On either side of the river lay the city, looking in the frosty sunshine like a vision, like a city in a dream. Tall houses crowded to the water's edge, old, dark, and gabled, or new, foursquare, and shining. Directly ahead soared what looked like another city erected on great stone pillars.

"London Bridge," said the obliging young lieutenant in command.

"Do folks live upon a bridge?" wondered Flora.

"Indeed they do, and they have since time out of memory."

Flora looked at the rush of the tide between the arches, shooting down like a waterfall as tall as a man.

"It must be vastly noisy," she remarked.

Beyond the bridge to the right stretched the City of London itself. Flora looked at it, and wondered how a handful of men from the outer edge of the North had ever hoped to conquer the king who had such a capital. A dazzle of slender white spires soared over the crowding houses into the sunshine, and the shining dome of a great church crowned the rising ground.

"St. Paul's," said the young lieutenant.

All this time they had been approaching an ancient stone structure looming on the right below the bridge. As they neared it, Flora knew in her heart what it was. There was no mistaking the most ancient building in London, part fortress, part palace, part prison. There frowning above the river in a sweep of gray stone walls and battlements rose the Tower of London.

A few more strokes, and they were under the wall. The boatmen found a low arched opening, and ran into it. The sun was blotted. Dampness and dark laid a finger on Flora's heart, and she shivered and pulled her plaid closer.

"The Traitor's Gate," said the young lieutenant thoughtlessly.

A thrill of horror ran through Flora. She knew enough of history to know how many had passed in through that ill-omened waterway, and how few had ever seen the sun again. Their blood was soaked into the sod of Tower Green.

The boat slid along between cold stone. They passed under a lifted grating. It had sharp iron prongs like teeth. It was like going into some dreadful mouth that would snap shut upon you. Then they were within the water gate. The boatmen held the boat steady. The young lieutenant handed them ashore, Flora, her maid, and her bundle.

Flora was suddenly cold and weary. She hardly listened while a fussy functionary took her in charge, with what flourishing of legal papers she was too tired to notice. It seemed forever before they took her to an upper room in the keeper's house and left her there. Without supper, fire, or candle, as she was, she lay upon the curtained bed, drew her plaid about her, and fell fast asleep.

She awoke on a misty morning. Far away she heard the hum of the city. Close by, carpenters were hammering. A raven croaked once, and somewhere near a wild beast was roaring. Now what strange turn would this crazy dream take?

Flora opened her eyes. Kate was at her bedside with bread and butter and tea. As she sipped, Flora looked about the room which might be her last home.

It was not an uncomfortable lodging. They did not mean to be cruel to her. There was a chimney piece with a little half-moon grate, and in it Kate had kindled a cheerful fire. Flora wrinkled her nose. It was not fragrant peat, but something black that had a disagreeable fume. They say if you have once smelled peat, you can never learn to like a coal fire.

There were tapestry hangings on the stone walls, and

an old red rug upon the floor. The bed was hung with red woolen. There was a low trundle bed for Kate. The scanty furnishings were heavy and dark with age. There was an oaken table with great lion's claws, and sharp-angled oak chairs from the same bygone day.

Flora set down her cup, and went to the window. She was in one of the gables of the keeper's house. Through the crossbars in the narrow window she looked out on Tower Green. There was the raven, parading about and croaking under his breath with misplaced dignity; but there was no wild beast in sight.

About the Green clustered ancient gray stone buildings and round towers. With their notched crowns on top, the towers looked exactly like chessmen. In the center stood the most ancient building of all, the White Tower. It was really four towers, one at each corner. Over the tallest tower flew the red flag of England.

There was a tap at the pointed carved wood door. Kate admitted the man who knocked, and stared at him. Flora stared almost as hard. Like everything here, he too belonged to an earlier day. The style of his dress had not been changed for two hundred years. He wore a full-skirted red tunic with a golden lion on the breast. His black hat was round and flat, like a pot set on a plate. He wore a stiff white ruff, which made his head look as if *it* had been set on a plate. For the rest, he was a large old man with a rusty face like Mr. Punch in the puppet show.

Flora soon got used to the Tower Warders, and this one came to be her good friend, once she was sure that he was not a figment of her dream. He was an old soldier, a vet-

eran of Marlborough's wars, and he took it upon himself
to see that she was cared for, advised, and informed in
every way that he thought necessary.

This morning he came to present the compliments of
the Deputy Lieutenant of the Tower, and inform the new
captive that she was at liberty, when she chose, to take
the air upon that part of the battlements called Raleigh's
Walk. He conducted her thither by an upper door. For a
while she strolled along the stone parapet on top of the
wall in the misty air, and looked along the river, and
thought about Queen Elizabeth's gallant Sir Walter, who
lost his head at last on Tower Green.

As Flora walked, she became aware that below on the
Green something like a small mob was gathering. To the
intermittent roaring of the beasts and the incessant clatter
of hammers on boards was added the uneasy hum of a
crowd.

At first Flora thought they were staring at her. But they
were staring at something beneath her in the keeper's house,
lower down and to the left. Flora couldn't see what it was.

She was able to study them unobserved. They were the
first Londoners she had seen. They looked like small
French fashion dolls, so far below her, especially the fine
ladies, of whom there were several. Their hooped skirts
were flat as a mattress from fore to aft, and broad as a
bed canopy from side to side. They had little tight caps
and broad flat hats tied above, bare bosoms and furred
capes with hoods. One or two wept into cobwebby
handkerchiefs. They were attended by dandies with long
canes, muffs, deep-skirted velvet coats, and gold-laced hats
under their arms.

Flora watched them until a sparrow-legged popinjay caught sight of her, put his quizzing glass to his eye, decided she was worthy, and blew her a kiss. Then she hastily slipped inside.

The long day dragged by. No one asked for her or noticed her. Tossing in her bed at the day's end, Flora wondered whether she was to endure more forgotten months before King George's vengeance got around to her. It was long before she fell asleep.

As she slept, she dreamt that she was upon the Minch in storm. In time to the pitching of the open boat, someone was singing an old island lullaby:

> Darkness walks on the face of the deep,
> Sleep, little daughter, sleep . . . sleep . . .

But the roar of the waves and the scream of the wind were growing louder and louder, until at last it was hopeless to sleep longer. She opened her eyes.

There was no face bending over her. All she saw was the shadowy top of the bed tester. But the awful surge and roar of the tempest was still in her ears.

It was no illusion. When she had risen and stepped out on Sir Walter's Walk on the battlements, it smote her ears and shook her heart. It was the roar of an unruly crowd.

They were somewhere just outside the Tower walls, on the uphill side. At the East Gate there were mounted men. She could hear horses stamp and harnesses jingle. As she looked in that direction, two Tower Warders went forward and pulled back the iron leaves of the gate.

Two solemn officials, staff in hand, held brief parley.

Then they were escorted into the Tower grounds. They vanished from sight into the Lieutenant's house.

She wondered what all this might mean. Had they come for her? She laughed at herself at once. Come for her, one small Highland lass, with a troop of horse and a mob at their backs?

For what then? She had not long to wait. Soon the solemn jacks-in-office and the gaudy Tower Warders were back on the Green, drawn up ready to receive—whom?

It was a gallant figure that they had come to fetch. He was tall and well formed, clad in blood-red velvet. The sleeves of his coat were turned up with black. His scarlet waistcoat was thickly encrusted with gold. He wore white silk stockings and shoes with glittering buckles. His hat was brave with a great white feather—a white cockade!

For a moment he stood stock-still on the Green and turned his face to the sky, a steady face with an old scar slashing it. It was the face of a stranger.

For a long moment he stood so. Then with graceful ease he stepped forward to where the officials were waiting to receive him. Bowing respectfully, they assisted him to step into an open landau which was waiting.

Then their ranks parted, and a companion joined the man in the carriage. Flora gasped, and gripped the parapet. The newcomer was like a figure of Death. He was clothed from head to toe in stark black. He held a great two-handed axe, and as he seated himself opposite the man in scarlet, he turned the edge deliberately in his direction.

As the landau was drawn slowly out at the East Gate, Flora stared fascinated upon the erect figure in the blood-red raiment. Now she knew why the crowd stared at him, and what the carpenters had been building on Tower Hill, and what the people there were waiting for.

As the landau went out the gate, the surge of the crowd swelled to a crash. She could hear the sound go with him to the top of Tower Hill. As she stood on the battlements, gripping the edge till her knuckles whitened, she heard the surge go down to a wave, to the stillness of a held breath, and then crash out in a sound that was not quite a sigh, not quite a groan, not quite a snarl, but a huge horrifying combination of all three. As well as if she had seen it, she knew that the great axe had fallen and the proud head was rolling on the scaffold.

As she stood fighting nausea with bent head and long-drawn breath, the rusty-faced warder appeared beside her.

"Bless me, miss, you shouldn't be here!" he cried with concern.

"Nobody told me not to," she said faintly.

"More fools they! Come inside, miss, do. Them beasts in the crowd outside is worse than the lions in the moat, they do love the smell of blood. But it ain't for the like of you. Come inside."

"Who was he?"

"Rebel, miss, an impident double rebel against his Majesty King George. Earl of Derwentwater, he called himself. Had Royal Stuart blood in his veins, too."

"He fought for the Prince?"

"For the Young Pretender? Not he. He fought for the Old Pretender, in the year '15, ah, and they caught him, and condemned him to the axe. But he broke prison and fled over the water. Do you think he had enough? Not he!

He must needs come back to fight again, and they caught him on the sea. 'My father condemned him once,' says King George, 'so lads, you may take off his head without further parley!' " He opened the carven door. "Here we are, miss, just you recline, and the young maid shall fetch you the smelling bottle."

Flora had steadied herself. If the dead man could face the axe twice in the Stuart cause, and smile as he faced it, she could surely watch him go without blenching. If she blenched at the fate of another, how should she stand firm when her own day came?

"I wonder," she said steadily, "that your King will waste the edge of the axe upon so old a crime, while the leaders that beat him from Prestonpans to Moy go free!"

"Ah," said the warder. "He'd catch 'em if he could. But he can't, do you see. Where's Lochiel? Where's young Clanranald? Where's the Pretender himself? There's three rebels that would make a pretty show on Tower Hill!"

Now that they had finished with the Earl of Derwentwater, the officials had some time for Flora. The Deputy Lieutenant was stupid and kind. He advised Flora to be ready with her defence in writing, and furnished her with long sheets of laid paper, oak-gall ink, a box of sand to blot with, and a gray goose-quill pen. Sitting at the oak table by the crossbarred window, Flora labored earnestly to set her thoughts in order. But how could she put on paper the gaunt bronzed face, the desperate eyes, the gay smile of courage, the tender hands that had impelled her to do what she did, and sustained her in the doing of it? What use to sit scratching stupidly over and over:

THE TRUE STORY *of* FLORA MACDONALD, *now
imprisoned in the Tower of London* . . .

Nothing she could say would make them let her out.
She seemed to hear Felix O'Neille saying: "Be careful to
make your conduct all of a piece. Never once pretend to
repent or be ashamed of what you have done . . ."

For the tenth time, Flora slowly shredded the paper before her. Let them ask her what they pleased. She was not
afraid of them.

As if to test her resolution, at this moment there was a
bustle on the stair, and a sharp rap at the door.

"Quick, miss, make ready, you're wanted."

It had come. Flora rose slowly, and drew her clan plaid
across her bosom, half as if she thought it was a shield.

"I am ready," she said.

The friendly warder's eyes were popping.

"It's unheard of, miss," he said. "It's the Prince of Wales
himself has come to question you."

Flora flickered her ghost of a smile. *Her* Prince had left
her with two kisses in the smoky inn of Portree. To her
this fellow was the Pretender.

The bustle increased. There was an insurge of pompous
waiting gentlemen, a flutter of kerchiefs and cravats, a
flash of gold lace, and Frederick Lewis, usurping Prince of
Wales and undoubted heir to the Elector of Hanover,
strutted into the room.

For all his gold lace, he was not nearly so frightening as
Captain Ferguson, nor for that matter as distinguished as
General Campbell. He carried far less gross tonnage than
his surly father the King or his butcher brother of Cum-

berland. His smile was silly, and his eye was full of doubt.

"Hem," he said. "Now then, miss, what's this I hear of you? How have you dared to give your assistance to a rebel against my royal father?"

As he peered at her, he was such a sad contrast to the gallant young Prince she remembered, that to her amazement she found herself pitying him. Words of defiance died on her lips.

"Sir," she replied sincerely, "if you had been in similar distress, be sure I would have done the same for you."

After they had all gone away, Flora did not know whether her bold answer had ruined or bettered her chances. There was no use trying to guess. She set herself to continue waiting in patience.

While she waited, her fate was settled, and they say that Frederick had a hand in it. Very soon a warrant came down to the Tower. Miss Flora Macdonald was to be released.

It was not an unconditional release. A King's officer was told off to keep an eye on her until her trial. The officer was a silent man named William Dick. He brought the warrant down himself in a hackney coach. The coach waited while Kate tied up the bundle. Then the ladies were handed in, Mr. Dick took his place, the coachman snapped his whip, and off they rolled.

They did not go out at the Traitor's Gate. They rolled out under the heavy arch of the Byeward Tower, over the empty moat in which the lions were caged, out at the Middle Tower Gate, and westward into the heart of the great City of London.

CHAPTER 17 ❦ *Mayfair*

As Flora's hackney coach joggled and clattered over the London cobbles, all the church bells began to ring. They rang because it was Sunday morning, but to Flora it seemed as if they were ringing for her. They rattled down Cheapside and came to St. Paul's to the chiming of the bells of St. Bride's. From St. Paul's the great bell solemnly chanted them on their way.

Kate Macdonald had not eyes enough to take it all in. As they jogged over the Fleet Ditch into Fleet Street, her head was whirling trying to look at every painted board hung out for a shop sign. Both girls were laughing heartily at the sign of the Devil Tavern, St. Dunstan with his tongs chasing a comical devil, when the shadow of Temple Bar fell before them, and Flora looked up. Over the arch stuck on long spikes were three human heads. She closed her eyes with a cry.

When she took her hands from her face again, the coach was drawing into a paved court. In another moment the Scottish lasses had alighted and were mounting a narrow stair.

Mr. Dick escorted Flora into the one-pair-of-stairs front, which was a comfortable withdrawing room. The room was full of people. As Flora looked about bewildered, an old gentleman came forward and took her hand.

"You are welcome, my dear," said he, "back among your own people."

It was old Clanranald. About him were her own people indeed, a knot of Jacobite prisoners lodged with Mr. Dick on parole. They pressed about her to kiss her hand, and Flora greeted them from a full heart. Among them were Clan's brother Alexander, handsome Malcolm Macleod from Raasay, whom she had last seen a prisoner on board *The Furnace*, and young Gordon of Glenbucket, peering with his purblind eyes.

"How happy I am," she cried, "to see you all again; and could I but hear that my Prince is in safety, then all would be to a wish!"

"My dear, have they not told you? He is safe, and pure well. He got off from the mainland in a French vessel that came to fetch him. With him went off Lochiel and some hundred of his friends both high and low."

"When?"

"Almost three months after you left him."

"Three months! To what misery must he have been reduced! But tell me the way of it. I long to know it all."

"Here is the one that can tell you," said old Clanranald, nodding at Malcolm.

"I will tell you in few words. With my nephews I came to Portree in the wild rainy night you remember. Donald Roy brought the Prince to us from the inn, and we took him over the water and hid him on Raasay. There we stayed only long enough to shake off pursuit. Returning then to Skye, I guided the Prince to the country of Mackinnon, and there I bade him farewell. From there the old laird and his kinsman, John Mackinnon, took him off to the mainland. But there was no refuge on the mainland. His way was traced. The redcoats threw a cordon of sentries around the district where he landed, each in the sight of the next, lighting the countryside with great fires by night, so that to pass through seemed impossible."

"Yet he succeeded?"

"By help of a guide who knew the byways, he crept in the night along a hidden way among rocks between sentry and sentry. Then having broken through, he made his way towards Badenoch. Once he tarried for a week with eight sturdy outlaws in the Braes of Glenmoriston, and there lived merrily.

"At Badenoch," continued Malcolm, "he comes up with Lochiel, to his great joy, for he ever loved Lochiel best of his clansmen. There the Camerons make him safe in secret caves and shielings, or in a tree-cage artfully built in the face of a rock. Here he lingers until two French ships put in at the coast. Being advised of it, he and his companions walk back, and so our Prince embarks again at Lochna-nuagh, the very spot where first he landed on Scottish ground."

"No sooner was he got to Paris," added young Gordon, "but he went in state to wait upon the King of France. They say he wore gold brocade, with all his orders and all his jewels, so that he glittered like the sun. In his train went twenty Highland gentlemen, of whom my father had the honor to be one. King Louis embraced him like a father, and the French Court makes much of him; so that we may hope that soon he will return again in force."

"Amen!" said Flora.

There was still so much news to hear from the Isles. Donald Roy and Hugh of Armadale had begun to come out of hiding. Her mother was well. Old Kingsburgh was still jailed in Edinburgh Castle. In Skye, Allan was hard at work trying to keep his father's affairs straight without him.

"Lady Clanranald?"

"A prisoner too, in London, but in another house. She is frail, but keeps up her heart."

"Lady Margaret?"

"This two months widowed. Sir Alexander died suddenly in his route from Skye to Edinburgh, and it is the world's belief that he died of a broken heart."

"Well he might, for he played a sad part among heroes. What of my Cousin Clan, who played his part so well?"

"It is believed that he is now in France; therefore if," said old Clanranald slyly, "he lives quietly with kin in the North, who shall disturb him?"

"And Neil Maceachen?"

"Followed the Prince to France."

"Would we were all so fortunate!"

"Well, well, my dear, we must make the best of it!"

Flora soon found that to make the best of it in London was to have a very good time indeed. As Felix O'Neille had predicted, friends and admirers flocked about her. They were eager to show her all the sights. They took her to see Gog and Magog, the Giants of the Guildhall. In nearby Fleet Street, outside St. Dunstan's Church, stood two other giants. Clad only in carven leaves, these wooden wild men would heave up their clubs every sixty minutes and beat out the hour, to the admiration of all beholders, and especially wondering Kate Macdonald. She never tired of the performance.

Kate would have gone as often to see Mrs. Salmon's Waxwork, close by, if shillings had been easier to get. It seemed to her another work of enchantment. Over "Charles I on the Fatal Scaffold" simple Kate shed tears. Her eyes popped to see the waxen High Dutch lady upon a bed of state having 365 children all at once. When the mechanisms were set going, the executioner swung his axe, and the 365 children began arriving upon an endless belt, simple Kate was between ecstasy and downright fear.

At the theater Kate was no less vocal with wonder. The feats of the harlequin in the afterpiece left her breathless as he leaped, flew, jigged, and coaxed his way into her heart and Columbine's together. Flora enjoyed the tragedy itself better. Famous Mr. Quin spouted like a whale. Young Mr. Garrick was like quicksilver.

Soon Flora was taken up by high society in Mayfair. Old Lady Primrose, a prominent Jacobite dowager, introduced her everywhere. She learned to pass compliments and to fend them off, to parry a fixed quizzing glass with a fluttering fan, to listen to everything, to say yes to most things, and to believe few.

The polite world thought Miss Flora Macdonald vastly pretty, vastly witty, and vastly sensible. She was included in many a party of pleasure. The sparks took her to Ranelagh and treated her to chickens in wine and frothing syllabubs. Ranelagh was a huge pleasure dome circled with two tiers of boxes where one might feast. In a third tier sat the musicians sounding their fiddles and bassoons, their oboes, horns, and kettledrums. Round and round in the center, dressed to the teeth, paraded the somebodies and the nobodies of London. It made Flora's head swim.

Except for the chickens, she liked Vauxhall better. Vauxhall was a garden up the Thames. It was enchanting to go thither in a barge, some evening in June, hearing music echoing on the river between the cool green shores. One could walk in the groves and hear the nightingales sing; or, just as good, when the band struck up, listen to the music of the famous Mr. Handel.

Certain other pleasures of the city Flora preferred to abstain from. Nobody was so stupid as to invite her to go along and see Lord Lovat beheaded for following the Prince. She knew however that many went. There were specially built grandstands for the spectators. Flora almost felt it served them right when one of the stands fell and killed some people.

Her fine friends coaxed her to make one in a party of pleasure to laugh at the mad folk in Bedlam. They were funnier than the comedians, so she was assured, especially if one tipped the keeper to prod them up with a stick. Flora declined. She also declined to join a party going to view the lions in the Tower, even though they too were to be prodded up with a stick. She had had enough of the Tower.

She found more than enough to fill the day at the plays and the pleasure gardens, boating on the Thames, walking in St. James Park, or attending fashionable routs and parties at cards.

Meanwhile the French war dragged on. The French

King kept the Scottish plans dangling. The Jacobite Co-
terie at Mr. Dick's longed to hear word from Prince
Charles; but no word came.

"We shall not hear," said Flora sensibly, "until he comes
again. What could he say that he has not already said?
We have his promises. We shall hear from him, when he
can keep them."

The weeks dragged on. It became harder and harder to
endure even so little captivity. As summer came close,
Flora began to long to get back to the misty Isles, and to
the friend—the friends—whom she loved. King George
seemed to have lost all thought of hanging her. If he would
only let her go!

King George's people were tired of blood. In June, Parliament made it official. They passed a law called an "Act
of Grace," pardoning the rebels that survived. In July they
turned them loose to go home.

"Are you not grateful to our gracious King George," a
courtier asked the dour old laird of Mackinnon, "for his
kindness in sending you back to your own country?"

"Aye," growled old Mackinnon, "so grateful I'd be glad
to do the same for him!"

"But, Flora," cried kind old Lady Primrose, "you can
neither walk nor swim to Scotland. I shall send you back as
befits your station and your fame, in a post chaise, and you
shall choose any gentleman to escort you."

"I choose Malcolm Macleod," said Flora.

So on a summer day, when the lasses in the fields were
making hay, Miss Flora Macdonald and Captain Malcolm
Macleod, with Kate in attendance, rolled in their high post

chaise out along the Great North Road, bound for Scotland and the home that neither one of them had ever hoped to see again.

CHAPTER 18 ❦ *Home to Skye*

> Late, late in the gloaming when all was still,
> When the fringe was red on the westling hill,
> The wood was sere, the moon in the wane,
> The reek of the cot hung over the plain
> Like a little wee cloud in the world alone;
> When the ingle glowed with an eerie flame,
> Late, late in the gloaming Kilmeny came home!

Though King George had let her go, it seemed to Flora as if the enchantment still held. There were still so many demands on her. There were duty visits to pay at Edinburgh, at Armadale, at Monkstadt, at Benbecula. Months dragged by before she was free to follow her heart home.

At long last she stood with Allan in the wood above Kingsburgh. The hills were purple with heather. On the horizon, across blue water, glimmered the misty lavender shape of the Isle of Lewis. It was many months since they had parted in anger at Armadale. They stood in silence and looked at one another.

They were both older. Flora was slimmer than ever.

Allan's firm mouth had tightened. Flora saw with a pang the sadness in his eyes. These years had not been easy for him either. Now it was over. The white cockade was only a memory. It was time to begin living in earnest.

"Allan," said Flora, "I have brought you a fairing from London."

"What is it, Flory?"

Flora put the gift in his hand. It was a broad finger ring of gold. On it were two hearts intertwined.

"You must read the posy," said Flora.

Allan tilted the ring, and read softly: "*I am thine, as thou art mine.*"

"If it is true," said Flora gravely, "will you wear it for my sake?"

"I will wear it forever," said Allan, and took her in his arms.

In a handsome house in Paris, Neil Maceachen and young Clanranald were dining with the Prince. The finest French sauces and the rarest wines were spread before the man who had once been glad to eat mutton giblets off a wooden spit and to drink milk from a rough stone bottle, "Jock-fellow-like."

As the wine went round, a messenger came in haste with a warning.

"Prince," he cried, "the French King designs to have you arrested this very day, and banished from France. He says he has promised it to King George by the treaty of peace, and if you will not go peaceably you shall be expelled by force."

"It is a promise," said Charles contemptuously, "dishonorable for him to give and unfit for me to comply with. I will not go. Let him expel me."

"Forgive me, sir, they are his words, not mine. I come only to warn you that they are prepared to arrest you when you go to the Opera today."

"Be it so," said Charles coolly. "We will not make them wait for us."

He was deaf to argument. He arrayed himself splendidly, and set out. He looked every inch a king as he rolled in his crested carriage through the Rue St. Honoré.

"Prince, turn back!" cried a voice from the footway. "The Opera is beset! Turn back! Turn back!"

Charles did not even turn his head.

As soon as he alighted before the Opera, Charles was seized by six men, roped from head to foot with cords of crimson silk, and carried off bodily.

Throughout he held a contemptuous silence. Only once did he speak.

"Where are you taking me? To Hanover?"

Certain death by secret assassination was waiting in Hanover. But they were not bound for Hanover. They took him to the French King's prison at Vincennes. There he was imprisoned in the remotest top of the old stone tower. Of all his followers, only Neil was allowed to stay with him.

It was a tiny stone cell, lighted from the smallest slit in the roof, and furnished with a wretched camp bed and a single chair.

"This," said Charles coldly, "is not very magnificent."

The jailers bowed in silence, and withdrew. Then once

again Neil saw that incomparable patience break. The Prince threw himself down in a passion of angry tears.

"Oh, my faithful Highlanders!" he cried. "You would not have treated me so. Would I were still with you!"

The French dared not hold him long. When they put him over the frontier and let him go, he disappeared.

His friends did not know which way to turn. It was the end of all their hopes. Until he died, Charles would never admit defeat; but it was over just the same.

Flora and Allan were married quietly at Kingsburgh. Flora's admirers made her a handsome dowry. They sent rich gifts. There was neither gift nor greeting from Prince Charles Edward. Nobody knew where he was.

But perhaps, opening an old newspaper one day in a back room in some mean street in Liége or Avignon or Warsaw, Charles would once again recall with tenderness the small steadfast face, asleep between his hands in the storm-tossed boat, or wet with salt tears under his lips at Portree, as he read:

MARRIAGES, NOVEMBER, 1750.

Nov. 6. Allan Macdonald, eldest son of Alexander Macdonald of Kingsburgh, married to Miss Flora Macdonald, daughter of Ranald Macdonald of Milton, deceas'd. This is the young Lady who aided the escape of the young Chevalier.

𝔅𝔬𝔬𝔨 𝔉𝔦𝔳𝔢 ✤ Flora and Allan

Farewell, lovely Skye, sweet isle of my childhood,
　Thy blue mountains I'll clamber no more;
Thy heath-skirted corries, green valleys and wildwood,
　I now leave behind for a far-distant shore.

Once more, dearest isle, let me gaze on thy mountains,
　Once more let the village church gleam on my view;
And my ear drink the music of murmuring fountains,
　While I bid to my old and my young friends adieu.

Farewell, lovely Skye, lake, mountain and corrie;
　Brown isle of the valiant, the brave, and the free;
Ever green to thy sod, resting place of my Flora,
　My sighs are for Skye, my tears are for thee.

CHAPTER 19 ❦ *The Emigrants*

On an autumn Sunday in the year 1773, two travelers might have been seen riding in the rain along the way from Portree to Kingsburgh, over the same path Flora had followed on that rainy day in 1746.

One was a huge, burly old man, who wore a large great-coat that flapped about his booted heels, and rode on a little horse. The other rider was a lively young fellow with a dark complexion. The young chap had a long nose, a sharp eye, and an eager ear. He delighted in meeting and listening to famous people. The burly old gentleman was a very famous person. He was Samuel Johnson, the best known writer and scholar of England. His young friend was a Scotsman named James Boswell.

The odd pair of travelers had come to the Western Islands to visit the Highland chiefs and see how they and their people lived. They were finding great changes in the old-time life. The power of the chiefs had been deliberately broken. The people were even forbidden to wear their clan tartans. Many of the chiefs had been exiled for their part in the rebellion of the '45. Others were trying to compete with the wealthy English lords. Instead of staying home and taking care of their people, they went off to the

Lowlands or to England to be educated, and stayed there. In order to pay their debts in the great world, they had to raise the rents.

One of these absentee chiefs was young Sir Alexander Macdonald, Lady Margaret's son. Mr. Johnson and young Boswell did not approve of Sir Alexander. He had raised rents and neglected his clansmen to such a degree that they could no longer make ends meet. Many of them had had to give up everything and go off to make a new life in America. Among others, Hugh Macdonald had given up Armadale and gone to a far-off place called North Carolina. He took with him Flora's mother and Annabella and her husband. Every ship that sailed carried off a load of Macdonalds.

Such a ship was even then lying in the harbor at Portree. Mr. Boswell, who never missed seeing what there was to see, had gone on board. He thought it a fine vessel. He found the cabin commodious and elegant, admired the library of books for reading at sea, and approved of the sleeping quarters, lined with square beds, each one big enough for four sleepers. But he still considered emigration a very bad idea, and Mr. Johnson agreed with him.

"It is hurtful to human happiness," said Johnson, "for it spreads mankind, which weakens the defence of a nation and lessens the comfort of living. Men thinly scattered make a shift, but a bad shift, to get along without many things. A smith is ten miles off; they'll do without a nail or a staple. A tailor is far from them; they'll botch their own clothes. Meanwhile these Isles are made a desert. I wonder the government does nothing to stop emigration."

"Perhaps," said Boswell, "the government is willing

enough to be rid of the Macdonalds, as being former rebels."

"Suppose they were once rebels," growled Johnson, "will they learn better among the Americans?"

"What ails you at the Americans?"

"A nest of malcontents! Refusing to pay his Majesty's just taxes! Flouting Parliament! Setting themselves up to make their own laws! Mark me, sir, there's insurrection brewing!"

"Nay, sir," said Boswell, who admired the Americans, "they are his Majesty's loyal subjects, and desire only their just rights."

"Sir," roared Johnson, "clear your mind of cant! The Americans are a set of rebels born. Let me hear no more of them!"

Mr. Boswell hastily changed the subject. The two friends were approaching Kingsburgh. They were on their way to visit the famous heroine of the Isle of Skye, Mistress Flora Macdonald.

It was late in the afternoon when they rode up to the house. They were expected. No sooner were they before the door than out came their host, Allan Macdonald of Kingsburgh.

Allan was now middle-aged, but he was as handsome as ever. Mr. Boswell noted his appearance carefully so that, when later he should write up his trip, he could describe the handsome Highlandman exactly.

"He was quite the figure of a gallant Highlander," wrote Boswell, "having the graceful mien and manly looks. He had his tartan plaid thrown about him, a large blue bonnet with a knot of black ribbon like a cockade, a brown short coat, a tartan vest with gold buttons and gold buttonholes, a bluish philibeg, and tartan hose. He had jet-black hair tied behind and with ringlets on each side, and was a large stately man, with a steady sensible countenance."

The tartan attire was quite illegal, but Allan did not care. He shook hands with his guests, and led them into the house. There in the parlor where once Betty Burke had warmed her long shanks, the two visitors dried their rain-damp clothes before a good fire, and made friends with their host.

Soon in came supper, which they relished no less than Charles had enjoyed his roasted eggs and collops. It was a better supper. There was a fine large roast turkey, and porter, claret, and punch to drink. A numerous company sat down to the feast; but the visitors had eyes for only one, their hostess, Flora Macdonald. Although Flora was over fifty, she was still erect and slim, "a little woman," Boswell described her, "of a mild and genteel appearance, mighty soft and well-bred."

When she came into the room, Mr. Johnson went to her, took her hand, and kissed her cheek. They were friends at once. Samuel Johnson liked pretty women, and he admired brave ones. Flora was both. Soon they were such good friends that Flora was teasing him.

"While I was visiting on the mainland," she told him, "I heard that Mr. Boswell was coming to Skye, and one Mr. Johnson, a young English buck, was coming with him."

Old Mr. Johnson, in his rumpled traveler's clothes and his rusty matted wig, with his heavy homely face, was far from a fashionable young buck. The idea tickled him. He put back his head and laughed out loud. Flora laughed with him. Soon she was telling him all about herself.

"We are blessed with seven children," said she. "The oldest is a lad of twenty-one, named—"

"Let me guess," said Mr. Johnson. "Charles."

"You are right. But how did you know?"

"Because, ma'am, with my friend Boswell here I share your politics. We are both of the *old interest*, and think with affection of him that's away."

"God bless you for it, sir, and God bless him, wherever he may be."

"Well, and is young Charles in his service?"

"No, sir. Charles is in the service of the East India Company. Of my four other sons, Ranald is at sea, in the Royal Marines. John is my youngest; he is in school in Edinburgh. Then there's Alexander, he's eighteen, and James is fifteen. I have them still at home."

"And, Flory," said Allan affectionately, "you'll not slight the lasses. Nannie is nineteen, and wed to a son of Macleod. She has already made me twice a grandfather. And Fanny at seven is the baby of this house."

"Five sons and two daughters," said Flora. "We have been blessed indeed."

"May you still be so," said Mr. Johnson.

"You shall wish us well in a new life," said Flora, "for as soon as our affairs are set in order, we intend to say good-bye to Skye and sail away to our friends in North Carolina."

Mr. Johnson forbore to ask questions. The truth was that Allan Macdonald was deep in debt. He had tried to follow his father in the management of his chief's affairs;

but the new chief gave him no help, and soon he was hopelessly entangled. It would take all he had to settle his debts and get a new start. Flora faced the future, as she had faced the redcoats, with her head held high; but there were hard days ahead.

Mr. Johnson was tired after his long ride in the rain. He and Flora put their heads together a moment. Then he rose and bade the company goodnight, and Flora led him upstairs.

Boswell stayed below. Like Allan's jovial father, he liked a good glass of punch and a rousing song. Allan had learned his father's recipe for the punch that the Prince had so enjoyed. He had not learned his father's favorite song, "Green Sleeves and Pudding Pies"; but his sister had, and later she taught it to Boswell.

The gentlemen sat late, and were merry together. Boswell was grieved to think that his kind host was forced to emigrate; but he pleased himself in thinking that so spirited a man would get along well anywhere. At last Boswell went up to bed. He was to share the best room with his friend. He found him sleeping soundly in a bed with tartan curtains.

It was the very bed in which Prince Charles had slept so sweetly twenty-seven years before.

"I would have given a good deal," said Mr. Johnson at breakfast, "rather than not have lain in that bed."

"You are a lucky man," said Boswell, "and I think your luck was contrived between you and Mrs. Macdonald."

"That is true," said Flora, smiling at her favored guest, "for you know *young bucks* are always the favorites of the ladies!"

"To think," said Boswell, "that the Prince was here, in this very house!"

"And *who* was with him?" said Johnson slyly. "We were told, madam, in England, that there was one Miss Flora Macdonald with him."

"They were very right," said Flora.

Mr. Johnson was too polite to ask questions; but Flora did not wait to be asked. She could see that this big Englishman loved the memory of the bonnie young Prince as she herself did. She began to tell the story. Once more, in the house which was now her home, and which she was so soon to leave, she remembered the adventure that she had shared there so long ago. She recalled the flight from Benbecula in an open boat. She said nothing of the moment on the stormy Minch when she awoke to find Charles bending over her to guard her from harm; but she told how they were fired on, and how they escaped and got safe to Monkstadt.

"There at dinner I met with Lieutenant Macleod, on the watch for the Prince. I have often since laughed at him in friendship, over the way he was deceived."

Flora described to her hearers the Sunday walk to Kingsburgh, the tall figure of the odd muckle slattern, Betty Burke, striding awkwardly along, pulling his petticoats too high or letting them draggle in the burn. She remembered his gaiety at supper, and his long sweet sleep in the bed with the tartan curtains.

She would never forget the moment at his bedside, when he laid his blond head in her lap and she cut off a curl to keep. But it was nobody else's business; she said nothing about it. Nor did she mention their moment of farewell at Portree.

"When the Prince left Kingsburgh," she said, "Allan's mother took the sheets from his bed, and saved them as they were; and according to her wish, when she died we laid her to rest wrapped in those very sheets."

"All this should be written down," declared Mr. Johnson.

Then it was time for the travelers to part. Once more Mr. Johnson took Flora's hand and kissed her cheek. The name of Flora Macdonald would live in his heart—"a name that will be mentioned in history, and if courage and fidelity be virtues, mentioned with honor."

After they were gone, Flora found on the table by Prince Charles's bed a slip of paper. On it Mr. Johnson had penciled a Latin proverb. He had been thinking of the reward on the Prince's head, and of Flora and the other Highlanders who had preferred loyalty.

"*Quantum cedat virtutibus aurum*," he had written— "How much better virtue is than gold."

CHAPTER 20 ✤ *The New World*

Flora and Allan Macdonald stood side by side on the deck of the ship *Baliol*, out of Campbelltown for Cape Fear. It was the autumn of 1774.

They had had a peaceful voyage of long blue days, and now their destination was in sight. Here was their new country. They looked at the long white beaches, crowded with woods to the edges, and wondered what awaited them. It seemed a lonely wilderness, save that once they saw the thin thread of smoke among the trees that told where a plantation lay.

Soon they were sailing between the wooded banks of the Cape Fear river. On the left they passed Fort Johnston, a square structure of timber and lime, crumbling in spots, with cannon peeping from between the sticks.

Up river they sighted the first town, Brunswick, a mean little scattering of houses between the woods and the waterline. Soon after that, the *Baliol* came to anchor off the town of Wilmington.

It was here that Flora and her family first set foot on the new world. They were a numerous group. There was Flora's pretty daughter Nannie, young at twenty to be the mother of the bouncing youngsters pulling at her skirts. Her soldier husband, Alexander Macleod, was almost twice her age. Flora's two sons helped their mother ashore at the wharf. Alexander was nineteen, and James was not quite seventeen. Eight servants followed with the baggage.

Wilmington was the finest town in North Carolina. It was built along straight streets between two hills. The Scottish party admired the handsome houses. There was nothing like them in Scotland. The red brick houses were two and three stories high, with double porticoes supported by tall columns painted white. The church had a slender spire like the spires of London.

At Wilmington Flora had her first taste of Southern hospitality. There was a ball in her honor. As she and Nannie picked their way on foot along the muddy, unpaved street, following a servant carrying a torch, the new world did not seem much like London. But once in the long hall, lighted by many candles in sconces, as Flora trod a minuet with her handsome husband, she was reminded of home and that first minuet in Edinburgh so long ago. What if Allan was heavier and quieter, she herself thinner and older? Here life would begin again.

At Wilmington too, along with the ways of home, Flora caught her first glimpse of a new world, savage and strange. She saw with repulsion the strange scaly creature called the alligator dragged up from the river in triumph. She saw Negroes for the first time, and the occasional figure of a red Indian stalking along with lank black hair and bright feather was a strange sight to her.

The Macdonalds were completing preparations for their journey upcountry to the Scottish settlements, when one morning a disturbing thing happened. The sound of fife and drum brought Flora and Allan to their upper window.

The fifer was playing a quickstep. An advance guard of little boys scampered along ahead, shrilling the words:

"Yankee Doodle keep it up,
Yankee Doodle dandy . . ."

Behind them a strange procession straggled down the street. Save for the musicians, they were all women. Women of every age and rank trooped along. There were

gowns of butternut homespun topped with clumsy kerchiefs; there were gowns of damask and falling lace. There
were loose-flying elflocks and powdered pompadours. One
thing only united them. Every woman bore a look of determination and a caddy of tea.

In the market square the men had kindled a large bon-
fire. The fife and drum led the embattled ladies to the fire,
and into the fire went every last leaf of the tea. With a
wild shout from the bystanders it went up in smoke.

"What ails these ladies, that they burn good tea?" wondered Flora.

"We'll burn it before we will drink it," said the landlady
grimly. "Listen!"

Among the savage shouts Flora could distinguish a
phrase now and then: "Down with King George! Down
with the tax on tea! Taxation without representation is tyranny!"

"Why," exclaimed Flora, shocked, "this is rank treason!"

"If this be treason, ma'am," said the landlady trucu-
lently, "let George III make the most of it!"

After this, Flora began to perceive the seething unrest
in the colony. She began to see the resentment of the
American-born colonists at being ruled from across the
ocean, and ruled in such an arbitrary manner by King
George and his ministers. It seemed as if anarchy was at
hand. She was glad to leave Wilmington.

One hundred miles up the river was Cross Creek. The
houses were more modest, of logs or boards chinked with
clay. Even the church at Barbecue Creek was little more
than a log house. But in it she heard no treason.

Coming to the Highland settlement at Cross Creek was

like coming home. There once more Flora saw the tartan, and heard the bagpipe. Nearby on his plantation Hugh of Armadale waited to welcome Flora and her family. With his help Allan soon found a tract of ground to his liking. It was called Cameron's Hill. There they began to make a home.

At Cameron's Hill, as spring came on, Flora began to think she had come to paradise. She heard for the first time the song of the mockingbird, as sweet as the trilling of the nightingale at Vauxhall, and infinitely more varied. She saw the flash of the redbird, the white and pink planes of blooming dogwood, the shimmer of the redbud tree. Then the magnolias bloomed, like great oaks fragrant with a thousand white roses, and the hummingbird shimmered his wings in the wild honeysuckle. Flora was enchanted.

Some of the wild creatures made her laugh. Sitting still among the tangled leaves on some stream bank, she could see the sharp-nosed raccoon washing his dinner of roots held in his tiny black paws, or catch sight of an opossum hanging asleep from a branch. She couldn't laugh, however, when a great bear carried off a piglet, and left his tracks behind; nor when in the path she heard the dry whirr of a rattle, and pulled back from the cold heavy folds of the snake they called the rattlesnake.

They lived well at Cameron's Hill. Game was plentiful, and all the Scots knew how to bring it down with the gun. Flights of pigeons darkened the sky. The wild turkey, the partridge, the deer, and the duck fell to their firearms. The little ricebird of the swamp was as fine as the English ortolan. On turtles brought up from the coast they could feast like London aldermen. Flora learned to eat the succulent

Indian corn, the watermelon, the squash, and the sweet potato. Grapes grew wild in the woods for the pulling.

But they were not to be left in peace in their new paradise. Every traveler that passed brought uneasy news. Treason and rebellion were brewing fast. In early spring the Provincial Council had the impudence to flout the King's Governor, meet independently, and send delegates to the treasonous Continental Congress.

Soon after, guns began to blaze. Flora and Allan heard with indignation that at Lexington in Massachusetts a handful of farmers, "Minute Men" they called themselves, had fired upon the soldiers of the King.

A like spirit was stirring in North Carolina. There in Mecklenburg County the leaders met and called upon the colony to arm for its defence. Worse, they put out a declaration full of stark, bald-faced treason. In it, these dangerous agitators took it upon themselves to absolve Americans from all allegiance to the Crown, and to declare themselves a free and independent people. Anarchy could scarcely go further.

Four days later, Governor Martin ran away. He ran to the King's ship lying off Fort Johnston. He felt safer there.

All the Highlanders of the Cross Creek settlements were horrified. To a man, they had been brought up to be loyal, and they knew where their duty lay. They resolved to take up arms, if need be. Allan was one of the most respected men of the colony, and he took the lead. He went to Governor Martin and offered his services. Soon he received an officer's commission. So did his son-in-law, Alexander Macleod, and others among the Highlanders.

They held themselves in readiness to rise when the King's Governor called.

In the meantime, in June, the Americans and the redcoats fought a pitched battle on Bunker Hill near Boston, and the American sharpshooters shot down King George's men in heaps. Among the wounded was Ranald Macdonald of his Majesty's Marines, though this was not yet known to his mother, Flora Macdonald.

In July, the raggle-taggle mob of Americans in arms was taken in hand by a commander, a Virginia planter named George Washington, and the war began in earnest.

North Carolina was still enjoying an uneasy peace. Flora hoped that the war would keep away. She sometimes wished Allan would stay out of things, but, of course, if it was his duty he must go.

Her hope of staying at peace soared when Allan decided to leave Cameron's Hill and move upcountry. He bought a fine plantation in the piney woods. It had eighty cleared acres, a fine house and outbuildings, a gristmill that brought in an income, and an orchard of peach and apple trees. They named it Killiegrey. Riding up to her new home through the stately forest, glimpsing the misty heights of the Blue Ridge, Flora hoped that they were leaving war and rebellion behind them.

Martin, the King's Governor, did not mean to leave them in peace. Sitting safe on board the ship of war, he was busy with a plan to put down the spirit of rebellion by force. Admiral Sir Henry Clinton with seven Irish regiments would sail for Cape Fear. The loyal Highlanders would assemble at Cross Creek and march to the coast to meet him. Between them they would chase the rebellious buckskins back to their homes, and Governor Martin would return in triumph to govern the province for the King.

Sir Henry Clinton had not even set sail from Ireland when Governor Martin sent a message bidding the Highlanders to rise. The first man named was Allan Macdonald.

"Flory," said Allan, "I must go."

Just thirty years ago, his intense spirit of loyalty had led Allan Macdonald to take up arms for King George. He was the same man still. Then Flora had opposed him. Now he was her husband, and Britain was her country.

"I'll go with you," said Flora.

Allan smiled at that, but Flora meant it. Together they rode down to Cross Creek. Alexander, now twenty, went along. So did young James, much against Flora's wishes. He was quite old enough for the wars. Thus of her five sons only one, the youngest, at school in Scotland, had not taken up arms for Britain, and soon he too would do so. When her daughter's husband came from his plantation to join them, Flora's family had given six men to the service of her country.

On February 1, 1776, the royal standard was raised at Cross Creek. Once more Flora saw the swing of the tartan philibeg and heard the skirling of the great war pipes. When the clansmen had gathered and the march began, she rode along upon her white horse, wearing the King's cockade in her broad hat. Her heart was full of pride in her tall sons, and in the soldierly figure of her handsome husband striding along at their head. When it was time for her to turn back, she stood on a bank and watched the tall figure until it was lost in the dust of the road.

She did not see him again for years.

Only James came home to Killiegrey. He came with news of defeat and capture.

"These Americans are devils," said he. "I remember that you have often told me that facing the cold steel of the Highland charge the best trained regiments will break and run. No enemy, you have said, can stand before it.

"Well, the Americans can. They have discovered a new way to fight. They shoot from cover, like red Indians. No man knows where the enemy is hid. Every bullet finds its mark. And they have learned how to make things fight for them."

"How can *things* fight?"

"I will tell you. On our way to the shore, we had many burns to cross—creeks, the buckskins call them. Sometimes we found that they had taken away the bridges. Then we had to walk through the water. Once when the stream was swift, we floated a raft for a bridge. When we came to Moore's Creek, the bridge was standing. The buckskins were in the woods beyond. We marched to the attack. Oh, it was a fine sight to see, with the tartans swinging and the banners flying and the pipers sounding the great war pipes! At the bridge the word was 'Claymore!' and the front ranks drew steel and charged.

"Watching from the second rank, I could not believe my eyes. They fell from the bridge like leaves. They could not stand. The tricky Americans had taken up the planks and put grease on the long tree trunks underneath!"

"And so the bridge fought for them. I see what you mean."

"Then the firing began from the woods. The charge was

broken. Our men were floundering in the water. A body of buckskins was coming around behind us. The battle was lost. To put it bluntly, the rest of us ran away."

"What of your father?"

"I saw him captured, and Alexander with him. The buckskins took his silver-mounted rifle and marched him away. I stayed hid all night, and when the morning rose, I came away home. Oh, Mother, now what shall we do?"

"Do?" said Flora, setting her firm chin. "We'll do what has to be done. We'll work the plantation till the rebels are subdued and your father comes home."

Allan Macdonald never came home to Killiegrey. Flora sometimes wondered whether she would ever see him again. She kept things going as well as she could, but everything seemed to go wrong. The servants grew insolent. In the disturbed state of the country, wandering robbers preyed upon the estates that had lost their masters. Flora never knew when blacklegs would invade her house and with hideous threats try to force her into revealing some hidden store of money. It happened to her more than once. They found she could not be frightened, and after a while they left her alone.

Half the people she lived among were enemies. Her very friends were sulky when they reflected that it was Allan Macdonald who had led them into their misfortune. At first Flora was too sick to care. Then she tried to make friends. She rode from house to house, visiting. Riding thus, one day, she was thrown, and broke her right arm. It was long in healing, for there was no doctor left among the Highlanders.

Her enemies watched her behavior with suspicion. What

was she up to, riding about from house to house that way? They called her before the Committee of Public Safety and questioned her.

Flora had not been afraid of King George's judges. She was certainly not going to be afraid of a parcel of back-woodsmen. She answered their questions with spirit. They decided to let her go back to Killiegrey.

Meanwhile, on July 4, 1776, the Continental Congress followed the example of the rebels of Mecklenburg. They declared American independence.

At this open disloyalty, Flora felt as if North Carolina was no longer her home. She still hoped to see the rebels put down; but in October 1777, Burgoyne's invasion was stopped at Saratoga, and all hope of an early end of the war was lost.

In November 1777, the Provincial Congress declared Loyalist estates to be forfeited. Among the confiscated estates was Killiegrey.

When Flora left Killiegrey, she had to leave most of her possessions behind. She managed to save her silver service, and a few other treasures. The one thing above all others that she would not leave behind was a strand of light hair set in a brooch. How changed she was, how many things she had left behind her, since she had cut that yellow curl in the upper room at Kingsburgh!

After she lost Killiegrey, Flora lived on a friend's planta-tion near Cross Creek. James stayed with her. She was in continuous anxiety for news of her husband and her other sons. Ranald had recovered from his wound. Both he and Charles were in the army stationed at Halifax in Nova Scotia. After dragging about from jail to jail, Allan and

Alexander had finally been exchanged. Now they were at British headquarters in New York. Allan had been assigned to the 84th Highland Emigrant Regiment, with headquarters at Halifax. Soon he would join his regiment.

One more winter Flora spent, homeless, in North Carolina. In the new year, to her great delight, her husband sent for her. Under a flag of truce she sailed from Wilmington to New York. The wild Atlantic off the Capes stormed the whole time; but Flora did not care. Her husband and sons were waiting for her at the end of the voyage.

To anyone who had seen London, New York did not look like a big city; but it was larger than Wilmington. Along the wharves barrels of pitch and tar scented the salty air. Drays clattered over the cobbled streets. Some of the houses were old, Dutch, and gabled. Some were new and fine, of brick, with balconies and porticoes. Red coats were everywhere.

The broadest red coat was Allan's. In a breath Flora was in his arms. Alexander was beside him, dressed in the same gaudy uniform, scarlet turned back with blue. James, shaking his brother's hand, deplored his own sober citizen's garb.

James soon enough got into uniform. He joined the dashing light horse corps of Tarleton's Loyal British Legion. When Allan and Alexander were summoned to join their regiment in Halifax, young James was left behind in New York.

Flora went along to Halifax. It was autumn when they sailed, and the Atlantic was rougher than ever. This time she was so worn with travel and difficulties that the wild sea almost finished her. When they landed at Halifax, she could not hold up her head. She never looked at the forest of masts, the cloud of sails in the harbor, or the slender church spires with their look of London, or the raw blockhouse that frowned over the city from the snowy hill. The icy, rutted streets seethed with sailors in wide slops, lobster-backed grenadiers in mitre caps, gaudily dressed Negroes, drunken Indians, and all the motley hangers-on of an army. At Pontac's hotel officers in scarlet feasted ladies in furbelows. Flora was too ill to join them.

When Charles and Ranald came to her bedside, she clung to them until she had to leave them again. Too soon it was time to go on.

Allan's detachment was at Windsor, farther west, on the Bay of Minas. Five days they toiled through snowy woods. Woodsmen in fringed skins guided them, sliding smoothly along on strange webfooted runners for the snow. Muffled in furs, Flora rode in the army supply wagon under the canvas top. Allan rode beside her.

At Windsor, they told her, the winter that followed was one of the worst that Nova Scotia had ever known. Flora had seen snow in Scotland, but never had she seen such snow as now fell incessantly from the leaden sky and covered the world with a deep pall of white. Wolves howled in the death-still forest. The fierce forty-foot tide of Fundy spewed icy water and sucked it down again. As Flora sat huddled in her plaid beside the fire, listening to the wind howling down from the Arctic, the resolve grew in her heart to go home to Skye.

Spring came with hope. The paper birch shimmered pale green among the pines. The mayflower, breathing perfume, pushed aside the dead leaf on the forest floor. The sun shone, and the waters sparkled. Now surely Flora could go home.

She had always been small. Now at fifty-seven she was frail. In the midst of her preparations, she fell and shattered her wrist. But her heart was still stout. She would not give up her plans.

Finally, in September, there came into port at Halifax a ship of twenty-four guns, the *Lord Dunmore*, with letters of marque to take the King of France's ships upon the sea. Allan arranged for Flora to sail on the return voyage. In October they parted once more.

It was the business of the *Lord Dunmore* to fight the French. When they sighted a French vessel, they cleared for action. The ladies were ordered below. Flora had better sense than to clutter up the deck of a fighting ship. She hurried to go below; but her foot slipped, down she fell, and crack! went the shattered arm again. She spent the rest of the voyage in her bed with the arm in splints.

"I have now," she remarked with her unconquerable spirit, "risked my life for both the House of Stuart and the House of Brunswick; and I have got very little reward for my pains!"

CHAPTER 21 💥 *Home to Stay*

Flora Macdonald sat in the sun on a bank of turf outside her little cottage in the Isle of Skye. She had wandered halfway round the world. Now she was home again. She was very frail now, but her stout heart was unchanged.

She sat and looked north, toward the Minch, where a lifetime away, forty-two years ago, a man and a girl on a desperate night of storm crossed together in an open boat. Three miles away was the mansion house of Kingsburgh, where they had briefly found refuge. Not many miles farther was Portree, where they parted.

Now he was dead. He lay in a coffin of cypress wood, wrapped in purple velvet and ermine, with his sword at his side and his sceptre in his hand. The huckstering courts of Europe had broken his heart at last; but in death he slept like a king.

He was better than a king, thought Flora. He was tender and brave.

It was the end of the House of Stuart. There was no heir to fight for now. The chapter was closed. Slowly Flora shredded the letter that told her he was gone.

She had been more fortunate than he. With her little

smile, Flora fell once more to counting her blessings in the old-fashioned way.

She was sixty-six years old. That was a blessing in itself, to have come through so many trials by sea and land, and live to see home again.

She had bred up five sons for the service of Britain. At the bottom of the sea, among the bones of wrecked ships, lay two of them, Alexander and Ranald. Charles, the oldest, was the most polished gentleman of the five, and perhaps the wildest. He was in the King's Rangers. John, the youngest, was in India. He was the wealthiest and the most accomplished. It was he who had sent the money for the home Flora now lived in, the tack of Penduin. James, to whom she was closest of all her sons, had left the service to marry and settle in Skye.

Her two daughters had married Skyemen, and they were both near her. Flora took great delight in their growing families. Among her descendants were to be counted at least twenty brave soldiers and civil servants, prominent among the valiant Scots who built the British Empire in the years after the '45. She had surely done enough for the country that bonnie Prince Charlie called his own.

The greatest of her blessings was still to be counted. She turned to Allan where he sat beside her, and put her hand in his. They had been together for almost forty years, and now, for Flora, there was very little time left.

The Minch was howling in storm. Wild gusts of rain lashed through the darkness. Thunder rolled, and lurid lightning cut through the black downpour.

In the wild night a funeral procession was moving slowly along the path from Penduin to Kingsburgh. The coffin was borne on six men's shoulders. When they came to the stream, it was swollen from bank to bank. The bearers stood in doubt. Should they risk the passage, or turn back?

"She never turned back," said one of them. "She never flinched from anything she had once undertaken. We must carry her forward. We owe it to the memory of Flora Macdonald."

So they carried her forward. All the pipers of the Isles played the lament. They laid her at last in the churchyard of Kilmuir, between valiant old Kingsburgh's dust and the place where in two short years Allan was to lie. Over her head they set these words:

Flora Macdonald

who died in March, 1790, aged 68—

a name that will be mentioned in history, and if courage and fidelity be virtues, mentioned with honour. She was a woman of middle stature, soft features, gentle manners, and elegant presence. So wrote Johnson.

ELIZABETH R. HAYES, Ed.D. Stanford University, is Professor of Health, Physical Education, and Recreation and Director of the dance-major program at the University of Utah. She previously held positions as Secretary and Chairman of the National Section on Dance of the American Association of Health, Physical Education, and Recreation, and has served on numerous national committees in connection with dance in education, theatre, and recreation. Dr. Hayes, well known in the field of dance education, has written many articles for professional dance magazines and is the author of *Dance Composition and Production for High Schools and Colleges,* published by The Ronald Press Company.

AN INTRODUCTION TO THE TEACHING OF DANCE

Elizabeth R. Hayes

UNIVERSITY OF UTAH

THE RONALD PRESS COMPANY · NEW YORK

Copyright © 1964 by
THE RONALD PRESS COMPANY

3-VR

Library of Congress Catalog Card Number : 64–13940

Preface

To attempt to present a method for teaching dance that guarantees success could only be regarded as foolish, or to say the least, presumptuous. Teaching is a creative process, and as with painting, or writing, or dancing itself, there is no *one* right way of doing it. The fact is that successful teaching depends more upon the teacher himself as a vital, creative individual capable of inspiring others, than it does upon his personal methodology. Nevertheless, experience has shown that students who are preparing to become teachers of dance can be helped to achieve their goals (and avoid needless errors in the process) by understanding certain concepts and by following certain general practices and suggestions. A talent for organizing and presenting teaching material in a fashion that has meaning for the student is seldom inborn. This book has been written with the purpose of offering assistance in the development of such ability; its intended function is like that of a pilot vessel guiding an ocean liner to the sea—when the initial unseen dangers are past, guide lines are severed so that the captain can chart his own course in accordance with his chosen destination.

The text is designed to demonstrate how various forms of dance can be developed from an understanding and mastery of movement fundamentals. Specific dance materials and lesson units have been included to illustrate how these materials can be organized and presented to provide students with rich experiences and sound understandings of dance elements and principles; but these examples are intended merely as a means of pointing the way for the teacher's own creative planning. Because the dance teacher is also intimately concerned with the task of providing satisfactory dance accompaniment, some practical help has been given in this area. A discussion of problems pertaining to the supervision of extracurricular club activities and dance performances has also been included, since the responsibilities of the dance teacher are seldom limited to class teaching. No attempt has been made to discuss dance composition as such, or the technical details of dance production, since these aspects of dance have been the subject of another textbook by this author entitled *Dance Composition and Production for High Schools and Colleges.*

The writer is deeply indebted to many people who have generously contributed time and effort to the preparation of this book: to Maja Schade of the University of Wisconsin, who has graciously given her permission for the inclusion of a description of her method of teaching relaxation; to the staff of the University of Wisconsin Women's Physical Education Department for the syllabus of their course in Movement Fundamentals, which has served as a model for the chapter on "Movement Fundamentals as Preparation for Dance"; to Hanya Holm, professional teacher and choreographer, to Lucas Hoving, professional dancer and teacher, and to Margaret H'Doubler, Professor Emeritus of the University of Wisconsin, for some of the technical material and movement ideas presented in Chapters 2 and 4; to Shirley R. Ririe of the University of Utah dance staff, who collaborated in the planning and presentation of the material on ballroom dance; to Mary Bee Jensen, folk dance specialist of Brigham Young University, who served as a consultant and guided the author in her selection of folk dances appealing to high school students; to the California Folk Dance Federation, to Richard Kraus, author of *Folk Dancing,* and to the authors of *Dance Awhile,* for some of the folk dance source materials used as a basis for this writing; to Wilford Marwedel for his help in interpreting folk dance descriptions; and to Joan J. Woodbury and Maurine Dewsnup of the University of Utah dance staff, who provided the material for the chapter on accompaniment for dance classes. The author also wishes to express her gratitude to Mrs. Woodbury and to countless other friends and colleagues who read portions of the manuscript and offered suggestions of inestimable value.

ELIZABETH R. HAYES

Salt Lake City, Utah
   January, 1964

Contents

AN INTRODUCTION
TO THE
TEACHING OF DANCE

1

Dance as Education

What is dance, and how does it differ from gymnastics, swimming, or basketball? As bodily activity, dance shares many movement elements with other physical activities. What, then, distinguishes dance from these other movement forms? Dictionary definition indicates that dance is set apart by being *rhythmic movement usually with musical accompaniment*. But all movement is rhythmic, whether its rhythms are recognized and identified or not; and not all dance is performed to music. We must, therefore, look further for the characteristic that distinguishes dance as a form of human activity.

Regardless of the kind of dance under consideration, its primary appeal as physical activity is in the satisfaction or enjoyment its particular rhythm and pattern of movement evoke within the performer. This satisfaction may be physical or emotional, or aesthetic; but basically it is pleasure in the kinesthetic sensation of movement that impels the dancer to move as he does. It should not be inferred that only dance is pleasurable in this way and other physical activity is not; or that dance pursues no other function than that of arousing pleasure. The key to its distinction lies in that the dancer's immediate concern is not with lifting weights, transporting himself through water, balancing on skates or skiis, or winning a game, but rather with movement per se—*movement that has been consciously given form and rhythmic structure to provide physical, emotional, or aesthetic satisfaction*. If dance happens also to promote good physical condition or otherwise contribute to the welfare of the dancer, so much the better; but the derivation of such benefits is not the essential reason for the existence of dance.

Thus it becomes the responsibility of the dance educator, above all else, to see that dance is a pleasurable, satisfying activity for

3

its participants: that physical and social enjoyment, especially, are the immediate outcomes of folk and ballroom dance; that physical, aesthetic, and sometimes social enjoyment are the outcomes of that form of dance which for want of a better term is called "modern" dance. To arrive at this goal of enjoyment, certain fundamental movement skills and understandings are requisite; these are not skills that pertain only to dance, but are skills and understandings requisite to almost all effective muscular response. The dancer, like the athlete, or the mechanic or the housewife, must know how to relax, so that he can use efficiently those parts of his body that are called upon to act, without meeting unnecessary resistance from muscles that have nothing to do with the action. The dancer, like every physically educated person, must develop his body as an intelligently responsive instrument through exercises designed for that purpose; he must know how to stand, sit, rise, and walk correctly, how to push, pull, lift, and carry efficiently, as well as how to spring into the air, land properly from a leap or jump, perform well the basic modes of human locomotion, and fall without injuring himself. The learning of such fundamental movement skills can hardly be called *dance,* but many of these learning experiences may be looked upon appropriately as means to that end. Unless a program of physical education is designed to accomplish these goals it is failing as "physical education." Nor is it alone the responsibility of the general physical educator, the correctives teacher, the dance educator, or the teacher at any given grade level, to pursue these objectives. The teaching of fundamental skills and understandings basic to good movement should be the constant aim of every movement educator for every age level, and these skills should be the source of experience from which specific sports and dance skills may be derived.

Whether such fundamental movement or "basic movement" is taught in isolation or in conjunction with other phases of physical education as the need arises, depends upon the requirements of particular situations. What is important is that dance and physical educators teach students to move well, in conjunction with teaching them to create dances and to play games. This education should not commence in high school or in college; it should begin in childhood; but even when valuable learning years have been lost, much can be accomplished by a teacher who has the patience to help students to unlearn poor movement habits and replace them with efficient ones.

Much that is taught in the name of the dance could really be classified as basic movement. Dance, however, is much more than basic movement; and it is essential for classwork to be extended to the point of providing students with actual *dance* experience. Although mastery of movement fundamentals is requisite to success in dance, movement becomes dance only when the mover has become sufficiently free of technical or mechanical considerations to be able to enjoy movement for its own sake and the movement experiences have been so directed as to exploit the physical, aesthetic, social, and creative satisfactions which movement can provide. The experiencing of movement as dance need not be reserved for some far-distant future; it should be a day-to-day reward that inevitably crowns each small gain in movement technique and understanding effected through dance education.

2

Movement Fundamentals as Preparation for Dance

The aspects of movement which concern the dancer are numerous or limited, depending upon the kind of dance under consideration. Square dance, while often involving intricate floor patterns and varied group relationships, is limited in the demands it makes in movement of the body as a whole. In "modern" or creative dance, on the other hand, there are no limits except those imposed by the anatomical structure of the body. Perhaps the only phases of movement fundamentals or basic movement with which the modern dancer is not quite as much concerned as the athlete are those in which the performer must relate his movement to an outside object, such as a racquet or ball. For the sake of brevity, it seems wise to restrict discussion in this book to those aspects of basic movement which most immediately concern the dancer. Such activities as throwing, catching, and striking will therefore be left for others to discuss.

The teaching of movement fundamentals as preparation for dance has the following intermediate objectives: first, development of kinesthetic awareness of body position and action, including such aspects of movement as direction, range, tempo, and energy release; second, development of intellectual awareness of how body movement is controlled; third, elimination of unnecessary muscular tension; fourth, stretching of muscles to permit maximum joint flexibility; and fifth, development of general muscular coordination and desirable habits of movement. The following material on basic movement has been selected with these objectives in mind; it is organized, not as a course outline, but rather as a presentation of the various facets of basic movement in which a student of dance is likely to require experience. The content and order of presentation of lesson material will have to be determined according to student needs in particular situations.

RELAXATION *

Moderate body tension is a necessary part of being alive. In a healthy person, it is normal for skeletal muscles, as well as the smooth muscles in the walls of the blood vessels and abdominal organs, to be in a state of contraction; the nervous system and some hormonal glands are active: all of the body parts are vibrantly alive and responsive, like the parts of a finely tuned violin in readiness for performance.

Modern life, with its complexity, pressure of competition, and continual race against time, often produces such excessive tensions in people that their energies are exhausted and dissipated rather than conserved and channeled to useful ends. It becomes necessary to educate people in relaxation techniques, to free their bodies of these unnecessary tensions.

There are several theories as to the best approach to the teaching of relaxation. Some authorities advise a "total relaxation" of the body by making it completely passive except for breathing; then, when total relaxation has been experienced and can be achieved at will, relaxation is localized and applied to movement. Other authorities prefer teaching first a partial or localized relaxation with specific exercises designed for this purpose. The former is the method described in this chapter.

Environmental conditions are important to the successful teaching of total relaxation. The physical environment should include nothing that tends to produce tension, such as low temperature, too much light and distracting noise. The room in which relaxation is to be practiced should be warmed in anticipation of lowered body temperatures, and if possible somewhat darkened. Floor mats and towels should be available. The environment should be free from noise and other sensory distractions that can disturb the concentration of the participants.

The instructor must have complete control of the class, because an uncooperative student not only fails to benefit from the experience, but also, if he creates a disturbance, can ruin the experi-

* This material on relaxation has been extracted from a syllabus for a class in "Fundamentals of Physical Education" which is under the direction of Maja Schade at the University of Wisconsin. The syllabus, compiled by Miss Schade and a faculty committee, describes a technique of relaxation which she developed.

ence for others. Instructions should be given in a voice that is soothing in quality and inflection and thus conducive to relaxation. And finally, the teacher should train himself to be sensitive to signs of restlessness and fatigue in his students and to be able to recognize and evaluate relaxation when it occurs.

The approach to complete relaxation must be a gradual one. The process cannot be rushed, but should be extended over several weeks. At first only a few steps of the process should be undertaken, during short practice periods. Finally, when passive relaxation has been achieved, what has been learned can be applied to the body in movement.

Technique of Total Relaxation

Position

The technique of total relaxation begins with the body in a position that is natural and completely supported, requiring no physical exertion in order to maintain it. Relaxation is more easily achieved when the skeletal joints are in a slightly bent position than when completely extended. The subject lies supine on a mat or bed, arms at the sides, slightly flexed at the elbows, palms down. Structural peculiarities in the shoulder joint may make this arm position uncomfortable for some students; in such instance, a rolled-up towel or a sandbag placed under the wrists can be helpful. The legs are almost together and slightly rotated outward in response to gravitational pull. A rolled up blanket or towel can be placed under the knees to relieve all tension in the back of the legs and to keep the lower back from hyperextension. The head is tilted slightly to the side; it may be elevated if desired; or it may be kept straight, but arching of the neck should be eliminated. Painful neck tension may make it impossible to keep the head comfortable; in which case turning the head to the side and resting it against some support (sandbag or book) may prove helpful. The eyes are kept closed; but if this produces strain, they may be held open in the beginning.

Breathing

During the process of relaxing, it is necessary to let the mind focus upon something to keep it from reverting to problems of the day. Breathing, because of its constancy and tendency to regularity, makes a good point of focus for concentration, but the breathing must be passive, without strain or tension.

The instructor should begin relaxation practice by having students observe their own breathing without interfering with its rhythm. Breathing should be easy and comfortable. The students should be instructed to let the breath come and go naturally, assuming an attitude of passivity toward it, and associating strongly the idea of relaxing with the exhalation phase of breathing. After the first breathing practice, the students should be told to begin to extend the exhalation slightly by passively "letting go" a little further; they should give in to it, rather than attempt to force the exhalation, and should wait for the new inhalation to come. Thus, a pause develops at the end of the breathing cycle.

Practice should last only short periods of a few minutes. The instructor should watch during all steps of the procedure for signs of tension such as strained breathing or restlessness, and should interrupt whenever they appear. Students should be encouraged to stretch and sit up whenever they can no longer maintain their concentration. These two breathing practices must always precede the conscious release of muscular tension, in order to produce a preparatory attitude of quiet and passivity.

Conscious Release of Muscular Tension

Attention is now turned to one arm. With the exhalation, the students should let one arm become "heavy." * Not by doing anything, but by thinking of the arm as heavy, they should imagine that the arm is "sinking" onto the mat and becoming heavier with each exhalation. Terminate the trial actively. Have the students, with a deep inhalation, raise both arms overhead and stretch throughout the body. Students should practice concentrating upon one arm until spontaneous transfer to the other arm is experienced; from then on, they should always relax both arms simultaneously.

Next, the students should be told to feel that the shoulders are "sinking back," and that the upper back is becoming "wide and flat." The neck should feel "loose and long," with the head "resting heavily" on the mat, and the whole of the upper body "heavy, loose, and relaxed."

After there has been a spontaneous transfer of relaxation to the legs, these body parts should also be included. The students should allow both legs to become "heavy" with the hips "spreading" or "falling apart." The lower body can be thought of as a unit, "heavy and relaxed."

* The words in quotation marks are descriptive terms that can be used by the instructor to suggest visual images that may aid students in achieving the desired muscular response.

The exhalation is now slightly extended. Student attention should be directed to the drop in the abdominal muscles during the exhalation. The middle of the body can be observed to be giving in to gravity, "sinking," and the lower back "sagging." The whole body is "heavy, relaxed, spread out," and attention should be focused on the general sensations of relaxation, rather than on details.

The release of throat and facial muscles comes last. The throat will feel "hollow and wide," and the lower jaw will "drop," the lips parting slightly. The forehead will be felt to be "sliding apart" and the eyebrows "dropping down." Short periods of time should be spent in attending to these small details, and attention should be turned back repeatedly to the body as a whole and the sensations of all-over general relaxation.

During this relaxation period, instructions should be given in a quiet, soothing voice. It is not necessary to talk continuously; in fact, it is important to allow time for the students to carry out instructions and to concentrate upon their bodily sensations. The students should be instructed, beforehand, that they should not allow themselves to fall asleep but rather should seek *to gain the ability to release all bodily tension and to become active again at will.* During the practice of relaxation, all effort should be avoided. If concentration fails, short and repeated periods of practice will be helpful. Two daily ten minute periods of conscious relaxation are advisable at first. Later these periods can be gradually prolonged. While the ability to relax may not always be achieved during the first attempts, this is no indication that ultimate success will not be attained if the individual continues to practice. Once learned, the technique of relaxation can be applied at times of stress by maintaining the relaxed breathing with the slightly extended exhalation and by consciously relaxing the shoulder girdle.

Relaxation in Movement

Experience in passive relaxation can eventually be carried over into movement; this may begin with the raising of an arm from the shoulder (four or five inches from the mat) during the inhalation, and dropping the arm on the exhalation. The effort to hold the arm is centered in the shoulder and upper arm muscles; and the drop occurs when the tension in these muscles is released. The "let go" is continued throughout the arm after it has met the ground. Always, at least one breathing cycle precedes each lifting of the arm. Practice is continued in the same way with the other arm; then with both arms; also, with one knee, the other knee, and both knees. The leg is lifted from the hip with the knee slightly flexed. Activity can now be carried to the standing position. One arm is swung in a passive, pendular fashion, until the movement dies down. Later, both arms can be used. The trunk can be swung in a similar fashion, with the drop and lift coming from the lower back, and the upward movement running sequentially through the vertebrae to the head.

Other activities can be practiced to reduce tension in smaller parts of the body, such as neck, shoulders, and hands. Neck muscles can be relaxed by dropping and lifting the head in all directions, swaying it from side to side, or moving it in a circle. The shoulders, which are frequently overtense in beginning dancers, can be lifted and dropped, singly or together, and circled in order to release tension. Always coordinate the drop with the exhalation phase of breathing. The arms can be shaken to relax the lower arms and hands, or the hands can be shaken from the wrists. Legs can be similarly shaken, or swung back and forth from the hip joint.

Eventually an increase in force and control can be applied to certain muscle groups in the performance of swinging movement without the loss of ability to relax. Relaxed leg swings, which introduce the added problem of balance, and arm and body swings of increased complexity can be practiced. Dance swings are somewhat different from completely relaxed swings, but experience with total relaxation heightens one's sensitivity to tension and relaxation, and enables one to perform swinging movements of all kinds with increased control and understanding. Several such swinging activities involving localized relaxation are described later in this chapter in the section on Preparatory Techniques for Dance.

POSTURE

The function of a course in basic or fundamental movement is not remedial in the sense that it could be a substitute for a class in "correctives"; what it does is to provide knowledge of how to stand correctly, shift weight easily, balance on one foot, sit, rise, walk, and run with control, and so forth, knowledge that is essential to becoming a well-coordinated person.

Standing

Good standing posture involves aligning the body in a way that is both efficient, that is, in a position of readiness to move, and aesthetically pleasing. In proper stance, body parts are aligned one directly above another in line with one's center of gravity; wherewith gravity assists in maintaining one's posture. In practice, the feet are slightly apart and parallel, or turned out slightly and the body weight is over the center of the feet in front of the ankles; the knees are released, rather than hyperextended; the pelvis is tilted neither backward nor forward; the space between the pelvis and the rib-cage is elongated, with abdominal muscles tightened; the shoulders are level and completely relaxed; and the head is perched directly on top of the spine. Kinesthetic awareness of body position can be developed by consciously shifting the alignment of body parts and observing the effect of these changes: increasing the pelvic tilt and noticing the effect upon the knees; releasing the abdominal muscles and noticing the effect upon the pelvis; shifting the weight back to the heels and forward again at the ankles; and lifting and pressing back the shoulders instead of relaxing them. In experimenting with these postural changes, it will become evident that when one body part is permitted to deviate from its normal relation to the center of gravity, a compensatory adjustment must be made by another body part or parts for balance to be maintained. It becomes important to know how to make temporary adjustments in body alignment during certain movements; but it is also important to avoid having to make habitual compensations to offset postural carelessness.

Good posture, whether one is standing, or sitting, or moving, cannot be achieved merely as a result of brief practice periods; it is a constant consideration with which a student of dance is perpetually concerned, and about which he will need to be reminded when concentrating on other problems.

Sitting and Rising

For the dancer, there are many ways of sitting and rising. In this discussion, the concern is not so much with eliminating postural faults as with learning to sit and to rise for practical purposes in a manner that is efficient and aesthetically pleasing.

Normally, when a person wishes to sit on some object, such as a chair or bench, the correct procedure is to approach the object as closely as possible, pivot turn, placing the calf of one leg lightly against the edge of the chair and the foot directly beneath the seat to serve as a base under the center of gravity that will enable him to control the lowering of the body onto the chair. The other foot is slightly forward. The weight is then shifted to the foot in the rear, and as the body is lowered to the seat, the trunk is inclined slightly forward. The shift of the base of support from the feet to the hips begins with the hips as close to the chair as possible. The feeling of the chair against the back of the leg certifies that the chair is actually where it is expected to be and eliminates any insecure fumbling. Placing the foot directly under the seat shifts the base of support sufficiently far back that the sitter can remain in balance, without bending noticeably from the hips, while lowering himself to the chair. Rising is a reversal of the procedure used in sitting; again the trunk is inclined slightly forward, and the weight is shifted from the back foot to the forward foot as the act of rising is completed.

Sitting on the floor usually entails keeping the weight on one foot while the body is lowered to the floor. One very satisfactory method is begun by centering the body weight over one foot. The free leg is then crossed behind the supporting foot so that the body can be lowered perpendicularly to the floor. As the supporting knee bends, the top of the free foot touches the floor first, then the side of the leg; and finally, the hips are lowered to the floor. In rising, the action is reversed. One leg, turned out at the hip and bent at the knee, is placed on the floor, across as far as possible in front of the body. The other leg is then crossed on top of this bent leg, and the foot is placed on the floor very close to the body. The center of gravity is now shifted directly over this foot and the sitter rises vertically to a standing position. One hand may be used, if necessary, to initiate the rising motion, but this assistance should be given as inconspicuously and as briefly as possible.

Regardless of the form used in sitting and rising, the problems remain the same; in sitting, the task is that of keeping the weight balanced over the original base, as long as possible, while lowering the center of gravity; in rising, it is one of shifting the center of gravity over a foot, or whatever part of the body is to be used as a base of support. The correct way to rise or sit depends to a large degree upon the starting position and the purpose for the action. Under ordinary circumstances, the best way is the simplest, most direct method that can be followed with control. For the dancer, the problem is a different one, often involving expressive meaning in addition to practical considerations. Further discussion of variations in level change in connection with dance is included in Chapter 4.

Balancing

The problem of maintaining body balance under difficult circumstances is of immense concern to the dancer. When standing normally, body balance is achieved by aligning the body parts over the base of support and by stabilizing the spinal column. One of the best means of achieving this stability is to retract and elongate the neck which elongates and stabilizes the whole spine. When balancing on one foot, the center of gravity must be shifted over the supporting foot and the body alignment adjusted accordingly. Stability can be increased if both the supporting leg and the free leg are turned slightly outward at the hips by tightening the outward rotators. The turned-out, supporting foot offers a broadened base upon which to stand, and the oppositional force of the turn-out at the hips provides added body control by stabilizing the pelvis. It is of utmost importance, however, to keep the force of the turn-out equalized between the two legs so that the body facing remains centered.

Rising onto the toes decreases the size of the dancer's supporting base. He should concentrate upon exerting all of his energies upward, again elongating the spine, especially in the neck, and tightening thigh, hip, and abdominal muscles. A moderate turn-out, combined with an effort to press the heels forward, helps to stabilize wobbly ankles. This same feeling of lifting the body upward, in resistance to gravity, should be maintained as the heels are lowered to the floor.

When part of a dancer's body, such as a leg, is moved away from the center of gravity, the body alignment must be adjusted, or some action taken by another body part, to maintain stability. Thus, when the left leg is lifted sideward, the trunk shifts slightly to the right. Still further stability can be effected if the right arm is extended sideward and the left one straight ahead. Experimentation, with observation of the natural adjustments that are made in body alignment when a portion of the body is moved away from the center of gravity, will increase kinesthetic perception and understanding of the physical forces affecting movement control.

When large and forceful movements are to be performed by the arms and torso, body equilibrium is again jeopardized. Stability can be increased by broadening the supporting base in the direction of the force, and by bending the knees, thus lowering the center of gravity. Again, a strong turn-out in the legs from the hip joint can help to stabilize and further broaden the supporting base.

Pushing, Pulling, Lifting, Carrying

A dancer is not usually as much concerned with pushing and pulling and lifting resistive objects as is a piano mover, or even a housewife; nevertheless, there are occasions in dance when the dancer may wish to exert pressure on real or imagined objects, and he must be able to perform or portray such activity efficiently and communicatively. Two important factors should be borne in mind: force must be exerted in the direction in which the object is to be moved; and the mover must relate himself to the object in such a way that the strong muscles of his body can be employed to that end. These strong muscles are in his legs and back.

In pushing and pulling, the principles are basically similar; only the direction of the force in relation to the object is changed. When pushing a heavy object, a step must be taken toward the object, broadening the base of support in the line of direction of the force to be applied. The body leans forward from the ankles, moving the center of gravity ahead of the pushing foot, thus directing the body force forward. There is flexion in the knee and hip joints to utilize the power of the leg and hip extensors. The back is kept straight and the hips down. Contact with the object to be moved is made as nearly as possible at its weight center. The muscles are then made ready for the task to be accomplished. The pushing is done with the back and legs, not with the shoulders and arms. In pulling, the step is taken directly away from the resistant object, and the body forces are also exerted in that direction.

When lifting a heavy object that is directly in front of the body, it is important to get as close to the object as possible, since the closer the weight is to the body's center of gravity the easier it is to lift. Again, a wide base is needed to increase stability. Then it is necessary to lower the body weight through the line of gravity by bending at the hip, knee, and ankle joints. The object should be grasped firmly near its center, if possible, and held close to the body. It is important to keep the back erect to avoid back strain and to make use of the leg muscles in lifting. When one dancer is lifting another dancer, the one being lifted can assist by taking a deep breath, tensing his body to hold it together, mentally lifting his body weight out of the floor in an attempt to make it weightless at the exact moment that the upward force is being applied by his partner. Lifts should never be attempted by inexperienced students without the presence of an experienced person to supervise.

Once an object has been lifted, the body and the object become a single weight unit that must be brought into equilibrium. A portion of the body (the upper back and often the opposite arm and leg) is placed in a position to counterbalance the weight of the object held. The farther the object is held from the body the more oppositional force is required to balance the weight; hence the more the body weight must be shifted in opposition to the load. Efficiency, therefore, requires that the load be carried close to the body and centered over the pelvis whenever possible. Heavy weights are most easily supported when they can be carried on the shoulders or head or upper back. Carrying a load directly in front of the body places strain on the lower back muscles and should be avoided.

Pushing, pulling, lifting, and carrying can be practiced with pieces of furniture, gymnasium equipment, and boxes of supplies or 10–20 pound beanbags.

Falling

Falling implies loss of equilibrium and succumbing to gravity. Most falls are accidental; but with the dancer, they are deliberate. When a person falls accidentally and suffers no injury, it is usually because he is consciously or unconsciously relaxed during the fall. The more rigid the body, the more it is likely to be bruised, jarred, or shattered. Dance falls involve varying degrees of relaxation, but are consciously controlled; and the relaxation is not sudden and total, but sequential, so that not all parts of the body reach the ground at the same time. The relaxation may start at the top of the body and progress down through the hips, knees, and ankles; or it may start in the ankles and progress upward. In the latter method one's "under-pinnings" give way, very much as in a natural faint. Whenever possible, the weight should be taken by the body levers (legs and arms) that gradually absorb the force of the fall.

Many falls used by dancers are not relaxed at all, but involve a continuously controlled lowering of the center of gravity. Here, as in the technique of sitting down, the secret of control lies in staying centered over the base as long as possible while the body is being lowered onto the floor. And, as previously discussed, there is the need for counterbalance of body parts. In a sideward fall, for example, when the hips are thrust to one side as the center of gravity is being lowered, the arms and upper body reach in the opposite direction to counterbalance the weight of the hips. In a controlled fall, the force of impact with the ground can be reduced if the dancer makes an effort to resist gravity just before he reaches the ground. In many types of falls, the force of the impact can be further diminished by making the direction of the fall oblique rather than perpendicular to the ground. The principle is the same as applies to an aircraft in landing. The more nearly its movement parallels the landing surface, the smoother the landing. The smoothness of execution of a forward fall, for example, depends largely upon the distance in front of the starting position that the body first touches the floor and the continuation of the forward motion after initial contact. A body roll in the direction of the movement is another way of gradually spending the force of the fall. It is also important that fleshy rather than bony parts make first contact with the ground. Especially the knees, elbows, and the head need to be protected, because their solid structures are uncushioned and vulnerable to injury.

The chief concern of the average person is to learn to relax when he falls. A fall in which relaxation progresses from the ankles upward is a good one to practice. Students can be told to reach upward, focusing upward and rising high on the toes with both arms overhead as if hanging onto a rope; they now begin by relaxing the ankles, then the knees, then the hips, allowing them to bend successively; and pushing the hips sideward, releasing one foot, so that the side of the lower leg touches the floor first, and then the hip. They should continue reaching upward as long as possible, still grasping the "rope" and focusing on the hands, so that the arms and head are the last to touch the floor.

Other falls, more intricate in their movement controls, are an important part of the dancer's technical vocabulary. Experience in the performance of falls, consciously controlled, is valuable, not only in teaching the student how to relax to avoid injury in falling, but also in helping him to overcome a natural fear of falling, which is often the chief cause of bodily tension.

PREPARATORY TECHNIQUES

Preparatory dance techniques are a form of gymnastics designed to prepare the body for dance; their purpose is practical rather than aesthetic, though they may contain elements that evoke aesthetic response. Dance exercises should not be confused with dance; they are not ends in themselves but merely the means to an end and that end is dancing. Such exercises may be rightfully included in a course in movement fundamentals; or they may be used as opening "warm-up" activities for dance classes, in which case they should be performed with a "dance quality" insofar as it is possible to do so. Performing movement with a dance quality means not only performing it with skill, but concentrating upon the kinesthetic feelings and aesthetic satisfactions that attend it.

These exercises contribute to the dancer's development in a

number of ways, depending upon the purposes for which they have been designed. The instructor must understand the purpose of each of the exercises so that among them he may choose those that are appropriate to the needs of his students or that are necessary as lead-up material for a specific dance lesson. Furthermore, this knowledge should be shared with his students, so as to enable them to derive the most benefit from the exercises.

The general purposes of conditioning exercises are to:

1. Rid the body of unnecessary muscular tension.
2. Stimulate the body physiologically to prepare it for efficient action.
3. Stretch muscles in order to increase joint flexibility.
4. Increase muscular strength and endurance by making demands upon particular muscle groups.
5. Develop balance and general coordination by training the body to become responsive to the mind.
6. Develop kinesthetic awareness and sensitivity to body position and movement.
7. Enlarge the scope of movement experience.
8. Develop desirable habits of movement in terms of good body mechanics that can be transferred and adapted to both dance situations and everyday living.

In selecting and teaching preparatory techniques for dance classes, certain considerations need to be borne in mind; one is in the allotment of time. In many schools the class period for dance activity is no longer than thirty to thirty-five minutes, wherein the time allotted to preparatory exercises must of necessity be quite limited. The exercises must be so organized that the best possible use is made of the time available. One method of saving time is to group the sitting and standing exercises so that the class does not waste time alternately getting up and sitting down. Much more time is required for teaching new exercises than for performing familiar ones. For this reason some teachers have found it practicable to develop a short series of general preparatory techniques that can be repeated daily with only minor variations. The danger in this lies in that students may become bored and commence to perform the movements carelessly and unconsciously once the exercises have become habitual. When students become careless, the work should be stopped and the activity repeated after the proper movement controls have been re-emphasized. Such carelessness usually indicates a need for the substitution of new material that can provide the students with further physical and intellectual challenge. Ideally, of course, conditioning activities should be taught from the same creative standpoint as the other parts of a dance lesson; and when exercises are selected to explore the same phases of movement as those stressed in a session's dance activity, the additional time required to develop the preparatory exercises creatively is certainly justified. Ordinarily, however, in planning a thirty-five minute lesson, the teacher will have to limit his introduction of new exercises so that there will be adequate time left to *dance*.

It is usually wise to begin with free, big body movements that will encourage students to relax. Sitting and lying down exercises might be introduced next, and the series concluded with some standing and locomotor activities. Exercises should always be practiced on both sides of the body; and, generally speaking, the teacher should try to see that all parts of the body are exercised. In this way the conditioning activities can sometimes compensate for neglect of some parts of the body in the rest of the lesson. Above all, it is necessary to see that muscles to be used in strenuous dance activities should be minimized for safety reasons.

For lessons on leaping and jumping, the muscles in the feet and legs must be thoroughly warmed and conditioned before any high elevation is attempted. The preliminary exercises should also afford the necessary practice in the correct performance of "push-offs" and landings so that proper movement habits are established; otherwise, students are in danger of injuring themselves. On unresilient gymnasium floors—e.g. wooden floors laid over cement—high elevation activities should be minimized for safety reasons.

Preparatory exercises can also be used to establish the quality and style of movement for the lesson to follow. Most dance exercises are easily adaptable; their movement qualities and rhythmic structures can be so altered as to enable the exercises themselves to serve as an introduction to the dance movement.

In certain instances, the dance movement itself can *be* the warmup; that is, the dance movement can begin at such a basic level that no strenuous physical demands are made and no special preparatory exercises are necessary. Here, in the process of developing the dance movement, the muscles are gradually warmed and "educated," in readiness to respond as technical demands are increased.

Following are some general conditioning exercises presented as examples of techniques that can be used to prepare the body to dance. If these specific exercises are used, an instructor should feel free to change the movement organization, the quality, the rhythmic pattern, or the point of emphasis in any way that will adapt the exercises to the purpose of the lesson. When musical accompaniment is used, exercises should be adjusted as far as possible to fit the musical phrasing. If the movement phrasing is irregular, special accompaniment may have to be devised.

A classification of preparatory exercises according to function is difficult because throughout many of the exercises the functions are variously combined. Simpler, and possibly of some value in the planning for maximum use of class time, is the grouping of the exercises according to the sitting, kneeling, lying, and standing positions.

In order to clarify descriptions, certain basic positions are illustrated below:

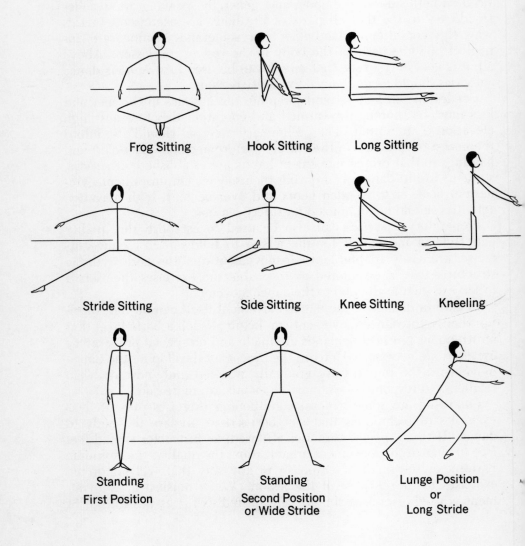

Frog Sitting   Hook Sitting   Long Sitting

Stride Sitting   Side Sitting   Knee Sitting   Kneeling

Standing
First Position

Standing
Second Position
or Wide Stride

Lunge Position
or
Long Stride

Sitting, Kneeling, and Lying Down Exercises

1. *For Outward Rotation at the Hip Joint*

Frog sit, with the feet as close to the body as possible.

Place hands, or elbows, on the knees, and press them down as far as they will go comfortably, then, with small, continuous bounces, push the knees further toward the floor (32 counts).

2. *For Spinal Flexion*

Frog sit, with the hands holding the feet.

Round the back and bounce forward, four times, attempting to touch the head to the feet (4 counts) (*a*). On the last bounce stay down. Then grasp the ankles, and start from the base of the spine to unroll the back, one vertebra at a time, keeping the back pressed as far forward as possible, until it is completely straight (4 counts) (*b*).

Do the entire exercise four times.

a   *b*

3. *For Hamstring Stretching and Spinal Flexion*

Long sit, with ankles completely extended.

Grasp the ankles with the hands and bounce the head toward the knees, with rounded back (16 counts) (*a*). Now flex the ankles completely and straighten the back, and with the arms reaching toward the feet, or grasping the toes, bounce forward again (16 counts) (*b*).

a   *b*

4. *For Spinal Flexion*

Stride sit.

Grasp the right ankle with the right hand and extend the left arm overhead to the right as far as possible (*a*). Releasing the ankle grasp, swing the body and arms forward and across to the same position on the other side (3 counts) (*b*). In the same manner, return to the original position (3 counts) (*c*). Now, moving to the left again, swing the body and arms in a complete circle and a half, reaching as far as possible in all directions, including backward (6 counts), finishing to the left, grasping the left ankle with the left hand (*d*).

Perform the entire exercise four times, starting from alternate sides.

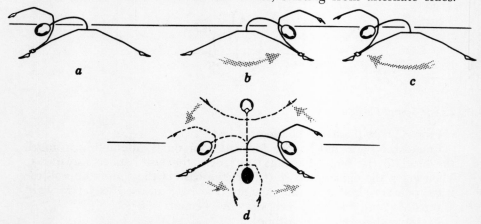

a   *b*   *c*

d

The same exercise can later be transferred to a standing position (*e*).

e

5. For Strengthening and Stretching the Longitudinal Arch

Hook sit, with the arms held "softly" in front.

Lift one foot, and touch the toes to the floor with the ankle extended completely, the heel pulled up into the leg (count 1) (*a*). Without releasing the toes from the floor, lower the heel to the floor, pressing it forward so that the foot is turned out slightly (count –&) (*b*).

Repeat with the other foot, and continue to walk away from the body 8 steps, until it becomes difficult to make the toes touch first. Walk back toward the body again, and repeat several times. Keep the back straight throughout the exercise.

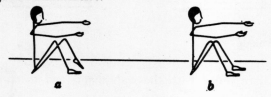

a   *b*

6. For Leg Stengthening and Coordination

Stride sit, with the legs uncomfortably far apart, the back straight, and the legs turned out.

Keeping the heels stationary, bend both knees and ankles until the feet are pointing upward (*a*), then extend both legs, trying to touch the floor with the little toes (*b*).

Alternate these two actions, working slowly and in the greatest possible range.

Now bend the knee and ankle of one leg, while extending the other, and alternate these actions (*c*). Perform the movement slowly at first, then increase the tempo until the movement becomes very fast. Guard against allowing the movement to become sloppy when the tempo is increased.

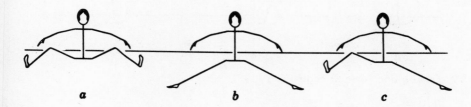

a   b   c

7. For Knee and Ankle Flexion and Extension and Thigh Strengthening

Stride sit, and grasp the right instep with the right hand, the fingers underneath the arch. If this grip is physically impossible to maintain move the hand up to the ankle or to the inside of the leg, and lower the leg until both knee and ankle can be completely straightened.

Lift the leg diagonally to the right, straightening the knee and ankle completely, keeping the back as straight as possible (*a*). Now, without allowing the heel to move from its position in the air, bend the knee and ankle as much as possible (count 1) (*b*); then extend (count –&). Alternate these two actions, slowly, eight times (8 counts); then, without supporting the leg with the hand, repeat twice as fast, eight times (4 counts). Complete the exercise by rounding the back and bouncing the head toward the knee of the lowered leg four times (4 counts) (*c*). The other leg remains completely extended on the floor throughout the entire exercise.

Repeat on the other side.

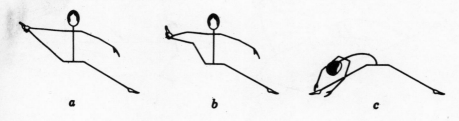

a   b   c

8. *For Thigh Strengthening and Hamstring Stretching*

Stride sit, and bend the left knee, grasping the left heel with the right hand, the other hand resting lightly on top at the ankle; extend the ankle, pressing the toes downward.

Lift the left leg, raising the heel as close to the forehead as possible (count 1) (*a*). Holding the leg with both hands, extend it forward, lifting it as high as possible (count 2) (*b*). Let go of the lifted leg with the hands, but don't allow it to drop. At the same time, straighten the back, opening the chest and separating the arms (counts 3–4) (*c*).

Make the entire exercise very smooth and expansive. Repeat four times with each leg.

a   *b*   *c*

9. *For Leg and Torso Strengthening*

Side sit.

Lift the sideward leg from the floor (count 1) (*a*); extend it sideward, rotating it so that the knee is facing upward (count 2) (*b*). Move the extended leg to the front of the body, keeping it as high as possible (count 3) (*c*); return it to the side, rotating the knee forward (count 4) (*d*). Move the leg around to the back as far as possible, bending the knee and twisting the body toward the lifted leg, focusing on the lifted foot (count 5) (*e*); return the leg to the side with the knee bent (count 6) (*f*); lower the leg to the floor to the original position (count 7) (*g*).

a   *b*   *c*

d   *e*   *f*   *g*

Repeat the exercise.

Then, using an additional two counts, extend both legs together and swing them around to a side sitting position on the opposite side and repeat the pattern for the other leg.

Make the movement very smooth and continuous throughout the pattern.

10. *For Hip Rotation and Thigh and Hip Strengthening*

Side sit, with the left leg bent, the knee turned out and pushed as far as possible to the left. Extend the right leg into the air, diagonally forward and upward, with the body facing the extended leg and the arms reaching out toward it. Keep the back straight, with the chest lifted high.

With three slow sustained counts, twist the body to face left, moving the arms around with the body and keeping the head up and the shoulders pulled down—rotate the hip so that the extended leg is stretched directly behind the body with the knee pointing downward, and keep the knee straight with the leg not touching the floor (counts 1–2–3) (*a*). Return to the original position with one quick movement (count 4) (*b*).

Do the movement four times; then repeat on the other side.

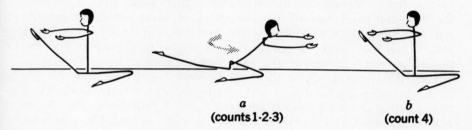

a
(counts 1-2-3)

b
(count 4)

11. *For Spinal Flexion and Abdominal Strengthening*

Long sit.

Round the back, initiating the movement in the lumbar region by contracting the abdominal muscles, and gradually lower the body to the floor (*a*); while so doing, press each vertebra, particularly in the lower back, to the floor in successive order (counts 1–2–3–4). When the body is extended on the floor (*b*), reverse the process, rolling up from the floor with the head leading, releasing the vertebrae one at a time (*c*), keeping the lower back pressed to the floor as long as possible, and allowing the hands to slip forward on the legs in an attempt to touch the feet (counts 5–6) (*d*). With an impulse in the body, scoop the arms still further forward (count 7), and bring the arms and body up to a vertical position (count –&) (*e*), lowering the arms sideward to the starting position (count 8).

Repeat seven times.

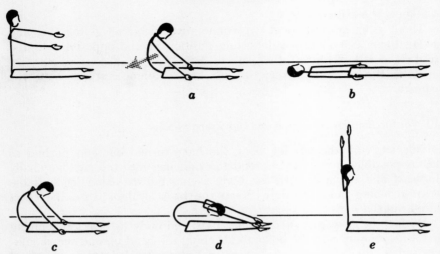

a   b

c   d   e

12. For Abdominal and Back Strengthening

Assume back lying position, with arms by the sides.

Contract the abdominal muscles, and keeping the heels in place on the floor, bend the knees and ankles, pressing the small of the back down to the floor. Simultaneously, raise the upper back and head from the floor and reach toward the feet with both arms, which are rotated out and straight at the elbows; the heels of the hands are pressed toward the feet, with the palms at right angles to the wrists and the fingers at right angles to the palms—there should be a feeling of tension down the inside of the arms (counts 1–2) (a). Now, lift the chest, dropping the head back and arching the upper body; at the same time rotating the arms inward with the palms facing down, the elbows moved sideward and the chest opened as wide as possible, and with ankles extended, but the knees still bent (counts 3–4) (b). Return to position a (counts 5–6) (c). Lower the body to the floor (counts 7–8) (d).

Do the exercise eight times, using a slow, sustained movement throughout. It is probably advisable at first to do only a and d. Later, when the coordination is mastered, the entire sequence may be done with fast, percussive changes.

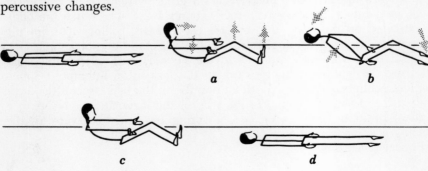

a   b

c   d

13. For Back and Abdominal Strengthening and Pectoral Stretching

Hook sit, with the heels raised and only the toes touching the ground, and the feet well extended. Sit tall and hold the arms straight forward from the shoulders, with the elbows bent and the forearms extended directly upward, the palms of the hands toward the face and the fingertips stretched toward the ceiling.

Quickly extend the legs just barely off the floor and at the same time swing the arms downward and diagonally backward, placing the palms of the hands flat on the floor and keeping the elbows straight, arching the upper back, with the top of the head almost touching the floor, the chest lifted as high as possible (count 1) (*a*). With another percussive movement, return to the original position (count 2) (*b*).

Repeat the exercise several times.

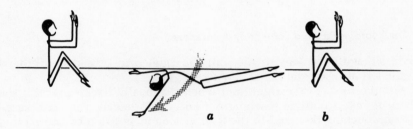

a   *b*

In learning this exercise, it may be advisable first to practice the leg action and upper body action separately. Because this exercise places considerable strain on the lower back, it should not be attempted by persons with weak abdominal muscles until after those muscles have been strengthened by simple abdominal exercises.

14. For Abdominal Strengthening

Hook sit, with the heels raised and only the toes touching the floor, and the feet well extended, the body is rounded forward over the knees, with the arms circling the knees lightly. Use sustained movement throughout the exercise.

Extend the legs straight forward on the floor, at the same time straightening the back and extending the arms overhead with the shoulders held firmly in place (counts 1–2) (*a*). Keeping the back and legs straight, tilt the body backward until the extended legs are lifted slightly off the floor, at the same time opening the arms wide until they are extended sideward (counts 3–4) (*b*). Hold this position and move the arms oppositionally up and down in a small, sequential wave-like motion, the movement being initiated from the shoulder blades (counts 5–&–6–&) (*c*). With the chest leading (*d*), return to the original starting position (counts 7–8) (*e*).

15. *For Coordination and Total Body Awareness*

Side sit, with the legs to the left, the right arm extended overhead and the left arm sideward.

Twist the torso to the right, and reach diagonally backward with the right arm (*a*). Continue reaching out and down toward the floor, keeping from touching the hand to the floor as long as possible by contracting the muscles on the left side of the body. Finally, extend the body com-

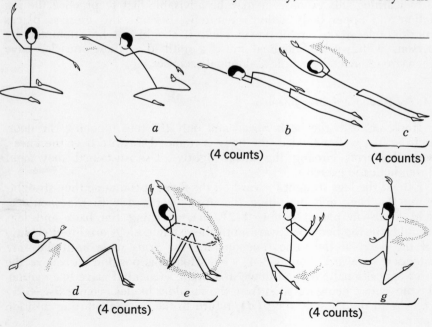

pletely on the floor in the diagonal, lowering the left arm to the side of the body (4 counts) (*b*).

With the top shoulder leading backward, turn over onto the back and swing the left arm around on the floor to overhead (4 counts) (*c*).

Turn the palms down, and using the hands to push against the floor, lift the upper back off the floor, with the chest leading and the head back (*d*), and come up to a hook-sit position. Bringing the arms, fully extended, forward and upward to overhead (4 counts) (*e*).

Keeping the arms parallel bend the elbows sharply, and swing them to the left (*f*); at the same time, twist the knees to the right into a side-sit position. Separate the elbows, and with a very large movement bring the arms to the original starting position—a quarter turn will now have been completed (4 counts) (*g*).

Repeat the exercise three more times so that a whole turn is made.

At first, do the exercise very slowly and smoothly. Later the exercise can be done percussively, using only one count for each of the four parts.

Do the sequence on both sides.

16. For Thigh, Abdominal, and Hip Strengthening

Kneel sit, with the upper body rounded forward over the knees. Make the entire movement pattern very smooth.

Slowly unroll the back, keeping the hips tucked well under, until the body from the knees to the head is in a single, slightly curved line (4 counts) (*a*).

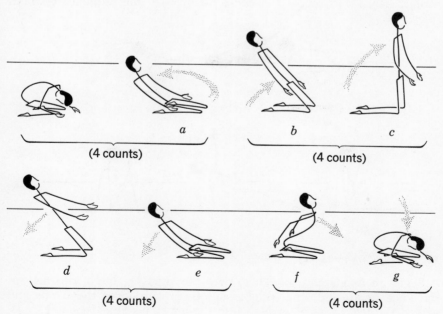

(4 counts)   *a*   *b*   *c*   (4 counts)

d   *e*   *f*   *g*

(4 counts)   (4 counts)

Then contract the hip muscles, lifting the hips off the heels. By using the thigh muscles, continue to carry the body forward to a kneeling position, keeping the hips in a straight line with the rest of the body (4 counts) (*b–c*).

Continuing to grip with the hip and thigh muscles, and keeping the body as long as possible in a single line from knees to head, lower the hips to the heels (4 counts) (*d–e*).

Finally, bend sharply at the hips, and with a chest lead, return to the original starting position (4 counts) (*f–g*).

17. For Awareness of Total Body Extension in Contrast to Flexion

Side sit, with the legs to the left, the right hand on the floor for support, the left elbow raised sideward left, the forearm relaxed.

Using sustained movement, with a shoulder lead, sweep the left arm down across in front of the body and up to overhead on the right side; continue reaching to the right until the hips and the left leg are lifted off the floor and the body is completely extended sideward (4 counts) (*a*). Bring the left arm down and lower the· left leg (still extended) to the floor; turn the body to the left, and place the left hand on the floor, releasing the right hand (4 counts) (*b*). With the right arm bent directly in front of the chest, fingers pointing upward, raise the body and right arm slowly upward until the body is extended in a straight line (4 counts) (*c*). Return to position (*b*), initiating the movement with an abdominal contraction (4 counts) (*d*).

Shift hands and repeat the entire action. Do the sequence on both sides.

(rear view)   a

b   c   d

18. For Hip Strengthening

Begin on hands and one knee, with the right leg lifted into the air, the knee bent. Shift the weight slightly forward over the hands and extend the leg, lifting it as high into the air as possible (count 1) (*a*). Return to starting position (count 2). Repeat three times, but on the count of "8" instead of bending the lifted leg, keep it extended and lower the whole body to the floor (*b*). Return to the starting position with the other leg lifted (count –&) (*c*).

Repeat with the other leg raised. Because a large amount of weight is placed upon the knee it is advised that persons with previous knee injuries refrain from this exercise.

a

b   *c*

19. For Knee and Ankle Flexion and Extension and Hip Flexion

In back lying position bend one knee to the chest, holding it with the hands; keep the other leg extended on the floor.

Pull the bent knee closer to the chest with small bounces (4 counts) (*a*). Now straighten the leg completely and try to bring it a little closer to the chest on each bounce (4 counts) (*b*). Keeping the leg close to the chest and the heel in one spot in the air, bend and extend the knee and ankle of the lifted leg eight times while the leg on the floor remains completely extended (8 counts) (*c*). Slowly lower the lifted leg to the floor (7 counts) and (on the 8th count) raise the other leg into position with the knee bent ready to begin again.

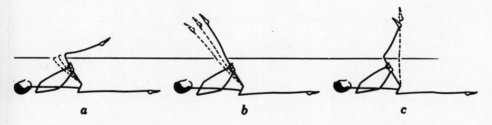

a   *b*   *c*

20. For Strengthening the Upper Back

In front lying position extend the arms along the floor above the head. Use a slow, sustained movement that is initiated in the shoulder blade area of the back.

Raise the arms and entire upper body (from the pelvic bones upward) from the floor—do not lead up with the head, or arch the lower back, but rather tighten abdominally, keeping the shoulders in place, the neck very long, the head in line with the body, and the eyes on the floor (2 counts) (*a*). Maintain this position off the floor and move the arms sideward (2 counts) (*b*). Return to position *a* (2 counts) (*c*). Lower the body slowly to the floor (2 counts) (*d*).

Repeat the pattern four times.

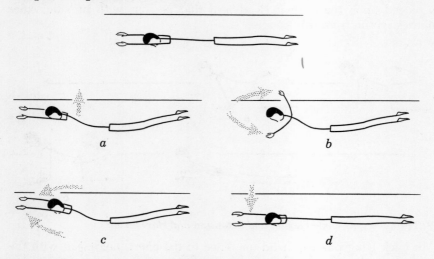

a

b

c

d

21. For Back Flexion and Hamstring Stretching

From back lying position do a shoulder stand with the hips in direct line with the rest of the body and the toes pointed toward the ceiling—

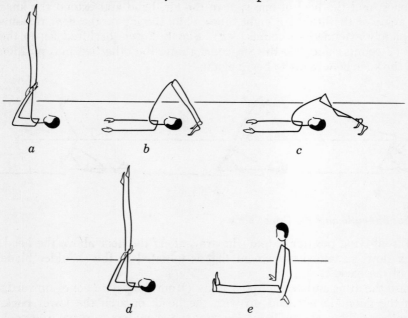

a   *b*   *c*

d   *e*

the body is supported by the hands (*a*). Lower the legs from the hips until the toes touch the floor behind the head (*b*). Keeping the toes in place, bounce the heels down toward the floor several times. Walk away from the head as far as possible (*c*) and back again. Lift the legs into a shoulder stand again (*d*) and roll down to sit (*e*).

Standing Exercises

22. Body and Arm Swings for General Relaxation

In learning this exercise, begin by swinging the arms easily backward and forward, bending the knees with a bounce on each swing. Gradually increase the range of the swing and the bend of the knees until the hands are brushing the floor. On the backward swing, lift the arms as high as possible, so that the knees are forced to straighten. Relax the back (including the neck) and the arms as completely as possible.

Now, begin the exercise by standing tall, arms stretched overhead, shoulders pulled down (*a*). Swing the arms and body forward, with elbows leading (*b*) and downward, bending the knees (*c*); straighten the knees as the swing continues backward to its completion (*d*). (3 counts)

Then reverse the direction of the swing, bending and extending the knees as before (*e*) returning to the original standing position (*f*). (3 counts)

At the beginning of each downswing, the neck is relaxed and the head falls back first, before dropping forward. The entire spine is relaxed to permit the sequential movement to pass up and down it easily. On the return swing, the hips are pressed forward as the body moves into its extended position. Make the movement free and swinging, not sustained. This is a two-part swing.

a   *b*   *c*   *d*   *e*   *f*

Perform this sequence eight times.

With more experienced groups, the activity can be further developed:

Stand tall, arms overhead. Drop the arms forward and circle them backward and upward to overhead. As the arms swing to the back, bend the knees, allowing the whole body to lean slightly backward—don't hyperextend the lower back (3 counts) (*a*). Continue by swinging the arms and body forward and downward, brushing the floor as above, until the arms are extended in back (3 counts) (*b*). Keeping the knees straight, swing the arms and body forward, stopping the movement when the arms and body are in a forward horizontal position (3 counts) (*c*). Still keeping the knees straight, swing the arms to the rear again (3 counts) (*d*). Bending the knees, return to an erect position with the arms overhead (3 counts) (*e*). This is a five-part swing.

Do this exercise four times.

a   *b*   *c*

d   *e*

23. *Forward and Backward Bounces, For Back and Hamstring Stretching*

Stand in a moderately wide stride position. With the hands holding the elbows and keeping the knees straight, round the back and bounce forward and downward from the hips eight times, attempting to touch the elbows to the floor (8 counts) (*a*).

Straighten the back from the hips and extend the arms straight forward so that the back, head, and arms are in a horizontal line. Keep the arms as high as possible, creating a slight hollow in the small of the back. Bounce the chest toward the floor eight times (8 counts) (*b*).

Shift the torso, from the hips, toward the right, keeping the shoulders parallel to the floor, and bounce four times (4 counts) (*c*). Shift the torso to the left, and repeat the action (4 counts) (*d*).

Stand erect, with hands on thighs; then, bending the knees, push the hips and thighs directly forward eight times, keeping the abdominal muscles firm and pressing the knees outward (8 counts) (*e*).

Repeat the entire series, cutting the number of bounces in half (4–4–2–2–4). Then cut it in half again, and perform the sequence twice (2–2–1–1–2; 2–2–1–1–2).

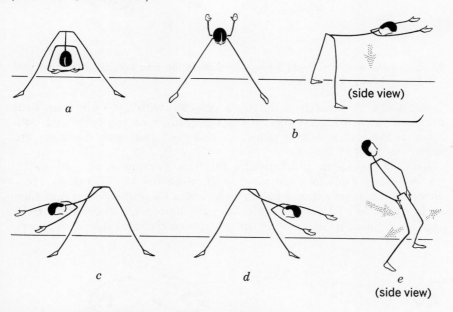

a

b (side view)

c   d   e (side view)

24. *Sideward Bounces for Lateral Stretching of the Torso*

Stand in a moderately wide stride position with the legs turned out, with the left arm reaching overhead to the right, the elbow slightly bent, and the hand, palm down, in line with the arm; and the right hand on the right thigh with the elbow pointing directly sideward.

Keeping all parts of the body in this lateral plane, stretch the left arm and the body to the right, bouncing four times, keeping knees straight and the hips centered so that the sideward stretch occurs mostly in the upper torso. (4 counts) (*a*). Now, bend the right knee sideward and continue for four more bounces (4 counts) (*b*).

Repeat the pattern to the left (8 counts).

Then cut the number of counts in half on each side; and in half again, repeating the very last sequence, so that the count for the entire series is: R–4–4, L–4–4, R–2–2, L–2–2, R–1–1, L–1–1, R–1–1, L–1–1.

a   *b*

25. Sideward Arm and Body Swings for Relaxation and Lateral Stretching and Strengthening of the Torso

Stand in a moderately wide stride position, with the right knee bent sideward. Reach horizontally to the right side with the body and both arms, keeping in a lateral plane, so that the chest and shoulders are facing the front of the room.

Bending the knees and brushing the floor in front as you go, swing the body and arms into the same position on the left (3 counts) (*a*). Swing in the same manner to the right again (3 counts) (*b*); and then again to the left (3 counts) (*c*). Stop the movement, and with a fresh impulse initiated by contracting the muscles on the right side of the chest,

a   *b*

c   d   e

lift the arms and body up overhead (*d*) to the right side and on around in a complete circle to the left again (6 counts) (*e*). This exercise is a five-part swing.

Do the pattern four times.

26. Squat to Straighten for Hamstring Stretching

Crouch with the knees together, the hands placed on the floor in front of the body. (*a*). Bounce toward the floor three times, and on the fourth count extend the legs completely, with the hands remaining flat on the floor (4 counts) (*b*).

Do the sequence eight times.

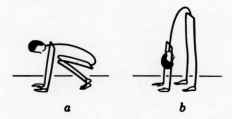

a   b

27. Lateral Knee Bounces for Outward Rotation at the Hips

Crouch with the hands on the floor in front of the body between the knees, with the knees well turned out. With small, percussive movements push the knees backward with the elbows (16 counts).

28. Pliés or Knee Bends for Outward Rotation at the Hips and Proper Alignment of Feet and Legs

Pliés are done in six basic foot positions related to sideward, diagonal, and forward–backward directions. The first two positions are related to moving *sideward*.

In first position, the heels are together; the feet are turned out at right angles to each other; the arms are at the sides, slightly open at the arm pits (*1-a*). Slowly rotate the legs outward at the hip joints and bend the knees sideward, directly over the center of the feet; keep the rib cage lifted directly upward and the hips so aligned that there is no hyperextension in the lower back (2 counts). As the knees bend, pull the *upper* arms, which are held very long, gently away from the body, keeping the wrists relaxed (*1-b*). As the knees straighten (2 counts), the arms return to their original position; the arm action is like that of breathing. This "breathing" action is used to eliminate tension in the arms and upper body. The arm movement is initiated in the shoulder blade area. Bend and straighten the knees slowly four times, keeping knees facing in the same direction as the feet.

In second position, the feet are in a moderate wide stride position (about eighteen inches apart), turned out at right angles to each other. The arms are extended softly sideward and a little forward, with the hands at about hip level (*2-a*). Slowly bend the knees sideward over the center of the feet, keeping the hips in place and simultaneously lifting the weight of the upper body out of the floor as in first position. As the knees bend, raise the upper arms and elbows slightly without lifting the shoulders (*2-b*). As knees straighten, press the upper arms downward as if pressing against the floor; with the elbows rolled under. Make the arm movement like that of breathing. Bend and straighten the knees, slowly, four times, concentrating upon keeping the legs rotated outward at the hip joint.

Third and fourth positions are related to moving *diagonally*.

In third position, the right foot is placed at the instep of the left foot, and the feet are turned at right angles to each other. The right arm is extended forward, the left arm sideward (*3-a*). As the knees bend outward (*3-b*) and straighten, lift the arms and press down as described for second position.

In fourth position, the right foot is moved about five inches into the right diagonal directly out from the instep (*4-a*)—now the left arm is forward, and the right arm sideward. The action is similar to that in third position (*4-b*).

Fifth and sixth positions are related to moving *forward* and *backward*.

In fifth position, the right heel is placed next to the big toe of the left foot, the feet are at right angles to each other, and the arms are held forward approximately level with the navel, with elbows slightly rounded (*5-a*). As the knees bend and straighten over the feet, the arms "breathe" out and in as in first position.

In sixth position, the right foot is moved forward about five inches,

with the right heel still directly in front of the toes of the left foot; the
arms are reaching directly overhead, slightly rounded, and the shoulders
are down (6-b). During the pliés, the arms "breathe" out and in, as in
first position.

Take four slow knee bends, or eight fast, percussive ones, in each
position. When doing the fast, percussive pliés, hold the arms quietly in
each position. The pattern should be done on the other side also, with
the left foot making the changes. With beginning students, pliés in first
and second positions may be sufficient.

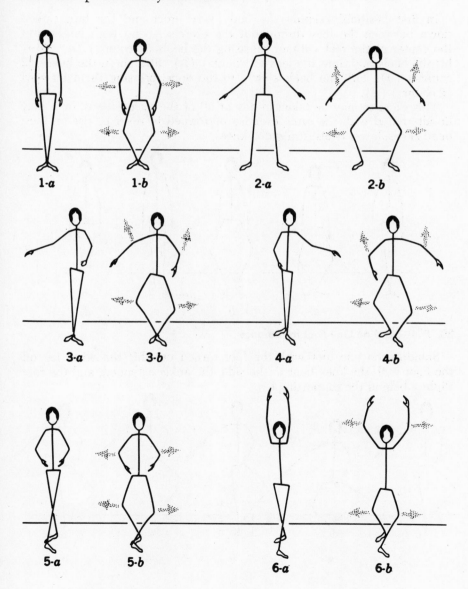

1-a   1-b   2-a   2-b

3-a   3-b   4-a   4-b

5-a   5-b   6-a   6-b

Pliés must be done very carefully, with the knees in proper alignment over both feet at all times. In fourth and sixth positions, one must take special precautions to see that the back knee and foot are in correct alignment. Slight individual adjustments can be made in the degree of turnout of the feet, depending upon the degree of turn-out possible in the hip joint. In all positions, the weight is evenly distributed between the two feet, and both the shoulders and the hips are facing directly forward.

29. Plié—Elevé or Bend and Rise for Leg Strength and Control

In first position, keeping the body very erect and the hips pulled down between the legs throughout the exercise, bend both knees over the center of the feet without releasing the heels (2 counts) (*a*). Now lift the heels high into the legs (2 counts) (*b*). Straighten the knees (2 counts) (*c*). Pull the heels slowly to the floor, pressing them forward (2 counts) (*d*).

This exercise may be taken in any or all of the six positions, or it may be alternated with the same exercise performed in reverse: rise on toes; bend knees; lower heels; straighten knees.

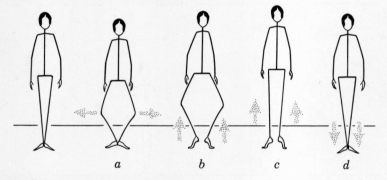

a   *b*   *c*   *d*

30. Plié—Elevé on One Foot for Balance

Standing on one foot with the foot turned out, lift the other leg off the floor with the knee bent to the side, the ankle extended, and the foot slightly behind the supporting leg.

a   *b*   *c*   *d*

Slowly, bend the supporting knee out over the weight-bearing foot (2 counts) (*a*). Straighten the knee (2 counts) (*b*). Rise slowly onto the half-toe (2 counts) (*c*). Press the heel to the floor slowly, with control (2 counts) (*d*).

Do the entire pattern smoothly four times on each side.

31. Brushes for Increasing Leg Strength and Coordination

Stand in first position with the feet at right angles and legs well turned out. Shift the weight onto the left foot, and keeping both knees straight, brush the right foot directly forward, extending the foot and ankle completely, while keeping the toes in contact with the floor (*a*); then quickly and forcefully pull the foot back to first position. Repeat the movement,

doing it eight times in all. Make the movements rapid and precise (8 counts). Do the same with the left leg.

Repeat the movement, brushing the foot to the side this time, with the leg turned out (*b*). Do the same movement with the left leg.

Repeat the movement again, brushing the foot directly backward, with the toes still in contact with the floor (*c*). Do the same with the left leg.

Make all directions very definite and be sure to return the foot exactly to first position each time. Keep the body very firm and erect over the supporting leg, and keep both knees completely straight at all times.

Repeat the entire sequence, brushing the leg slightly off the floor, with the knee straight. Immobilize the upper body by tightening abdominal and hip muscles. Work from the hip joint.

Repeat the sequence again, lifting the leg as high as possible without sacrificing body control. Be sure to keep the supporting leg turned out to equalize the turn-out of the moving leg. For some people the sideward lift may be slightly diagonal, depending upon the degree of turn-out possible in the hip joint.

32. *Extensions for Leg Strength, Coordination, and later for Balance*

Stand at arm's length from the barre (stall bars will do) in fifth position plié with the left side of the body toward the barre. Rest the fingertips of the left hand lightly upon the barre. Lift the right leg directly forward from the hip, supporting it underneath the inside of the thigh with the right hand. Knees and ankles of both legs are bent. Be sure that the calf of the free leg is not dropped, but is parallel with the floor.

Very slowly, extend (*a*) and bend (*b*) both knees and the ankle of the lifted leg, four times, keeping the heel of the lifted leg high in the air throughout the exercise. Endeavor to lift the free leg a little higher on each extension, and when the knee bends, pull the thigh closer to the body. Keep the body erect throughout the exercise (8 counts).

Move the free leg to the side without turning the hips (it will be on the diagonal for some people) and repeat the action (*a–b*). Both legs are turned out and the knee or the inside of the lifted leg is facing upward. Do not allow the body to lean toward the barre (8 counts).

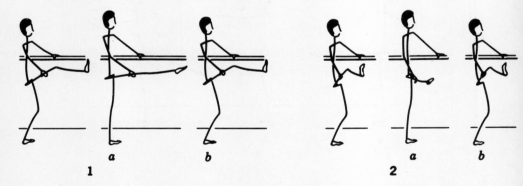

| a   b | a   b |
| 1 | 2 |

Move the free leg to the rear, with the knee bent and turned out. The body may tilt slightly forward, but the head and chest are lifted upward. The right arm is reaching forward. Push the hips and the small of the back down, and lift the leg as high as possible, while trying to keep both hips parallel with the floor. In this position, extend (*a*) and bend (*b*) both legs as before, lifting the free leg a little higher each time (8 counts).

With the knee of the free leg bent (ankle extended), turn the leg so that the knee is on top, bringing it around to the front (c); lower the foot into fifth position (d). Turn, ready to repeat the exercise on the other side (8 counts).

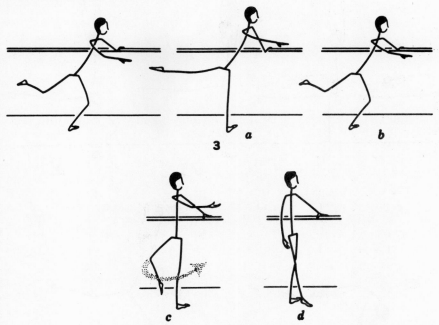

Later, when the exercise has been mastered, do it away from the barre, without depending upon any outside assistance to help with balance.

33. Barre Exercise for Spinal Strengthening, Flexibility, and Hip Rotation and Flexibility

In first position, face the barre.

Place one leg extended on the barre, and round the back over the leg on the barre, reaching with the arms toward the foot (a). Slowly extend the back and arms to a vertical position, initiating the action in the lower back (2 counts) (b). Keeping the leg on the barre, and both legs straight, turn the body to face away from the barre (2 counts) (c). Bend the supporting knee (2 counts) (d); and with a chest lead, reaching out with the arms, bring the arms and body down to the floor over the supporting foot (2 counts) (e).

Reverse the movement: Bring the body and arms up to vertical, initiating the movement in the lower back (2 counts) (f), and straighten the supporting knee (2 counts) (g). Turn to face the barre (2 counts)

(h); with a chest lead, and reaching out with the arms (i), return to the starting position (2 counts).

Do the pattern two times on each side.

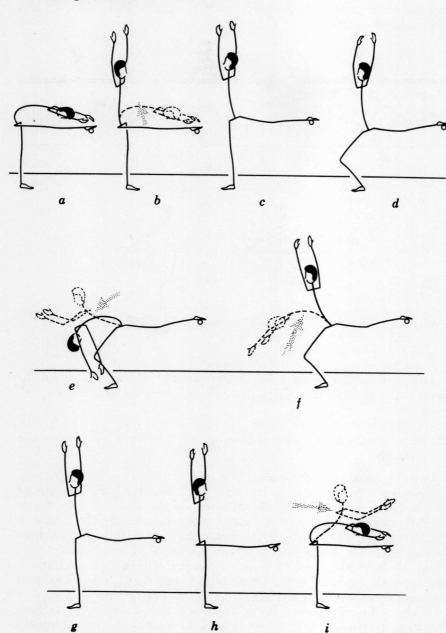

34. Pedaling and Prancing—Preparation for Locomotor Activity

Stand with the feet together and pointing straight ahead, with the body erect, and the arms extended slightly in front of the body.

Lift the right heel, and continue lifting until only the end of the big toe is touching the floor (*a*). Now begin to shift the weight gradually to the right foot, rolling the foot down to the floor sequentially (toe, ball, heel), with strong resistance, while simultaneously rolling the left foot off the floor. When the weight is completely released from the left foot, the toes (still in contact with the floor) should be pointing straight down. Do this pedaling movement very slowly at first. Gradually increase the tempo. Then, push the free foot from the floor completely so that the movement becomes a prance (*b*). Finally, bring the knee of the free leg up to hip height, with the lower leg extended straight down from it (*c*).

Keep the body erect, the rib cage lifted, abdominal muscles firm, shoulders down, and the arms held quietly in front. Straighten the knee of the weight bearing leg completely each time.

a b c

35. Leg Swings for Balance, Control, and Relaxation

FORWARD AND BACKWARD. Stand in first position and shift the weight over the turned out left foot.

Extend the right foot forward, slightly turned out, until only the toes are touching the floor. Tighten abdominally, and lift the free leg forward, with the knee slightly bent and still turned out (*a*). Extend the leg and bring it down through first position, brushing it backward until only the big toe is in contact with the floor. Lift the leg off the floor, working from the hip, and bend the knee, which is still slightly turned out (*b*). Extend the knee and brush the leg forward through first position.

Continue the movement, forward and backward, very slowly at first. Later, increase the tempo until the movement becomes a swing. It is important to keep both legs moderately turned out in opposition to each other throughout the exercise, in order to stabilize the pelvis and broaden the base of support. The body and arms, held in first position, are motionless, or the arms may be swung in opposition to the legs. Do 8 leg swings on each side; or do 4, then 2, then twice do 1 on each side.

SIDEWARD. Stand with the weight on the turned out left foot, with the right leg extended sideward and only the toes touching the floor. The right knee is turned out and slightly bent. The right arm is extended forward, the left arm sideward.

Brush the whole of the right foot across the floor diagonally to the left in front of the body, leading with the heel; lift the leg, still turned out at the hip joint, off the floor, bending the knee slightly and extending the ankle (*c*). Lower the leg and brush the whole foot on the floor sideward to the right with the toes leading. Lift the leg sideward with the knee bent upward, the ankle extended (*d*).

Be sure that the *whole* foot is in contact with the floor on each brush. Increase the tempo until the movement can be given a swinging quality. Do 8 complete swings on each side.

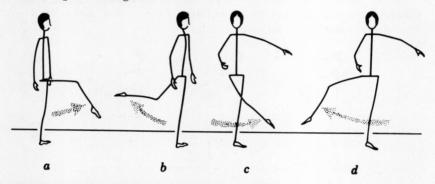

a   *b*   *c*   *d*

A Typical Series of General Exercises

The techniques described above are just a few of many excellent exercises that could be used to warm, stretch, and strengthen various parts of the body. A typical series of general exercises that might be chosen to begin an elementary dance lesson not requiring any *special* kind of emphasis might be as follows:

1. Body and arm swings for relaxation—No. 22
2. Stretches—Nos. 1, 2, 23, 24
3. Sitting swing for spinal flexion—No. 4
4. Abdominal and back exercise—No. 12
5. Foot and leg exercises—Nos. 5, 6
6. Pliés (in first and second positions only)—No. 28
7. Leg swings—No. 35

It is assumed that most of these exercises are not being taught for the first time; if they are, there will be little time left for dance.

As the students grow in proficiency, more difficult techniques can be substituted for simple ones. When exercises are taught carefully, with attention paid to details of movement control, right habits of movement will be established that can contribute greatly to the education of the student both as a dancer and as a well-coordinated human being.

LOCOMOTOR TECHNIQUES

Fundamental Steps

Certain locomotor steps are so basic to man's natural behavior that they appear to be a part of the experience of every normal person. Five of these steps are known as "simple" or "even" locomotor steps, because they require only one action for their completion. Since these five steps are the ingredients of all other steps, it is important to understand their structure:

WALK—a transfer of weight from one foot to the other without loss of contact with the ground.

RUN—a transfer of weight from one foot to the other with brief loss of contact with the ground during transfer.

LEAP—a transfer of weight from one foot to the other, similar to a run, but involving greater height or distance and requiring more energy for its performance.

JUMP—a transfer of weight from both feet to both feet or from one foot to both feet.

HOP—a transfer of weight from one foot to the same foot.

Three combinations of these simple, even fundamental steps are likewise so much a part of man's behavior that they, too, are known as fundamental steps; they are sometimes called "compound" or "uneven" fundamental steps, distinguished from the five simple steps in that each consists of two actions of different time value that form an uneven rhythmic structure:

SKIP—a step and a hop, with the step requiring twice as much time as the hop.

step _____ hop   movement
                   rhythmic pattern
                   underlying beat

SLIDE—a step (usually taken to the side) and another step (actually performed as a leap), closing to the first step. As in the skip, the first step requires twice as much time as the second one.

step _____ close

GALLOP—a step and a leap, with the step requiring twice as much time as the leap.

$$\begin{array}{cc} \text{♩} & \text{♪} \\ \text{step} & \text{leap} \\ \hline \text{♪} \quad \text{♪} \quad \text{♪} \end{array}$$

Because these eight fundamental steps are so familiar to everyone, their manner of performance is not always given the serious consideration that it deserves. The principles underlying good movement should apply especially to these steps, since they are the elements from which all other steps are made. Proper use of the legs and body in push-offs and landings are of great importance not only in jumping and leaping, but also in skipping, and in any other step involving elevation. The controlled use of arms and torso is also an important consideration in the performance of each of these steps, regardless of how else they may be varied. Habits of good movement need to be well established in the practice of these familiar locomotor activities if there is to be any carry-over at all in the performance of their more complex derivatives.

Walking and Running

Walking is actually nothing more than the subtle shift of the body's center of gravity into imbalance, and the step that is then taken to prevent the body's falling; but in a normal walk, the fall and recovery have become so habitualized that one is not conscious of them. A walk may be taken in any direction and in many different ways. Normally, the upper body leans slightly in the direction of the walk, except perhaps when walking backward.

When a natural, forward walk is performed well, the chest is leading; the body weight is held away from the floor by elongating the spine; the head is perched directly on top of the spine; the pelvis is kept stable, providing a point of resistance to allow the legs to swing freely from the hip joint and to prevent excessive hip sway; the weight shift is from the ankle joint, and is tranferred from the heel of the foot, forward along the outside border of the foot, through the ball to the big toe; the knees are never hyperextended, but the hips, knees, and ankles work actively to absorb the shock of the weight transfer and to provide a good take-off position for the next movement; the feet, pointing straight ahead, are placed in a straight line, with their inner borders along "the line of direction," which prevents any side-to-side waste of motion; and the arms are swung freely from the shoulders in opposition to the movement of the legs.

Some common errors in walking are the following: general poor posture; walking with the head forward, the weight back on the heels, and the pelvis so tilted that the abdomen appears to be leading; releasing the pelvis and hyperextending the knees with the hips swaying from side to side in an exaggerated fashion; toeing out excessively, producing a walk that resembles a waddle; or straddling the line of direction and throwing the body weight from side to side, in a lumbering, ape-like walk.

Dance frequently calls for a variation from the normal walk, though seldom in any of the ways described above. Often, for aesthetic reasons, a dancer may wish to reverse the use of the foot in stepping, extending the ankle and touching the toes to the floor first, then rolling through to the heel. In such a walk, the reach of the legs is emphasized and, if the walk is in a forward direction, the body weight is retained longer over the supporting foot, or even shifted slightly backward. In a slow walk of this kind, stability is increased by turning the foot out slightly so that the base of support is broadened and the line of direction passes obliquely through the instep. A smooth gliding walk in any direction is achieved by keeping the knees bent slightly, even after the transfer of weight has been completed.

In walking backward, the free leg is swung from the hip joint, not merely from the knee, and the toes touch the floor first. This backward reach of the entire leg from the hip joint is of particular importance to girls in the performance of ballroom dance steps. The body is normally not tilted back, which might give one an insecure sense of falling backward, but is usually upright between the feet, or, if the backward steps are very large, slightly forward.

Walking to the side can be accomplished by stepping sideward with one foot and closing with the other foot; or by stepping sideward with one foot and crossing alternately in front and in back with the other foot. The latter method, characteristically called the "grapevine step," can be done with the shoulders held in a frontal plane, but allowing the hips to twist on the cross-over steps, or by allowing the entire body to turn; or it can be done without turning at all, keeping both the shoulders and the hips in a frontal plane, in which case, both legs must be turned out sharply, and the cross-over steps taken with the heel leading.

Running is similar to walking; both involve the transfer of weight from one foot to the other, but in running there is a momentary loss of contact with the floor during the process of transfer. In a natural run, performed as if a person wished to reach his destination sooner than he could by walking, the forward lean of the body from the ankles is exaggerated and the force of the forward push or "take-off" is increased. In the transfer, the weight is received by the toes and shifted smoothly to the ball of the foot. Very little weight, if any, is received by the heels. The knees move straight forward in order not to divert any of the force of the movement from the line of direction. In running, the steps are longer and usually, but not always, more rapid than in walking.

The creative dancer, in his exploration of movement possibilities, does not confine himself to the normal way of doing things. His is a never ending search for new modes of expression through movement. He will want to try walking with the free leg swinging from the hip in a low, wide arc around the body, or with the knees lifted sharply to the sides, or in the manner of the German "goose step," or with changes of rhythm, dimension, and level. Probably he will experiment with backward and sideward as well as forward runs. The possibilities for variation are endless. But always, it is important first to understand the physical principles underlying normal movement before attempting to deviate from it.

Elevation—Jumping and Leaping

To leave the floor in defiance of gravity and return to it safely is always a challenging and exciting experience. The feeling of flying through the air is tremendously exhilarating, but it is fraught with danger of physical injury if improperly performed. For this reason leaping and jumping should be attempted only after the body has been conditioned and trained to coordinate efficiently, particularly on the landings.

The levers of hip, knee, and ankle and the arches of the feet are the mechanisms of force for elevation that must be used to the full. In addition to controlling these levers, the performer must also keep sufficient tension in his body that the movement force can project his body in the desired direction. All the energy must be exerted in the direction of the movement. The body must never, for one moment, be relaxed, but must constantly be in a state of resistance to gravity and ready to move. The ground is the springboard, and the dancers' legs are the springs, taut but never rigid. This control in the torso and legs must also be retained during the landing.

Beginners in dance usually lack both strength and coordination in the control of their legs and torso that can be acquired through proper movement education. The following general preliminary exercises are recommended for preparation in elevation.

General Exercises—Preparation for Elevation

Preparatory techniques for dance: Exercises 5, 6 or 7, 28 in at least first, and second and sixth positions, 29, 31, 34, and 35. These exercises, or others that accomplish the same ends, should *always* preface any activity involving elevation. Pliés and brushes are of particular value as preparatory exercises.

Technique of Jumping

A jump, which is the transference of weight onto both feet, can be performed in many ways, with varying degrees of elevation. When elevation becomes a major consideration, the technical demands are increased.

The take-off begins in a plié, with the legs turned out at the hip joint, and the knees directly over the feet. Hips, knees, and ankles bend simultaneously, and extend quickly and forcibly, propelling the body upward. The body must be held in alignment so that the force can pass directly through it without deflection. Hip and abdominal muscles provide stability for the pelvis, and the spinal extensors control the rest of the torso.

On the landing, the toes touch the ground first and the heels lower quickly to the floor with the aid of ankle, knee, and hip flexion; the weight remains over the balls of the feet. Hip and leg muscles are held taut to resist the downward thrust, and thus to lighten the landing. Instead of settling "into" the floor on the landing, one should use this contact with the ground as a preparation for the next push-off. The rib-cage is kept lifted, but the shoulders are relaxed.

In practicing jumps, it is important to make sure that the legs and feet are completely extended when in mid-air; that the heels are brought through to the floor on the landings for maximum leverage; that the knees for anatomical reasons, bend directly over the feet; that the back does not arch on the push-off, which would permit some upward force to be dissipated; and that there is no "sitting into" the hips on the landing, an action both inefficient and unaesthetic. It helps psychologically to concentrate on the upward phase of the action, and to resist the force of gravity mentally, as well as physically.

Special Preparatory Techniques for Jumping—

1. *Lateral Push-offs or Leg Extensions*

(For developing the ability to extend the feet and legs completely and rapidly from a plié position.)

Stand in a wide second position plié with the legs well turned out at the hips. Keeping the hips between the legs and not in back of them, the body centered vertically over the hips, and the arms extended sideward.

Without tilting the hips or the shoulders, shift the body horizontally to the right over the right leg, which is still bent. Simultaneously, release the left leg and (with tension) completely extend the knee and ankle to the side. A straight line is formed from the hip joint to the ends of the toes, which are pointing toward the floor. The leg is not lifted high, but rather, effort is expended to make the leg as long as possible and to thrust it away from the body. "Freeze" the position momentarily before shifting the body back to its centered starting position.

Repeat the action three more times. Then do the same thing with the other leg.

Now alternate right and left legs, keeping the base wide, the center of gravity low, and the extension of each leg "frozen" momentarily before returning it to the floor. Do not lean forward and thus permit the hips to go back.

Do the same pattern as in the paragraph just above, only progress slightly forward with each shift of weight. Be sure to keep the supporting leg bent and the legs widespread. Experiment with giving the movement a primitive quality: Try the movement with the focus upward or shifting from side to side, and the arms, which are sideward, turned up.

Do the same action, moving backward.

2. Double Leg Extensions

Stand in a wide second position plié, with the legs well turned out at the hips and with the torso upright.

Use the same controls described for the previous exercise to perform a low jump, completely extending both legs sideward simultaneously, and returning quickly to the starting position. Hold, and then repeat the action. Make the landings as silent as possible, rolling the weight from toes to heels.

Divide the class into several sections and let one section at a time take four of these jumps, listening to the sound of their own landings.

3. Heel Bounces

(Ankle extensions for the purpose of developing rapid rebound from the floor.)

In first position, begin on the half-toe.

Keeping the knees straight, press the heels to the floor very quickly, returning immediately to the half-toe, and hold.

Repeat this action sixteen times in an uneven rhythm (the touch of the heels has a very short time value, and the hold on the half-toe is twice as long).

Jumps— 1. Jumps in First Position

Stand tall, the heels together, the toes turned out at right angles to each other.

Take sixteen jumps in first position. Make the first twelve jumps small ones, performed with control, but without striving for high elevation. On the last four jumps go as high as possible into the air. Extend the ankles and feet completely while in the air. Bend the knees over the toes and press the heels to the floor on each landing. Keep the body in a straight line, avoiding hyperextension in the lower back, and keep the weight over the balls of the feet. Be sure to plié on the last landing.

2. Jumps in First and Second Positions

Do four jumps in first position (a–b) and then four in second position (c–d); continue the series four times in all.

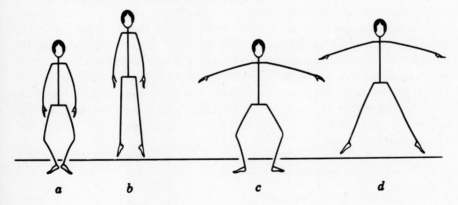

a   b   c   d

3. Jumps in All of the Six Positions

Do two jumps in each of the six plié positions, making sure that the foot relationships are definite, that both heels are touching the floor, and that the weight is centered between both feet on each landing.

Technique of Leaping

The leap, like the walk and the run, is a transfer of weight from one foot to the other. As in the run, there is a loss of contact with the ground during the weight transfer; but the increased height or distance involved in leaping requires more effort on the part of the performer. The form of the leap varies with the effect desired. In a series of leaps for distance it is necessary to extend both the reaching leg and the pushing leg as completely as possible, keeping the body centered between them while in the air.

The reach and the push should occur simultaneously; both legs are turned out and the foot makes contact with the ground in a slightly turned out position to broaden the base of support and to stabilize the ankle. Hip muscles tighten to prevent the buttocks from rolling and to increase the thrust of the pushing leg. The torso rides lightly on top of the legs, with the chest leading, rib-cage lifted, shoulders easy, and the arms swinging in opposition to the legs or held quietly in a comfortable second position. The head is erect with the eyes focused in the direction of the movement.

The principles of take-off and landing in jumping and leaping are similar, and the experience of performing jumps correctly is a good preparation for leaping.

In high leaping, force must be directed in an upward arc. It is mechanically difficult to do successive high leaps because momentum must be checked after each landing and the force redirected upward. For this reason, high leaps are often combined with runs.

With experimentation, many variations on the basic technique of leaping can be discovered. The front leg, or the back leg, or both, may be bent while in the air; or the reach of the forward leg can be allowed to precede the push-off of the back leg, to cause the body to rock backward and forward instead of riding smoothly between the legs; or both legs can be left in back on the weight transfer, or brought forward, as in a "hitch-kick." Other variations can be made by experimenting with rhythmic changes. Possibilities are innumerable.

Special Preparatory Techniques for Leaping—

1. *Stretch in Long Stride Position*

Stand in moderate long stride with the forward foot turned out, the rear foot pointing straight ahead, the knee of the forward leg bent, the back leg straight, the body weight over the forward foot, and the arms extended forward.

Bounce the heel of the rear foot down to the floor four times. Place the rear foot farther back and bounce it again four times. Place it still farther back and repeat the bounces. Place it back as far as possible and bounce it three times, and on the fourth count change feet, landing in moderate, long stride. Repeat.

On the very long strides, the heel cannot touch the floor, but the effort to make it touch stretches the calf muscles. The exercise also helps to establish kinesthetically a long reach with the legs.

2. Extension of the Back Leg in the Push-off

Start at one end of the room, in lines with several dancers abreast.

Progress forward by shoving the right foot forward, the foot in contact with or just above the floor, as though sliding on ice. Keep the body weight directly over the "sliding" foot, which is turned out, and the supporting knee bent. Lead with the chest and focus forward. The left leg, which has been used as a pusher to propel the body forward, should now be completely extended in back. The action is one of pushing forward, and at the transfer of weight leaving the free leg as far behind as possible, with the toes close to the floor. Keep this leg straight from the hip joint to the tips of the toes and turned out. Pause, "freezing" this leg extension momentarily; then shove forward on the left foot, extending the right leg behind. Continue forward in this fashion, each time using the supporting leg as a propelling force to shove the body forward as the weight is being transferred. Keep both legs turned out equally, gripping hard with the hip muscles. Keep the supporting leg bent and drive the movement horizontally forward with much force, eliminating all "over-curve" during the weight transfer, and staying very close to the floor at all times. Remember to "freeze" the backward extended leg during each pause.

Repeat the movement, but omit the pauses so that the forward shoves are taken in rapid succession, but without losing any tension and control.

3. Extension of the Forward Leg

Keeping both legs very much turned out throughout the exercise, lift the left knee high in front of the body (count 1); extend the leg, reaching strongly forward with it, while rising to the half-toe on the supporting foot (count 2); the body may be allowed to lean slightly backward to compensate for the forward extension of the leg, but try to minimize this action. Drop forward onto a turned-out left foot, rolling the weight down from the toes to the heel (count 3). Resist allowing the body to settle into the floor so that the landing will be as light as possible.

Repeat the action with the other leg, and continue forward in this fashion. Take the movement in a moderately slow tempo.

4. Prances for Proper Use of Feet and Ankles

Take light, prancy runs down the floor with the legs facing forward
and the knees lifted only moderately high. Keep the body aligned directly
over the feet. Roll the weight completely through from toe to heel in
placing the foot on the floor, and fully extend the ankle as the foot
leaves the floor. Keep the body weight lifted away from the floor, and
make the entire movement light and vibrant. Concentrate on foot and
ankle action.

Leaps

Commence running; gradually increase the effort and lengthen the
steps until they become leaps and a maximum distance is covered on
each leap. Be sure to keep both legs turned out.

Perform a continuous series of leaps for distance and not for height,
allowing the arms to swing in opposition to the legs. Focus directly
forward and lead with the chest. Use full power and range in the push-
off by the back leg and the fully extended reach of the forward leg;
but at the same time keep the hips from wobbling by tightening the hip
muscles and maintaining a strong turn-out with both legs. Try to extend
both legs simultaneously. Keep the body weight lifted and try to ride
easily on top of the legs.

Combine two runs and a leap, at first giving all three steps the same
time value; then, give the leap twice the time value of the run. Without
sacrificing control, make the leaps as high as possible. Use the runs as
preparation for the leap. Repeat the pattern for the length of the floor.

It will be noticed that here it is the push-off into the air that is called
the leap, rather than the landing, which is actually inconsistent with
our definition. Certain leap patterns, especially those in which elevation
is stressed, seem to be performed more successfully when the leap is
identified with the push-off (in order to emphasize the point at which the
greatest concentration of force is applied to the movement), rather than
with the landing. Such an inconsistency is permissible if the students
are made aware of the fact that the "air moment" now follows the word
"leap" (rather than preceding it), and are informed as to the reason
for this change in terminology.

Acquisition of the control that is essential to the correct performance of leaps, jumps, or any other steps involving elevation, is not
accomplished in one or two lessons. The activities must be practiced repeatedly until proper control becomes habitual. Above all,
leaps and jumps should never be attempted without adequately

preparing the legs for such strenuous action by means of preliminary warm-up exercises.

ARM EXERCISES

When students are asked to state what particular benefits they would like to receive from a dance class, almost invariably they say they would like to learn what to do with their arms. Awkwardness and insecurity are frequently revealed in the way a person uses his arms. In a course that deals with basic movement it seems appropriate, therefore, to focus, at least briefly, on control of the arms. One frequent cause of awkward, ineffectual use of arms is a tendency to move the arms from the elbow rather than from the back and the shoulder. Another very common fault is that of stiffening the elbow (when the arm is used as a whole) and bending too much at the wrist joint.

Of course one cannot generalize on the use of the arms in reference to specific situations, because much depends upon the special purpose of a movement. Once can, however, acquaint students with some of the controls possible and help them develop movement habits in the use of arms that are likely to be applicable to many situations.

A foremost need is that of learning to move the arm naturally from its point of attachment to the torso. The most normal alignment for the arms, as indicated by their position when they are permitted to hang comfortably at the sides, is with the elbows "easy," slightly bent, but not enough to create an angle, the hands continuing the line of the arms with no wrist flexion, and the fingertips gently extended with the thumbs in line with the fingers. In practicing arm movement, it is well to stress this natural alignment of the arms at first, regardless of where the arm is placed (sideward, forward, overhead, and so forth) in relation to the body, and then deviate from it as an exercise or movement may demand.

The following exercises are designed to help students to use their arms naturally with emphasis upon good alignment and upon initiating movement from the shoulder and upper back, where the arm is attached to the torso. In every exercise, the movements should be performed with an inner tension; that is, the muscles that oppose the movement should resist muscles that are executing it.

1. Shoulder Blade Circling

Stand with the feet slightly apart, the arms held down at the sides, as described above; increase the space between the upper arms and the body slightly, but at the same time make the arms very long, without stiffening the elbows.

Initiating the movement from the region of the shoulder blades, raise the arms slowly sideward until the hands are about waist high. Check the alignment of the torso to see that there is no hyperextension in the lower back. The line of the arms is curved so that the fingertips are pointing forward; the elbows are lifted. Move the shoulder blades in a circle, slowly several times, around to the back, down, and forward, being careful not to hunch the shoulders or to overtense the arms so that they are rigid; then slowly lower the arms by pressing down with the shoulder blades and upper arms.

Repeat the action several times until kinesthetic awareness of the point of attachment of the arms to the upper back is established.

2. Expansion in the Upper Back

Press the palms of the hands hard together in front of the chest, fingertips forward, widening the space between the shoulder blades. Now slowly extend the arms straight forward, and then separate the arms horizontally to a sideward position without losing the broad feeling of expansion in the upper back that was established when the hands were pressed together. Make the movement very large and expansive, but don't overstraighten the elbows or squeeze the shoulder blades together.

Repeat, until the kinesthetic feeling of widening the space between the shoulder blades is established.

3. Sustained Movement Arm Pattern

Begin with the arms down at the sides, and using 4 counts, raise the arms sideward, palms facing down, to overhead; on counts 5 and 6 bring the arms forward and down to shoulder level, palms facing upward; on count 7, separate the arms horizontally to each side, palms facing forward; and on count 8 lower the arms sideward to their starting position, palms facing down.

Make all movements very strong, and sustained, with the arms stretched long. Initiate the movements from the upper back and keep the shoulders down at all times. Let the elbows (not the wrists) lead slightly throughout the sequence. Keep the movement smooth, and by judging distances make sure the arms do not arrive at their destination ahead of the count.

Now relate the arm pattern to a walking base, taking one step, on every count, and making the walk smooth, continuous, and gliding. Allow plenty of space between performers.

4. Sustained Movement Arm Pattern with Forward and Backward Walks

Take four steps forward, starting with the right foot. On the fourth step, pivot halfway around to the left to face the back of the room and take four steps backward, continuing in the same line of direction; on the fourth step backward, pivot halfway around to the left to face the front of the room again; continue to alternate four steps, facing forward, with four steps, facing backward. On the four steps forward, raise the right arm forward, palm down, to overhead; on the four steps backward, lower the arm, palm up. Make the movement very strong and commanding, using the same controls as in the previous exercises. Be sure to keep the elbow easy. Move forward from one end of the room with several dancers abreast. The front row begins first, the row behind them commencing 4 counts later; the first row is facing backward as the second row moves forward and so on. The groups should direct their gestures toward those they are facing, both in front and in back of them.

Practice on the left side also.

5. Simultaneous Rotation of Arms

Extend the arms sideward with the elbows slightly bent and the line of the arms definitely rounded, but with wrists straight. Rotate both arms in as far as they will go at the shoulder joints, elbows on top; now rotate both arms out as far as they will go, elbows under, pulling the shoulder blades down; alternate these two movements.

Put this movement on a walking base, taking one step for each rotation. Now enlarge the movement: on the inward rotation contract the muscles of the abdomen and round the upper back, dropping the head forward; on the outward rotation arch the upper back, lifting the head and chest—guard against hyperextension in the lower back. Balance becomes increasingly difficult as the movement is enlarged and thus it is important in walking to step onto a turned-out foot, to broaden the base of support.

6. Alternate Rotation of Arms

Continue as in No. 5, but rotate one arm outward as the other arm rotates inward, alternating continuously. The body and head twist and lean slightly toward the side of the outward rotation.

Put this movement on a walking base also.

7. Exaggerated Arm Rotation Involving the Upper Torso

With one arm rotated out and one rotated in (as in No. 6), slowly raise the arm that is rotated in and lower the one that is rotated out. The elbows appear to be leading, but the movement is still controlled in the upper back. The torso bends toward the arm that is being lowered. Then reverse the rotation and do the same movement to the opposite side. Make the action very large and flowing.

After the arm movement has been mastered, move forward, taking two or three smooth gliding steps for each arm movement.

The achievement of proper control of arm movement demands that attention be paid in every class exercise and dance activity to the principles underlying correct use of the arms. Simple pliés can be every bit as much an exercise for control of the arms as for the legs if the proper attention is paid to the accompanying arm movements. Habits of good body control can be established only by being alert at all times to the total movement of the body.

AWARENESS OF RHYTHM

All movement is rhythmic. Every activity, well coordinated or not, has its particular rhythmical structure. Movement that is efficient and pleasing to watch usually has a rhythm different from that of inefficient movement, and the ability to analyze such differences and to control the rhythmic organization of movement is of great importance in establishing desirable motor responses. The following discussion and suggested explorations of rhythmic structures should help in developing rhythmical understanding.

Beat

The rhythmical structure of a movement is the particular organization of its elements in relation to time and energy. To find this organization, both time and energy must be measured. The measuring device for time is the *beat*, which is an underlying pulse that continues with unchanging duration and force. This underlying beat, as it is frequently called, can be fast, slow, or of moderate tempo, but once the tempo is established, it normally remains constant. Sometimes the beat is very obviously represented in a rhythm, as in a march or in jazz. At other times, the beat is not actually performed at all, but must be sensed in the movement or the music. A given movement will have a certain number of beats for its performance. If the movement is done in the same way every time, the number of beats will remain constant.

The following exercises have been designed to develop perception of the beat as it relates to movement.

1. Slowly raise one arm sideward to overhead and bring it down in front of the body, initiating the downward action with a bending of the elbow. Repeat the action several times and count silently the number of underlying beats that are required.

Ask various members of the class how many beats they used—not everyone will use the same speed or the same number of beats. Now choose a tempo and specific number of beats and let the group adjust to this rhythm.

2. Choose a familiar exercise from the preparatory techniques for dance. Do the exercise and try to sense the tempo and the number of underlying beats in relation to the movement.

Ask various members of the class to perform their patterns and have the class clap the beats underlying the movement. Then purposely change the movement to a different timing; try several possibilities.

3. Write on the board the following step combinations:

step–leap–step–leap–run–run–run

Ask the members of the class to perform this pattern in whatever rhythm feels comfortable and to keep repeating it—the pattern can be performed in several different rhythms. Have each student count the number of beats required for the completion of his pattern—remembering that the beat is the steady pulse underlying the movement pattern.

Ask several members of the class whose patterns differ to perform. Note the number of beats in each pattern and their grouping, and how the movement is altered as either the number or the grouping of beats is changed.

Measure

When one listens to the ticking of a clock or the regular drip of a faucet, or any other steady, recurring sound, one tends to group the ticks or drips and imagine that one is regularly louder than the others of a group; man's unconscious desire to see form in everything, makes him tend to organize the sounds that he hears into a pattern. To illustrate this, the instructor might precede his discussion by beating a steady unaccented rhythm on a drum and asking the class to determine the grouping of beats. Some students will probably answer that the beats are grouped in threes; others will say in fours, and so forth, when actually the beats were not grouped at all.

Because of this innate, human desire for organization, it is customary for man to group beats by means of *metrical accents,* and these groupings are called *measures.* A measure may contain any number of beats, provided the number is not so great that the sense of grouping is lost. When a measure contains many beats, the mind tends to divide it into smaller groups by secondary metrical accents. A measure of nine beats might be divided into three groups of three, or a measure of eight beats into two groups of four. Even a measure of six is normally divided into two groups of three, though not always. The following simple exercises illustrate how the measure is established by accent.

1. Clap a steady beat, accenting the first of every four beats; then the first of every three beats; and finally the first of every two beats.

2. Walk, accenting the first of every four steps by making it heavier than the others; then the first of every five steps; and finally the first of

every twelve steps. Continue this last pattern for a while, checking to see if the twelve counts are felt to be a single entity, or are divided by the mind into smaller groups; if divided, what are their groupings?

Rhythmic Pattern

Few rhythms are as simple and regular as the beat itself. An endless number of rhythms can be created by dividing or combining beats to form time intervals of various lengths. But to understand the structure of these different rhythms, the relation of the time intervals to the beat must be sensed. The beat can be divided in many different ways all based upon duple, triple, or quadruple divisions:

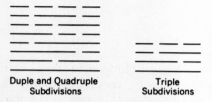

Duple and Quadruple   **Triple**
Subdivisions   **Subdivisions**

Even Division of a Beat

Working in couples, one person walks forward at a moderately slow tempo, establishing a steady beat. His partner walks beside him, taking two even walking or running steps to each beat. On signal, he changes and takes three steps, and finally, four steps to each beat.

Uneven Division of a Beat

The two change roles so that now the other person establishes a moderately slow beat; the partner now sets the rhythmic pattern by taking three steps to each beat and then omitting the second step, so that the pattern becomes uneven (a); he re-establishes the three steps to each beat, and then omits the third step (b).

They change roles again; the partner now sets the rhythmic pattern at four steps to each beat, and then omits the third step (c).

a   b   c

Numerous variations are possible which the teacher should feel free to try.

Combination of Beats

One person establishes a moderately fast beat, accenting the first of every four beats. His partner takes one step to every two beats (a);

and then steps on the first, second, and third beats, omitting the fourth beat (*b*).

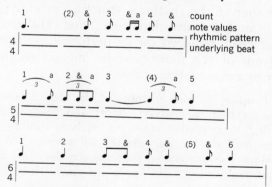

Again, numerous variations can be explored.

Divisions plus Combinations of Beats

Rhythmic patterns frequently involve both division and combination of beats. Furthermore, the intervals in a rhythm may begin somewhere in the middle of one beat and extend into another. Any division or combination is possible provided the intervals correspond to duple, triple, or quadruple beat divisions—with our system of musical notation, no interval can be, for example four-fifths of a beat. The following rhythmic patterns illustrate a few rhythms involving both division and combination of beats. Have the class count, clap, or move to these patterns and check the accuracy of the rhythmic response. When counting a rhythm relative to the beat, each beat in the measure can be given a number. Intervals beginning in the exact middle of a beat can be counted as "–&–." Intervals that begin either before or after the middle of a beat can be counted as "–a–." Three equal parts of a beat can be counted as "one–&–a–," spoken in an even rhythm. If no new interval occurs at the beginning of a beat, the beat is acknowledged silently.

Students may compose their own rhythms also, and put them into movement.

Accent of Execution

So far, the discussion of rhythm has been concerned chiefly with the element of time. Force or energy is the other aspect of movement that must be considered in determining rhythmic structure. Energy is required for the performance of any movement, but the amount of energy varies according to the movement and the way in which it is performed. Usually within a movement pattern some movements demand more energy than others. This sudden application of increased force within the pattern forms an *accent of execution*. For example, in the following step pattern, the jump requires a greater amount of force for its performance than the other steps in the measure, so that an accent of execution occurs on the third beat of the measure.

```
        run  run  run      jump    hop
   4 |____ ____ ____    ____   ____  |
   4 |
```

In sports that involve the projection of objects, such as a ball, an accent of execution will correctly occur as the performer imparts the force from his body to the ball. In dance, an accent of execution can be placed anywhere; as in speech, where meaning can be altered by shifting emphasis from one word to another, so in dance the character and meaning of a movement is changed when accent of execution is transferred within the movement pattern. It will be interesting for students to experiment with change in placement of accent of execution and to observe the effect this has upon a movement pattern.

Analysis of Rhythms Found in Movement Patterns

In order to analyze the rhythmic structure of a given movement sequence, the analyst must determine, first, the tempo; second, the number of beats required for its performance; third, the exact rhythmic pattern of the movement in relation to the beat; and fourth, the accents of execution, if any.

Working in couples, let each member of the class choose a movement pattern for his partner to analyze. Sport activities, such as a tennis serve, or bowling; or everyday activities, such as shining shoes; or any dance sequence will do for the purpose of analysis. When everyone has finished, show the movement patterns for the class as a whole to analyze, so that each analyst can verify his results by comparing them with the class analysis.

The physical educator has a tremendous responsibility in helping the student to develop his body as an intelligently responsive instrument. With so many aspects of movement to be considered, a mastery of even the basic movement skills is not a matter of days, or of weeks, but of years. The instructor has, however, at least one point in his favor: Almost everyone enjoys moving and has a desire to move well; his students may not believe it is possible for them to succeed, but at least they would like to be able to do so. It is up to the instructor, then, to make that desire become a reality by conscientiously attacking the problem at every opportunity; by presenting even the simplest movements in a way that will challenge the students' best efforts; and by helping students to understand the principles underlying movement control that can be applied both in and out of the gymnasium; and by making their experience pleasurable. Such an approach to physical education should not be coldly academic, but can be an experience of stimulating discovery if the teacher himself is sufficiently dedicated in his desire to help his students, is creative in his approach to learning, and is convinced of the values to be obtained from the practice of good movement.

SELECTED BIBLIOGRAPHY

Broer, Marion R. *Efficiency of Human Movement.* Philadelphia: W. B. Saunders Company, 1960.

Hoye, Anna Scott. *Fundamentals of Movement.* Palo Alto, California: National Press, 1961.

Lockhart, Aileene. *Modern Dance—Building and Teaching Lessons,* rev. ed. Dubuque, Iowa: W. C. Brown Company, 1957. Chapter III.

Turner, Margery J. *Dance Handbook.* Englewood Cliffs, N.J.: Prentice-Hall, Inc., 1959. Chapter II.

Turner, Margery J. *Modern Dance for High School and College.* Englewood Cliffs, N.J.: Prentice-Hall, Inc., 1957. Chapter III.

Wessell, Janet. *Movement Fundamentals.* Englewood Cliffs, N.J.: Prentice-Hall, Inc., 1957.

3

Teaching Modern Dance Creatively

Modern dance is an art form in which movement is consciously used to express ideas, feelings, and emotions for their communication. Modern dance in education is not just the learning of dances or a system of techniques but rather more an exploration of movement that leads to creative expression. Dance in education is concerned with helping people to discover movement not merely in its superficial, visual phases, but also in its significant spatial, rhythmic, and dynamic aspects, *kinesthetically* perceived; it is further concerned with helping people to develop their organizational and discriminatory powers in applying movement to expressive purpose.

EDUCATIONAL OBJECTIVES

In order to set up a worthwhile curriculum of dance, the teacher would do well to review in his own mind the potential of modern or creative dance as an educational medium. When dance is taught creatively in an atmosphere that is challenging to the students' best efforts, the rewards can be great. Among the most important of these benefits are the following.

1. An improvement in strength, flexibility, endurance, general physical readiness, and coordination. Movement response is governed intelligently by the mind.

2. A broadening of knowledge and experience concerning the movements that the body is capable of performing, according to its anatomical structure and the physical laws of motion.

3. An increase in awareness not only in the kinesthetic perception of movement itself, but of the interrelation of body movement with emotional expression.

In most everyday situations, a person's powers of observation are seldom directed to movement, per se, or its accompanying sensations.

Instead, the mind is concentrated upon extrinsic objectives to be gained as a result of the movement, such as that of getting snow shoveled from the walk, or putting a basketball through a hoop. In dance, the student's attention is directed precisely to the organization of time, energy, and space involved in his movements, and his sensations of them. Through recall, the student can associate these movement forms with emotional responses that had similar organizations of time, energy, and space. For example, movement that is slow, sustained, high in muscular tension, and inwardly directed might be kinesthetically associated with feelings of apprehension; whereas, swinging or staccato movement that is quick, moderately forceful, and outwardly directed might be associated with gaiety. Such awareness is of tremendous importance to the student if he is to be able consciously to select and use movement as a medium of expression.

4. A deepening of enjoyment in moving for the physical exuberance and emotional release that such movement experience can provide.

5. A development of the power to observe and to understand human behavior, as it is revealed through movement.

6. The attainment of another medium of expression—movement—which, when his instrument of expression, his body, has been sensitively trained, can be used to communicate and share with others his feelings, ideas, and emotions.

7. An increase in appreciation of the aesthetic principles that enter into the construction of pleasing form, regardless of the medium employed; and, through a critical evaluation of his results in creating form, the further development of aesthetic discrimination.

8. A heightening—because of the very intimate relationship that exists between dance and the temporal arts, music, poetry, and drama, and also between dance and the space arts, painting, sculpture, and architectural design—of the students' appreciatory powers for all of these forms of art expression.

9. Pleasure in dancing with others—in sharing a common pulse; a deepened sense of security gained through group participation, as well as opportunity for individual expression.

10. The opportunity to work cooperatively with classmates in problem solving situations which should enable the student to develop qualities essential to democratic living: the ability to lead as well as to follow others and to evaluate with tolerance and objectivity.

11. Finally, and perhaps all-inclusively, dance as an educative experience, can add greatly to the student's ability to make an art of living itself.

ACHIEVEMENT OF OBJECTIVES

The achievement of all the benefits claimed above for dance education is indeed a large order. Certainly an instructor cannot hope even to touch upon all of them in any one lesson, but each lesson in modern dance should point to at least some of these potential benefits; and proper teaching techniques must be devised and applied to that end. Unfortunately, these benefits are not automatically showered upon the student as he steps across the threshold of the dance studio or gymnasium. Unless the instructor sets about consciously in his lesson planning and teaching procedures to accomplish these objectives, many educational benefits will be left unrealized.

Strength and Coordination

Improvement in muscular strength and coordination through dance will be missed unless students are challenged constantly to work to their fullest capacity. Such dance techniques as leaping, turning, and falling are sufficiently stimulating movements to receive a student's best efforts; but other less spectacular activities often require motivation by the teacher to elicit wholehearted pupil response. The most valid and effective means of motivation is that of providing the student with a complete understanding of the purpose of each dance activity and the benefits to be obtained through its correct performance. When the goal seems worth attaining, the student can be challenged to work to the limit of his capacity, not to outdo someone else, but simply to gain for himself the greatest possible reward from the movement experience. The idea that dance activity will be unpopular or unpleasurable if it demands real physical effort and mental concentration is a fallacious one. It is the manner in which a movement problem is presented that determines whether it is to be looked upon as a compelling challenge or as a form of busy work.

Kinesthetic Awareness of Movement

Development of kinesthetic awareness of movement does not automatically take place as a result of dance activity unless movement is presented in such a way that the student is certain to perceive kinesthetically, and analyze consciously, the movements his body performs. The student must be given sufficient time to think, to feel, and to select proper responses; and he must be given verbal guidance that will enable him to pinpoint his observations and provide him with criteria for making his movement selections.

Examples of class problems and of the types of questions that might be used to heighten awareness of movement are the following: Perform a skip in its natural rhythm. Notice whether the step and the hop are of the same duration. Which is longer? Now change the rhythm of the skip to an even step–hop. Does this rhythmic change affect the elevation? How? What is the difference in the movement quality? Or again: Raise one arm sideward to overhead, slowly, with considerable tension, and with a slight elbow lead. Do this movement a number of times, observing its movement sensation. Does the movement feel complete, or does it suggest to you that another movement should follow? Try to discover what that movement is—it may be different for each individual and may involve other parts of the body beside the arm. Now lessen the tension of the original arm movement so that the movement becomes delicate or weak. Does this change in tension cause you to feel the need of a different movement to follow? Try it several times and see. This type of teaching may seem slow at first in comparison with the results of imitative teaching; but the depth of movement awareness and discrimination that is achieved is well worth the additional expenditure of time.

Creative Development and Discipline

If the creative horizons of the student are to be extended by movement exploration, it is desirable that several variations of a given movement be experienced whenever possible. When dance activities are taught as routines to be performed without deviation, the learner, especially the beginner, receives the impression that there is only one correct way to move, and he ceases to look for any other. Sometimes he is actually made to feel guilty if he deviates from the specified movement form in any way.

The question, then, arises: Should students be permitted to feel that any kind of performance is acceptable; that it is not necessary to conform to the specifications of a movement problem, since one movement is as good as another? The answer is, of course, no. Students must learn to discipline their movements to satisfy the technical demands of the problem as it has been set up. When they deviate, the teacher can call attention to differences in performance of which the student himself is frequently unaware. Sometimes it may be desirable to have the class experience the movement several ways so that the students can differentiate between them, and in the future can select the manner of performance best suited to their particular needs. Thus, a movement is not labeled as "right" or "wrong," but "different." The rightness or wrongness is determined entirely by what goals are set up in the first place.

Some students will require much more practice in the mastery of a new movement than others and may find it necessary to concentrate upon only one aspect of the movement at a time. Such students must be treated with patience and understanding and be encouraged for their partial successes. On the other hand, slipshod movement response has no place in a dance class. It may be true, for example, in an activity such as hopping, that the foot of the free leg could be flexed or extended with results that are equally interesting, but a foot that dangles somewhere in between has no meaning. *Careless* performance should not be confused with *carefree* performance.

Students enjoy being challenged to their best efforts, provided they are also given help and encouragement to continue trying. The idea that students should have "fun" in a dance class sometimes misleads a novitiate teacher into using the sound of laughter and giggling in his class as a gauge for a successful lesson. While laughter is generally associated with enjoyment, it may also indicate acute embarrassment—which is anything but pleasurable; or it can also be a sign of inattention. Frequently, the richest and most satisfying experiences are those involving serious thought and a high degree of concentration. There is a vast difference between a serious expression of concentrated effort and a look of bored disinterest. Discipline in movement should be self-administered, arising from the student's own intense desire to master his body. The teacher's role here is to direct, inspire and encourage.

A second question now arises: Will emphasis upon correct performance curb creativity and also the freedom and pleasure that can be derived from moving? It will not if, in introducing a movement pattern to students, the teacher makes a practice of having them experience it in a variety of ways, nor if ample opportunity is given to the students to discover other possible variations for themselves. Nor will students be discouraged or cease to enjoy moving because a high performance level is expected, provided the technical demands are compatible with their current capabilities; the dance movement must be simple enough so that it can be mastered, not just by the talented few, but by the majority of the members of the class. This simplicity is particularly important if students are to direct their attention away from mere body mechanics to feeling states kinesthetically aroused by the movement, so that they can make of it a real dance experience.

Appreciation for Principles of Form

Guidance also will be necessary in helping students to an understanding of aesthetic principles of form and the intelligent application of these principles, both in compositional problems and in evaluation of dances. Such terms as *unity, variety, contrast, sequence, transition, proportion, balance,* and *harmony* will need to be clarified, because there is frequent misunderstanding regarding their meanings. Sometimes their meanings can be clarified by examples of their application in other art forms. Thematic variations in music can provide clear-cut illustrations of compositional devices that can be used to achieve variation in dance. Or again, the meaning of such terms as *proportion* and *balance* can be found nicely illustrated in architectural form.

Specific class problems in composition that focus attention upon manipulating and experiencing the effects of any one of these components of dance form also help to reveal its compositional properties. But the most profitable experiences of all can occur during an evaluation in which the students and teacher survey and judge the results of student compositional efforts. The students' judgment can be stimulated by such questions as these: Is the dance unified in form and idea? Have its movements been developed with sufficient variation to make it interesting and rich in meaning? Do the sections of the dance offer sufficient contrast to each other? or do they contrast so greatly that they appear to be unrelated? Are transitions well designed for the effects desired? Does the dance have a climax? Are the dancers so arranged spatially that their groupings and movements are pleasingly balanced? It is when the principles of form are given practical application that these components can best be understood and appreciated and can become useful compositional tools.

Appreciation of Other Arts

The teacher of dance is in an admirable position to acquaint his students with other arts as well, which is sure to lead them to discover relationships between the various forms of expression. For example, he can make available for listening music that the students can use as inspiration or accompaniment for dance, or can enjoy purely for its own sake. The necessary study of the structure of music to be used as dance accompaniment deepens the students' appreciation of form as it is found not only in music but in other arts as well. The meaning of ABA or of a rondo form in dance is more clearly understood when the student has become familiar with its musical counterpart. Interesting sculpture, in its plastic imagery, can suggest choreographic ideas and movement designs to the dancer. Discussion of the creative techniques involved in giving form to ideas will disclose that all the arts are similarly concerned with many of the same compositional considerations. The painter's concern with establishing a center of interest or focal point in a painting is similar to the dancer's concern with creating a movement climax. Just as the painter uses line and color to produce harmony and oppositional tension, the choreographer combines movement for similar results in dance.

The use of one medium of art expression as a source of inspiration for creative work in another brings a valuable enrichment of understanding and appreciation of both forms of expression. An art class might be invited to observe and sketch the dance students in action; and the students of dance, in turn, might find choreographic inspiration in abstract space patterns and linear designs created by art students. A similar exchange might take place between dancers and students in an English class who are involved in a poetry project. Here, the experience to be shared may not be so much concerned with structure or design as with concepts and feelings.

In such circumstances, students learn to appreciate not only the similarities in structure and subject matter among the arts, but also the differences between them, as dictated by the possibilities and restrictions of the materials from which they are formed. The poet can be specific in his use of language whereas the dancer can deal only with generalities. But the poet must limit himself in his appeal to the listener to those elements that can be perceived by the ear and the mind; whereas the dancer can reach his audience emotionally and intellectually through the eye, the ear, and most important, through the observer's empathic response to movement.

Dance, perhaps more closely than any of the other arts, is bound up with her sister arts. Although music is the usual accompaniment for dance, poetry and sometimes prose have also served in this capacity. The visual imagery in painting, architecture, and sculpture have supplied the dancer with choreographic inspiration; and novels and plays have provided subject material. By familiarizing students with examples of excellence from these various art fields, the teacher can both inspire his students to creative effort and educate their aesthetic tastes.

Social Skills

Teacher guidance is again essential in helping students to learn to work in harmony together on group projects. Merely placing students in groups for problem solving does not ensure the development of democratic behavior. As the teacher moves among these groups, offering compositional suggestions where needed, he must also be sensitive to the social relationships of the group members. With his help, timid individuals can be encouraged to offer their ideas, and students who are inclined to dictate can be persuaded to solicit and accept suggestions from others. Where there is no appointed leader, groups can be taught how to work cooperatively under a leadership that changes as different group members gain insight into a problem. Subtle teacher guidance can help each group member to feel a responsibility to contribute to the group effort and to cooperate in carrying out group decisions.

The evaluation period provides another opportunity for the development of desirable social behavior. Students can be taught to examine their own strengths and shortcomings objectively; they can be assisted in learning to offer criticisms in a constructive manner, to phrase their opinions tactfully, and to accept suggestions gracefully. The teacher's own personal example can lead the way with skillfully phrased questions and comments such as these: What did you like best about the dance study that was just presented? What did the group do to heighten the rhythmic interest? Can you suggest a way that they might solve their space problem?—questions which are a means of helping to shape student thought and behavior.

One of the most important things a student can learn that will aid him in becoming a well-adjusted individual is to evaluate honestly his own capabilities and to adjust his actions and goals accordingly. The teacher can be of immeasurable assistance in helping students to accept the fact that every person possesses distinct talents, worthy of respect. What is important for each person is to discover and so develop his individual capabilities that he can make a maximum contribution to his group, and, thus to society generally. Student dance performances, although sometimes a breeding ground for dissension, rivalry, and petty jealousies, can, if properly handled, provide the opportunity for students to learn to put aside their own personal desires and to work together for a common goal. To achieve this end, emphasis must be placed on the over-all goal, rather than on the work of individuals, and on the creation of an atmosphere in which, along with those of the best performer, the contributions of the most modest participants, the costume maker and the curtain puller, are appreciated. Dance provides many opportunities for the development of desirable patterns of social behavior, but if these are to be carried over into activities outside of school, the teacher must again help the students to relate their motives and actions to situations as they occur in the world at large. It may not occur to them that there is any relationship between their procedures in a dance group and their actions as a member of a community unless this relationship is called to their attention.

LESSON PLAN CONSTRUCTION

With these teaching objectives in mind, the next important consideration is the building of lesson plans that will provide students with the necessary opportunities to learn. What are the characteristics of a good lesson plan? To begin with, each lesson should be built upon a specific unifying purpose related to dance itself—the purpose of a dance lesson must not be just to provide physical activity, nor to develop desirable social attitudes, but to enlarge the the students' scope of experience and understanding of *dance*. It is through the specific medium of dance that the other, more generalized, educational objectives are achieved.

Too often dance lessons are formulated with little notion of increasing a student's conceptual understanding of dance. He is directed in a series of unrelated movements that may be quite pleasurable in themselves, but when the lesson is over the student has not really learned anything about dance that can be applied to future situations. A lesson that is well planned and well presented will have sufficient unity and clarity of purpose that the student could sum up in a few words what the lesson was about; he should feel a progress in technical growth and theoretical understanding. Generally speaking, it is better to concentrate on the teaching of movement concepts than on the teaching of specific movement techniques as ends in themselves. Often, however, it is through the experience of specific techniques that movement concepts are best comprehended.

Once the purpose of a lesson has been established, the next problem is the selection of experiences that will further that purpose. Progression is also important. Many students are afraid to attempt activities unfamiliar to them, and so it is particularly important that a lesson's introductory activities be simple, familiar ones that everyone can perform with assurance. A satisfying teaching progression involves a step-by-step construction of each new experience upon the previous one, gradually advancing from the simple to the complex; and in such a manner, the lesson should build to a climax. Sometimes the climax of the lesson may be a fairly difficult movement sequence that is a culmination of most of the preceding material in the lesson; or sometimes the climax may be a very short movement problem in synthesizing the lesson material, challenging the students' own creative powers. If the climax is of the former type, and the movement pattern includes difficult techniques that some of the members of the class are unable to master, it is usually desirable to conclude the lesson with a relatively simple movement sequence that can be performed enjoyably by everyone. By so doing, the class lesson is not ended on a note of defeat for anyone.

Even though the subject material in a lesson is centered around a simple idea, it does not necessarily follow that the lesson will lack variety of movement. Variety can be assured by changing such aspects of the movement as its range, direction, tempo, rhythm, muscle tension, quality, and style. A beginning teacher, however, may need to guard against becoming so engrossed in variations that he digresses from the chosen purpose of his lesson; one of the chief reasons for exploring the variations of a given idea is to enrich the student's understanding of dance in relation to that original purpose. On the other hand, one should not infer from this discussion that the teacher may never, under any circumstances, deviate from his plan of procedure. Occasions often arise in teaching a lesson, no matter how well it has been planned, that call for a complete change in teaching approach and even in subject matter. Perhaps the movement is too difficult, or there are certain gaps in the students' experience which prevent the students from successfully fulfilling the lesson assignment. Or, in some instances, a sudden flash of inspiration will open a new vista for creative exploration that is too intriguing to be by-passed. These are occasions when a deviation from the planned objective is not only permissible but highly desirable.

In some lessons the activity may be very strenuous. In order to avoid overfatigue, vigorous movements can be combined or contrasted with others less demanding. By changing from a vigorous activity to one that is less strenuous or that uses a different set of muscles, students can rest without having to take "time-out" when time is generally at a premium. Such a procedure not only permits increased time for accomplishment, but student attention is not allowed to drop and thus does not have to be revived when a rest period is over.

When there are boys or men in a class, some thought should be given to their particular interests and requirements. It is not necessary to devise special techniques for them. Almost any dance movement can be given a masculine appearance if performed by men with directness and vigor. On the other hand, it is well to avoid activities that might make men self-conscious; and to include a generous amount of big, body movement. Men enjoy techniques involving elevation, in which they can excel; and they respond well when movement concepts are related to sports and work rhythms of a masculine nature. As beginning students, men usually prefer an abstract approach to dance—from the standpoint of rhythmic structure, dynamics, and design—to an emotional or dramatic approach.

An effort should be made throughout every lesson to give the students as much real dance experience as possible. Mere mastery of the mechanics of movement is not enough. The movement quality, style, and general feeling must be experienced if the activity is to become dance. The instructor is required to do more than analyze and teach the anatomical joint action and general timing of the activity. He must be sensitive to subtleties in the bodily tension and manner of performance that provide the basis for emotional feeling; and this sensitivity will have to be imparted to his students. The teacher can do this by his discriminative choice of picturesque language in describing movement and also by asking provocative questions that will stimulate the students' own powers of observation.

When a creative problem is used to culminate a lesson, it is important to make sure that students have been given an adequate background of experience in the lead-up material. Not only is it important that the students have sufficient movement experience to draw upon, but the problem should be such that one can visualize a variety of workable solutions. A compositional assignment must be limited in its scope so that attention is concentrated upon only one or two movement factors at a time. Otherwise, students may get bogged down in a confusion of too many compositional considerations. Furthermore, if students are to learn about the effects upon movement form of any given element, there should not be too many other variables.

At the very beginning students feel far more comfortable and secure when they can do their composing in groups than when working alone. Groups of from three to seven people are of a convenient size for them to work together effectively, and there are many compositional assignments that are admirably designed for pairs. If the compositional problem is such that it must be solved by beginners individually, the practice of having several students perform at once is often advisable to minimize self-consciousness. It is important to encourage students to perform sincerely and without apology, even in the most elementary compositional presentations.

When students have overcome some of their initial fear of performance, very short compositional assignments that must be solved individually can be of great value in their artistic growth. Such assignments encourage the student to explore movement possibilities within his own body and to perceive kinesthetically the organic rightness or wrongness of a movement, listening to what the muscles themselves have to say about how it feels to perform it. This inner concentration, seldom possible in a group situation, is essential to the student's inventive and discriminating use of movement for dance expression.

Improvisation is no substitute for composition, but it can lead the dancer into unanticipated movement responses that may reveal to him beautiful and unusual movement patterns that might not have been discovered in any other way. Such experiences, if captured and recalled, give the dancer both inspiration and excellent movement material for composition. Group improvisation can also teach the student to respond sensitively to the movements of other dancers and to relate his own movements to them in a meaningful fashion. Although improvisation is a highly valuable experience in the student's development as a dancer, it is apt to be too indefinite to afford the security that most beginning students need. To improvise successfully, the student must forget himself as a person and concentrate intensively on solving the movement problem. If improvisation is used at all with beginners, the assignment should be limited in scope and clearly defined for them. Later, after students have grown in experience, improvisation problems can be expanded without arousing feelings of ineptitude and self-consciousness. The satisfactory outcome of improvisation as an approach to dance depends not only on student readiness but also, to a very large degree, upon the ability of the teacher to provide the necessary verbal or sensory motivation. Adequate time is another extremely important factor, because improvisation problems sometimes require a long preliminary period of orientation and practice perhaps an hour or more, before the proper creative frame of mind is established. Improvisation, if it is to be successful, cannot be rushed.

In planning a dance lesson, a new instructor sometimes finds it difficult to judge how much material to include. Often an activity requires more time in class than anticipated, or occasionally the material can be covered more quickly than planned. In either case, the instructor should be ready to make adjustments. He should be prepared with an intermediary goal if the real climax of the lesson cannot be reached in the time allowed; or, if the lesson is moving along too quickly, he should have supplementary movement material ready with which to expand the lesson. A common failing of beginning teachers is that of spending too much time with preparatory warm-up activities and not allowing enough time for the development of a lesson's principal subject material. As he grows in experience, the teacher will eventually be able to anticipate the various time requirements of his lesson material.

LESSON UNIT ORGANIZATION

Lesson units are nothing more than a series of lesson plans coordinated to arrive at a more comprehensive goal than can be attained in a single lesson. Sequential development of movement material is just as important within a unit of lessons as it is within a single lesson. As far as possible, each lesson should build upon the specific understanding and skill acquired in the previous lessons so that all may contribute toward an ultimate climax or culminating activity.

Ideally, the length of a unit is determined by the educational goal selected and the time required for its achievement. Sometimes, however, the unit length is established by time availability, and subject material has to be chosen accordingly. A creative project to be assigned as the culmination of a single class period is of necessity quite short, because there is little time available for it. Longer projects usually require a number of lead-up lessons for the students to get an adequate background of experience to handle the problem with confidence and understanding. Creative assignments that in themselves may require more than one class lesson for completion can be used as culminating activities for lesson units. It is often advisable for the teacher, in planning the lessons leading up to such assignments to start with the culminating project and work backwards; by first determining the various experiences his students will need in order to handle the creative assignment with ease, the instructor will be able to plan intelligently what dance material to include in the lead-up lessons.

A lesson unit that probes deeply into a given subject is better than one that covers a lot of material superficially. Most students can make superficial explorations themselves. It is in discovering subtle movement variations, combinations, and their kinesthetic implications that the teacher's help is especially needed. Such a thorough approach requires more thought and preparation by the teacher, but the results are infinitely more rewarding than when an attempt is made to cover a wide variety of movement concepts in a short period of time.

If the dance unit has such a function as the introduction of creative dance to the students, the teacher will have to pay special attention to the opening lesson. This lesson must generate enthusiasm; it must be challenging, but not too difficult, and deal usually with free, big-muscle activities, such as swings or locomotion—familiar movement experiences approached from a slightly new standpoint. Above all, the lesson must be fun!

The last lesson of a unit is also an important one. Not only should the lesson leave the students with a real sense of accomplishment, but it should be sufficiently pleasurable that students will wish to continue with dance in the future.

Summarization and evaluation are essential elements in the learning process. At the end of every movement project, a brief summary and discussion of the dance experience helps to crystallize for the students the movement concepts upon which the lesson or unit of lessons has been based. A successful lesson unit, when viewed in retrospect, should give the students not only a sense of physical and emotional enjoyment, but also an awareness of educational achievement.

Points To Remember in Unit and Lesson Planning

1. In planning a lesson unit, select one or two major objectives toward which all of the lessons will be directed. Plan the lessons for a progressive development from one lesson to the next toward some specific culminating dance experience.

2. Avoid the tendency to try to teach everything that you know about dance in one unit of lessons. Instead, teach thoroughly what you do teach, and save the rest for future units.

3. In making a lesson plan, be sure that your specific objectives are clear. Build each lesson upon an idea or movement concept to which everything in the lesson contributes.

4. Exhaust the possibilities of your material through variation of approach. Stick to your subject long enough for students to feel a sense of accomplishment.

5. Make sure that each lesson builds to a climax.

6. Decide what particular technical controls can be stressed in one lesson and try to see that the class accomplishes these objectives. Don't allow careless habits of movement to be established.

7. Analyze your material accurately before presenting it. Break down a difficult activity into its simple components. Be sure your progressions are logical.

8. Try to anticipate possible errors and devise ways of helping students to avoid or to correct them, but also be adaptable: when unforeseen problems arise change your lesson plan to meet the needs of the class.

9. Use picturesque word imagery, particularly when it can be used to clarify some objective aspect of a movement such as its quality. If one description is ineffectual, try another. In general, avoid emotional

imagery that might cause self-consciousness or produce overemotionalism in movement.

10. Give students a definite objective upon which to concentrate while practicing a movement.

11. Don't hesitate to repeat an activity if necessary. Students do not become bored with repetition so long as they continue to be challenged by new considerations. It is only after a student has become thoroughly familiar with all aspects of a technique that he can begin to dance it.

12. Do not overwork a strenuous exercise. Make your directions sufficiently clear that success may be attained with a minimum of repetitions; and if necessary, come back to the technique in another lesson.

13. Help students to become aware of movement controls by asking questions that will cause them to discover for themselves what is happening when they move; this is creative teaching.

14. In general, with beginners, give specific instructions for the performance of a movement. Do not ask a beginner to "take some arm movement." Vague directions of this kind are likely to arouse feelings of insecurity.

15. When presenting a new and difficult coordination, allow students to do the movement at their own tempos before having them perform it to a specific count or musical accompaniment.

16. Remember that until a student has become kinesthetically perceptive as to the right "feel" of a movement he has not yet mastered the movement, nor can it become a significant part of his movement vocabulary.

17. Build the experience of your students to the point where they will enjoy composing. Be sure that they have had a sufficient variety of pertinent movement experiences to be ready to handle the compositional task assigned. Frequently, a number of lead-up lessons will be necessary to reach this point.

18. Limit the complexity of the compositional assignment. Don't confuse a student by expecting him to achieve too many objectives at once.

19. In beginning classes, allow students to work together in small groups, or if the composition must be handled individually, allow several students to perform at the same time until they outgrow self-consciousness.

20. Urge everyone to contribute his creative efforts to the class. Even if a student has only one or two movements to present, accept these agreeably and encourage him to future effort.

21. Use compositional studies not only as a creative outlet for your students but also as an opportunity to judge how well you have succeeded in expanding their creative horizons and how well they have understood the principles of movement with which the lesson unit has been concerned.

22. Throughout your lesson planning, allow yourself frequent opportunity to measure technical achievement; do not wait until the end of

the term to do such testing. Within each unit in which technique has been emphasized, select certain indicative skills by which students are to be evaluated and encourage practice outside of class.

23. Choose certain definite criteria upon which to base your evaluations of dance techniques. Some of the possibilities are (1) correctness of motor coordination; (2) accuracy of rhythm; (3) appropriateness of style or movement quality; (4) ability, when such criterion is applicable, to relate one's movement to another person; (5) ability to *dance* the pattern. Let the students know in advance the criteria upon which they are to be graded.

24. Evaluate each lesson and lesson unit after it has been taught, to see what was actually accomplished and how it might be improved in the future.

Teaching Tips

1. See that the room is well lighted and ventilated, and when students are inactive, that they are not in a draft.

2. Know your lesson plan so well that you can teach it without constant referral to notes.

3. Teach verbally, whenever possible, instead of demonstrating or performing the activities with your class. Verbal instruction discourages imitative learning and encourages students to think for themselves. Demonstration can, however, be valuable at times, in providing a source of inspiration and in enabling students to check their own results for desired movement response.

4. When a demonstration is necessary, have students demonstrate if capable; but be careful not to choose the same ones each time. A demonstration should be performed well or not at all, and should be presented in the view in which it can be best observed. Never call attention to errors in performance by singling out a student and subjecting his movement to class criticism.

5. Don't stay in the front of the room throughout the lesson. Move among your students so you can observe their movements from all angles and can help those in the back of the room as well as those in the front.

6. Use various formations—straight lines, circles, diagonals, and indefinite formations—to give students as rich an experience with space relations as possible. Be sure to allow adequate space for ease and safety in movement.

7. Try to so organize the mechanics of a lesson in dance technique that everyone is busy. If it is necessary for students to take turns performing because of space limitations or for other reasons, so organize the activity that students will be moving into position to begin again while they are waiting for their turn, or if they must stand idle, give them something specific to observe or think about while they are waiting. Sometimes students can work together in couples, observing each other and helping to correct the partner's technical difficulties.

8. Remember that there is no experience that can substitute for movement. Explanations are necessary, but they should be brief and concise. Students want to move; so get them into action as quickly as possible, and, if necessary, talk while they are moving.

9. Use words you are sure your students understand, or explain your terms. Use anatomical terms correctly.

10. When a definite rhythm is required, set the rhythm and the tempo for the students and the accompanist; don't make this the accompanist's responsibility. See that the tempo is right for the particular activity and for the participants involved. Remember that the ideal tempo for an activity may vary with the physique and motor capabilities of the performer.

11. Give clear signals for starting and stopping an activity so that students and accompanist can commence with confidence and end together. "Ready"–pause–"and," or "ready"–pause–"begin," or occasionally, "ready" "here we go" are the usual starting signals.

12. Remember to praise as well as correct. Students need the reassurance of being told when they have succeeded and encouragement to continue trying when they have not. Give praise only when it is truly deserved, but try hard to find something worthy of praise in the work of every student. Make corrections either quietly to the student concerned, or make your criticisms undirected ones, from which the entire class can profit. After correcting a student, be sure to let him know when he has succeeded in remedying the error.

13. Above all, be enthusiastic; believe wholeheartedly in what you are teaching, and be genuinely interested in the progress of every student.

RATING STUDENT ACCOMPLISHMENT

Before attempting to appraise student accomplishment, a teacher must first decide exactly what he wishes to consider. What does a class grade signify: Does it represent the good conduct of the student during his class participation? Is it a record of the student's attendance, neatness of attire, and diligence in taking showers? Is it primarily an evaluation of the student's accomplishment in *dance* —in technical skill, in understanding and appreciation of movement as a medium of art expression, in creativeness and artistic sensitivity? Doubtlessly, attendance, interest, and effort to learn and improve will enter into the grading to some degree, but regular attendance and effort by the student should be a natural assumption provided the teacher has done his part. Students should not be conditioned to expect to be rewarded with high grades merely for being co-operative; sincere effort to learn is certain to bring about greater achievement than could possibly be attained by attitudes of indifference or hostility, and it is in this way primarily that student conduct is rewarded.

Another matter to be decided is whether the evaluation is to be made upon the basis of the student's individual improvement or upon his actual accomplishment according to certain established criteria; this is often a difficult decision to make. Awareness that human effort is intensified in response to praise and encouragement inclines the teacher to encourage by appropriate grading the student who starts at the bottom and works hard to improve. Thus the rankest beginner and the student who enters the class with the advantage of some previous knowledge and experience have an equal opportunity to earn a high grade. On the other hand, incentive to improve can also be increased when the student has some objective standards by which to measure his own achievement. In most cases, class grades are the result of weighing both of these considerations. Whatever system for grading is used, it is important that the students be informed of it; otherwise, a grade has little meaning.

The matter of setting objective standards by which student accomplishment may be evaluated is much more difficult in a modern dance class than it is in a swimming or bowling class where progress and accomplishment are self-evident. Frequently, in modern dance, the rightness of a given movement is entirely relative to the demands of a particular situation; and much of the time when dance is being used for expressive purposes, its rightness or wrongness can only be judged subjectively. Fortunately for the dance teacher, most lesson units do include some specific technical skills that can provide one basis for judging student progress. Brief practical tests on these skills as they occur in the lessons not only give the teacher a fairly objective means of grading, but they also become for the students an incentive to self-improvement. Here again students must be informed of the specific aspects of movement upon which their performance will be evaluated—not the least of these being the ability to bring to movement the awareness and expressiveness that make it *dance*.

Movement skills, however, represent only one facet of the student's dance experience. Sometimes a teacher may require a written examination to test the students' comprehension of anatomical, physical, rhythmic, and aesthetic principles governing movement that have been discussed in class. But one of the most important aspects of modern dance is creative expression. Here technical skill and intellectual understanding combine to produce dance expression arrived at through the creative process. Measuring such accomplishment is especially difficult because the evaluation must of necessity be almost totally subjective. Furthermore, in beginning classes especially, very little solo composition can be expected from students; and when group compositions are assigned, the ensuing choreography is the result of group effort and compromise. Although group composition provides an excellent learning situation and opportunity for dance expression, it does not provide a very sound basis for evaluating the separate student's creative contribution. To measure progress in creativity requires alertness and constant observation by the teacher to enable him to judge accurately the amount of creative leadership each student is contributing to group projects and to evaluate his originality and artistic sensitivity in solving individual problems.

When students have become sufficiently experienced to be capable of composing solos and directing group choreography, an objective–subjective scoring system can be established to rate their efforts. Composition objectives that have been the subject of compositional problems and compositional principles that have been discussed in class and deemed essential to good choreography can be listed and given a numerical weighting according to their relative importance. Then student performances can be measured against these items and graded on a point system. When the direction of group choreography is involved, a separate evaluation of the directing abilities of the student may also be included. Below is an example of what a rating card for a student director-choreographer might contain.

The Choreography

Points
_____ Was the concept both worth while and danceable?
_____ Was the concept expressed with unity and clarity?
_____ Was the concept adequately developed, yet economically delineated in movement?
_____ Was the choice of movement both appropriate and original?
_____ Was the dance development convincing in terms of sufficient motivation and effective transition?
_____ Did the dance have a good beginning, climax, and ending?

The Choreographer

_____ Was the choreographer able verbally to communicate his choreographic intentions to his performers?
_____ Was the choreographer resourceful in directing his choreography?

_____ Was the movement well chosen with respect to the capabilities of his performers?

_____ Did the choreographer use his rehearsal time economically?

When musical accompaniment, costumes, and stage sets are involved, the following additional criteria may have to be considered, though they will not be applicable to all dances:

_____ Was the musical accompaniment danceable and appropriate to the choreographic idea?

_____ Did the choreographer avoid using music that was commonplace, overfamiliar, or associated with preconceived ideas?

_____ Did the costumes support the dance in design and color?

_____ Was the set functional in creating the appropriate atmosphere?

_____ If the set was designed to be danced upon or in, did the choreographer make adequate use of this opportunity?

A value of ten points might be assigned to each question, but an instructor might prefer to weight the questions in accordance with the aspects of composing and directing that have been emphasized in class.

Although this rating of student performance and accomplishment serves obviously in grading, its most important value is in acquainting the student with his specific strengths and weaknesses in dance in order that he may continue to grow technically, intellectually, and creatively.

SELECTED BIBLIOGRAPHY

Hawkins, Alma. _Modern Dance in Higher Education._ New York: Teacher's College, Columbia University, 1954.

Hayes, Elizabeth R. _Dance Composition and Production._ New York: The Ronald Press Co., 1954. Chapter 1.

H'Doubler, Margaret N. _Dance: A Creative Art Experience,_ rev. ed. Madison: University of Wisconsin Press, 1957.

Lockhart, Aileene. _Modern Dance—Building and Teaching Lessons,_ rev. ed. Dubuque, Iowa: W. C. Brown Company, 1957.

Murray, Ruth. _Dance in Elementary Education,_ rev. ed. New York: Harper & Row, 1963.

Turner, Margery J. _Modern Dance for High School and College._ Englewood Cliffs, N.J.: Prentice-Hall, Inc., 1957.

4

Approaches to Modern Dance

Modern dance is not a simple subject. The body, as an instrument for dance, is so very complex, and movement has so many facets, both spatial and temporal, that the possible approaches to movement of the body in dance are almost endless. There is no such thing as "a technique" of modern dance any more than there is a single, right way of creating. A serious study of modern dance will involve learning as much as possible about the body's capabilities for expressive movement—discovering movement, mastering it technically, applying it creatively to expressive purpose. To learn all that it is possible to know would require more than a lifetime. In an academic situation one can hope to explore only a few of the many aspects of movement that one should understand in order to use movement expressively. Although it is desirable to give students as broad an understanding of movement as possible it is also important to avoid touching so superficially upon each aspect of movement that class experience has little meaning. As has been stated previously, students can make superficial explorations themselves without any help from a teacher; it is in penetrating deeply into the discovery and mastery of movement that the teacher's assistance is needed.

MOVEMENT CONCEPTS FOR DANCE UNITS

Exactly which facets of movement the teacher selects for his approach to modern dance does not particularly matter. No single aspect of movement can be studied in complete isolation anyway, since all movement at all times involves the use of time, space, and energy. For example, although one may concentrate primarily upon locomotion in a problem concerned with varying a given step pattern, it is impossible to avoid such considerations as floor pattern, rhythmic pattern, and body movement in creating those variations. Thus, it becomes evident that while a teacher may select only one or two points for particular stress in her presentation of modern dance to a class, it is inevitable that other aspects of movement will also come under scrutiny.

The following outline suggests to the teacher various possible approaches to the study of dance. A lesson or unit of lessons could be built around any one of the many sub-headings depending upon how deeply the teacher wishes to probe into her subject material.

I. LOCOMOTOR APPROACH TO DANCE

   A. Developing variations upon a single fundamental step, such as a walk, a skip, or a jump, by changing the direction, range, placement of feet, use of the free leg, rhythm, arm and body movement, quality, et cetera.

   B. Combining fundamental steps in various ways—

      1. Combining *different* steps, such as: run–run–leap; or step–hop–run–run–jump.

      2. Varying the *manner* in which two (or more) *specified* steps are combined, such as a step and a hop:

   C. Working with traditional or conventional dance steps, such as the polka, schottische, waltz, tango, jitterbug, or jazz forms—

      1. Developing the dance step from fundamental steps.

      2. Experimenting with ways in which the traditional step might be varied as suggested in A.

      3. Combining certain traditional steps that are rhythmically and qualitatively compatible, such as the waltz and the mazurka.

      4. Building new locomotor patterns upon the *rhythmic* structure of a traditional step.

II. BODY MOVEMENT APPROACH TO DANCE

   A. Exploring movement in terms of the anatomical capabilities of the body—

      1. Experimenting with flexion and extension—forward, backward, and lateral.

      2. Experimenting with rotation—exploring movements that are either instigated or dominated by the twisting action in a certain body joint or joints.

   B. Exploring movement localized in or initiated by certain segments of the body, such as the arms and hands, the shoulders, the hips, the torso, the legs, the head, or the peripheral parts as opposed to the central parts of the body or vice versa.

C. Experimenting with movement qualities—swinging, pulsating, sustained, percussive; explosive and staccato; and collapsing—
  1. Extending the movement vocabulary within a given quality.
  2. Combining and contrasting movement qualities.

III. RHYTHMIC APPROACH TO DANCE

A. Meter, accent, and phrasing—
  1. Performing movement in relation to a single meter, such as 3/4 or 5/4.
  2. Experimenting with changing meters.
  3. Exploring the effect of cumulative rhythms upon movement (see page 119).
  4. Experimenting with resultant rhythms—rhythmic patterns that are the result of super-imposing the metrical accents of one meter upon those of another.
  5. Experimenting with accent patterns created by accenting unexpected beats or portions of beats—syncopation.

B. Rhythmic pattern—
  1. Devising movement to fit a given rhythmic pattern.
  2. Performing a rhythmic pattern in contrapuntal form.
  3. Performing a rhythmic pattern as a several-voiced round.
  4. Performing two different rhythms contrapuntally.
  5. Experimenting with breath rhythms.

C. Tempo—
  1. Experimenting with accelerating and retarding the rhythm of the movement.
  2. Performing movement patterns twice as fast or twice as slowly as originally performed.
  3. Experimenting with contrasts in tempo.

D. Intensity or degree of energy—
  1. Experimenting with the effect produced by performing a movement pattern with weak intensity, moderate intensity, and strong intensity.
  2. Experimenting with creating contrasts in intensity within the movement pattern.
  3. Experimenting with the use of different combinations of tempo and intensity and observing their resulting effect upon movement.

IV. SPATIAL APPROACH TO DANCE

A. Experimenting with direction in reference to *floor pattern*—often combined with focus—
  1. Straight line patterns.
  2. Curved line patterns.
  3. Combinations of curves and straight lines.

4. Turns.
5. Symmetrical and asymmetrical design.

B. Exploring the use of direction, level, and design in reference to *body movement*—
   1. Specific direction of movement.
   2. Different levels and ways of changing level.
   3. Curved and straight line patterns.
   4. Expansive and contractive movement.
   5. Symmetrical and asymmetrical design.
   6. Oppositional, parallel, and sequential lines of movement.

C. Experimenting in the use of focus—
   1. One focal point.
   2. Conflicting focal points.
   3. Many focal points.

D. Experimenting with contrasts in movement range.

E. Defining specific planes, volumes, and shapes by means of movement.

F. Experimenting with positive and negative space patterns—negative space being the space that exists between the body parts, such as the shape of the space between the arm and the body.

V. SENSORY AND IDEATIONAL APPROACHES TO MOVEMENT

A. Experimenting with the use of sensory stimuli to inspire dance movement—
   1. Visual stimuli: colors, designs, pictures, movement of such natural phenomena as water, smoke and lightning, sculpture, architectural shapes, costumes, et cetera.
   2. Tactile stimuli: textiles such as velvet and silk, shapes and surfaces, tactually rather than visually perceived.
   3. Auditory stimuli: percussion sounds and rhythms, word sounds, music, et cetera.

B. Exploring ideational sources as bases for dance—
   1. Literal actions and gestures used as a basis for dance pantomime and its abstracted movement forms.
   2. Word images and moods.
   3. Dramatic ideas, stories and situations involving relationships of people.
   4. Authentic dances characteristic of special cultures or historical periods.
   5. Structural forms, such as ABA, rondo, or theme and variations.

EXAMPLES OF TEACHING PROGRESSIONS

Because modern dance, as John Martin states,* is not a system but a point of view, every teacher who is at all creative will

* John Martin, *The Modern Dance* (New York: A. S. Barnes & Company, 1933), p. 20.

want to develop his own teaching methods. Examples of teaching progressions, however, can suggest to the beginning teacher ways of organizing his own materials. The novice may also find that, in experimenting with other people's ideas, he will discover new teaching possibilities that had not occurred to him before. For these reasons, the following lessons are included in this chapter.

The units are varied in length, according to subject matter and the time needed for development. The material is designed for beginning and intermediate dance students of high school and college age. In general, the lessons are planned for class periods of approximately thirty-five minutes. None of the lessons, if taught thoroughly, would require less than thirty-five minutes; some would require more, depending somewhat upon the technical advancement of the students. For several of the lessons, more material than could conceivably be taught in one thirty-five minute class period has purposely been included, in order to present many variations of a lesson subject and to illustrate how one goes about exploring a movement idea. One must bear in mind that teaching should never be rushed at the expense of student achievement in order to complete a lesson by the end of a class period. If a choice must be made, it is better for a class to progress slowly and to cover less material, if by doing so students can better assimilate what is presented and enjoy the activity, than to rush through a lesson superficially. By experimenting, a teacher can discover how much time to allow and can decide, if necessary, which activities to omit and which lessons to extend over more than one period. Whenever adjustments must be made in a lesson plan, the instructor should try to arrange his teaching material so that the lesson still builds to a climax, even though it is an intermediary one. In the lesson units presented here, time has not been specifically set aside for testing skills or various other dance accomplishments. The instructor would probably wish to include at least one additional class period for testing, except in those units primarily involved with composition.

Teaching objectives have been listed at the beginning of each lesson. These objectives are concerned principally with potential benefits to the student from the class activities, in dance skill and understanding and in his development as a person and a dancer. There are other general benefits possible, such as improvement of muscular strength, flexibility and coordination, that are taken for granted.

Normally, the lessons commence with a brief series of basic warm-up activities such as are described in Chapter 2; but except in lessons requiring specific preparatory exercises, the choice of such exercises is left to the instructor's discretion. When students are not familiar with any preliminary dance exercises, it may be desirable to devote a lesson in the beginning unit to warm-up activities in which can be developed a basic series that may be varied as required. The descriptions of class formations and methods of presentation are offered merely as suggestions to the teacher.

While it is not essential that the units be taught in any specific order, a unit on fundamental steps or one on swinging movement often makes an excellent introduction to dance, since these activities are already a part of any student's natural movement experience. However, a fresh and interesting approach to these activities will be necessary if they are to be made challenging to the class. In selecting lesson material, a new teacher will do well to inquire into the previous dance experience of his students, in order to build upon and expand it and to avoid duplication. Fundamental steps, especially, have sometimes been "done to death" as a result of failure to make such inquiry or to explore other movement possibilities. In planning a series of units, it is wise to develop several that are contrasting in their approach to movement, in order to give the students as varied an acquaintance with dance as possible. Whatever approach is used, the important thing is to make it both worth while and thoroughly enjoyable.

Unit One: Fundamental Steps, The Schottische, and The Polka

Lesson I: *Review of the Eight Fundamental Steps, Experienced Singly and in Combination*

OBJECTIVES:

1. To give students an understanding of these steps in terms of weight transference.
2. To teach students to perform these steps with conscious technical control.
3. To provide a basic movement vocabulary for the lessons that follow.
4. To enable students to put these steps together in specific combination.
5. To develop an awareness of one's partner when dancing in pairs.
6. To give students an enjoyable dance experience.

PROCEDURE:

1. Preparatory techniques, with special emphasis on feet and legs (Chapter 2).

2. Discuss briefly, the eight fundamental steps in terms of weight transference; try to draw as much of this information from the students as possible—

   a. Review the simple fundamental steps—

      (1) *Walk:* a transfer of weight from one foot to the other, without losing contact with the ground.

      (2) *Run:* a transfer of weight from one foot to the other in which both feet are off the ground momentarily.

      (3) *Leap:* a transfer of weight similar to a run, but rising higher or covering more distance.

      (4) *Hop:* a transfer of weight from one foot to the same foot.

      (5) *Jump:* a transfer of weight from one or both feet to both feet.

   b. Compound fundamental steps—

      (1) *Skip:* an uneven combination of a step and a hop.

         step   hop

      (2) *Gallop:* an uneven combination of a step and a leap.

         step   leap

      (3) *Slide:* an uneven combination of a step and a close, which is usually a small leap, normally performed to the side.

         step   close

3. Moving around the room, informally, or in a circle, or in various other formations, re-experience these fundamental steps in the following fashion:

   a. Walk in normal everyday manner with heel touching first, with good body alignment, chest leading. Change directions frequently according to specified signals.

   b. Walk, toes touching first, measuring the length of step by the distance the toes can touch in front of the body. Pull the heels forward across the line of direction so that the feet are turned out slightly. Make the walk very smooth and give the movement an expanded feeling.

   c. Walk backward, reaching back with the toes before transferring the weight.

   d. Run, shifting the body weight forward and kicking the toes up in back. Keep the movement very light. Hold the arms quiet.

   e. Start with a moderately fast run, gradually extending the length of the step until it becomes a leap. Lead with the chest and focus forward. Stay close to the floor but reach with both legs while in the air. Swing the arms in opposition. (Normally, with beginners, it is wise not to do much leaping until students' leg muscles are properly conditioned.)

f. Do alternate jumps and hops, taking the hops on alternate feet. Experiment with various uses of the free leg on the hops. Then release the free leg to the rear the first two times, forward the second two times, and keeping the knee straight, to alternate sides on the next four times. Point the toes and keep the whole pattern very light. Progress slightly forward throughout the entire pattern.

g. Skip, bringing the free leg forward, the knee slightly bent and turned out, the ankle extended. Hold the arms quiet in first position or swing them in opposition to the legs.

h. Gallop very lightly, bringing the knees up high and pointing the toes straight down.

i. Slide in a circle, hands joined, changing directions: 8 Right, 8 Left, 4R, 4L, 2R, 2L, 1R, 1L, 1R, 1L.

4. Combine slides and skips—
Moving down the floor, four or six abreast, facing each other in pairs so that you are dancing with a partner, do two slides, facing partner, and two skips, facing forward and continue alternating in this fashion. Be sure to close the second slide before beginning the skips. The arms are extended sideward in second position on the slides; and down at the sides in first position on the skips. When this pattern has been mastered, make one complete turn, turning away from your partner, on the two skips, making a half turn on each skip. Continue moving into the line of direction, even on the skips. Be conscious of your partner and try to establish a feeling of dancing together, especially on the slides.

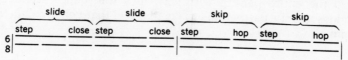

Lesson II: Combinations of Skips, Slides and Gallops

OBJECTIVES:

1. To provide an experience in combining skips, slides, and gallops accurately in specifically designated patterns.
2. To develop technical proficiency in the performance of these steps.
3. To develop an awareness of the other person when dancing in pairs.
4. To provide the students with an enjoyable dance experience.

PROCEDURE:

1. Preparatory techniques, with special emphasis on feet and legs.
2. In an informal class organization, take light prancy gallops around the room.

3. Review the combination of two slides and two skips.
4. Combine 1 skip, 1 slide, 1 gallop:

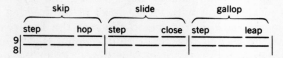

Practice the pattern in your own timing at first. Remember that, upon repeating, the pattern is begun on the other foot. When everyone has succeeded in working out the foot combination, do the pattern, in couples, diagonally across the room; do it with vigor and animation. This pattern is a little tricky for beginners and will require concentration and practice.

5. In couples, take the following pattern:
Four skips forward, starting by stepping with the outside foot; two skips backward; a slide and a half, i.e., step-close-step, to the side; four gallops diagonally forward toward partner (beginning by stepping with the inside foot); four skips turning around with partner by holding both hands; two slides sideward, away from partner.

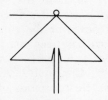

Do the entire pattern with zest, in a folk dance style. Be conscious of your partner and make him feel that you are dancing with him.

Lesson III: *Combinations of Fundamental Steps*

OBJECTIVES:

1. To provide experience in combining fundamental steps accurately and in specifically designated patterns.
2. To develop rhythmic sensitivity and accuracy in interpreting a rhythmic pattern.
3. To develop awareness of the other person when dancing in pairs or of one's relationship to a group.
4. To develop awareness of variations that are possible within a given step pattern.
5. To provide creative opportunity to construct an interesting movement variation of a given step sequence.
6. To provide the students with an enjoyable dance experience.

Procedure:

1. Preparatory techniques, with special emphasis on feet and legs.
2. In an informal class organization, clap and then perform the following pattern, working it out individually:

$$\frac{8}{4}\; \text{step} \quad \text{hop} \quad \text{leap} \; \text{step} \; \text{jump}$$

3. Moving forward down the room in lines of four abreast widely spaced, or two abreast if the room is narrow, take the following pattern:

$$\frac{6}{8}\; \text{run} \; \text{run} \; \text{run} \; \text{jump} \quad \text{hop}$$

4. Now do the same pattern, moving into alternate diagonals on each repetition of the pattern; in this way the dancers in each line of four will move alternately toward and away from each other:

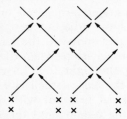

The second line of four waits to begin until the first line has completed one pattern. Cover as much space as possible. When moving toward another person, be aware of his presence, and make the jump–hop an act of recognition. The two center lines must remember to respond to the people on both sides of them. If the dance space is narrow, only two people should commence together in order to allow plenty of room for the movement.

5. In lines of four abreast, moving forward, perform the following pattern in the following ways:

$$\frac{6}{8}\; \text{step} \; \text{hop} \; \text{hop} \; \text{step} \; \text{hop} \; \text{hop} \quad \text{etc.}$$

   a. In your own way first.
   b. With the free leg bent in front on the hops.
   c. With the free leg straight behind.
   d. Alternating Procedures b and c.
   e. Alternating Procedure c, facing forward and moving forward; with b, facing backward and progressing backward into the line of direction.
   f. Facing front, with the free leg bent to the side, knee and ankle bent (country style).

g. Moving into alternate diagonals (skater's waltz style) with the free leg extended (straight) into the back diagonal, but the body facing front. Stay close to the floor and cover distance on the hops. Use the arms to help, as skaters do, avoiding letting them rise above shoulder level.

h. Making a complete turn, turning away from the free leg, on the first step–hop–hop; moving forward, with the free leg straight, and extended forward, on the second step–hop–hop.

i. Turning continuously in place, with the free leg trailing behind, on the first step–hop–hop; and bent in front, with the knee leading around, on the second step–hop–hop.

6. Perform the following pattern beginning with the left foot (a "touch" is a momentary shifting of the weight onto the toes of the other foot):

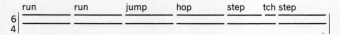

Now, with the class in one large circle or in several smaller circles, grasp the elbows of the adjacent people, and perform the same pattern. Face left, and move to the left throughout the pattern, except on the step–touch–step, when the body turns to face right. On the hop, swing the right foot forward into the direction of movement. This is the basic Israeli Hora step. Do the movement slowly and smoothly at first but with a light, easy quality, and gradually increase the tempo until the movement becomes quite fast and gay. Use any Hora music. The 6-count movement pattern is performed against a 4/4 rhythm in the music.

7. Learn the following pattern:

```
    step  hop  hop  step  hop  hop   run  run  run  jump      hop
 6 ─────── ──── ──── ───── ──── ──── │─────── ──── ──── ──────── ─────────│
 8
```

For the next class period create an interesting way of doing the pattern that progresses down the floor and can be repeated. Consider such possibilties as what to do with the free leg on the hops, directional changes, and use of arms and body.

This is a long lesson. It is probable that all of the material cannot be covered in a single class period. In such case, the teacher might omit some of the variations in Procedure 5 or omit Procedure 6 altogether, or might extend the lesson over two class periods.

Lesson IV: *Combinations of Fundamental Steps, Particularly Steps and Hops*

OBJECTIVES:

1. To provide experience in combining fundamental steps accurately in specifically designated patterns.

2. To develop rhythmic sensitivity and accuracy in interpreting a rhythmic pattern.

3. To develop an awareness of variations that are possible within a given step pattern.

4. To provide the students with an enjoyable dance experience.

PROCEDURE:

1. Practice individually the s–h–h–s–h–h–r–r–r–j–h variation that was assigned to be composed for this class period. When everyone has had enough practice time, do the patterns one at a time, moving diagonally across the room, each person starting after the person ahead has completed one sequence.

2. Discuss and perhaps repeat a few of the most interesting patterns.

3. Do the following step combination:

step   hop run run run

$\frac{6}{8}$

a. In your own way, but working for elevation on the step–hop.

b. Keeping the movement close to the ground; take the step–hop in a forward direction, bringing the free leg directly forward with the knee straight, and make the runs—backward, forward, forward. Swing the arms in opposition to the legs on the step–hop and change them on the first run only. Lean forward with the body, and drive the movement forward.

4. Do a series of free but well-controlled skips down the floor:

skip   skip   skip   skip
step   hop step   hop step   hop step   hop

$\frac{6}{8}$

5. Change the step–hop to an even rhythm:

st hop st hop st hop st hop

$\frac{4}{4}$

Notice what happens to the elevation when the rhythm is made even.

6. Do the following pattern:

step   hop step   hop st hop st hop st hop st hop

$\frac{4}{4}$

Work for elevation on the uneven step–hops. Keep the even step–hops close to the ground and be sure that they are even.

7. Do the same pattern but make two complete turns into the line of direction on the even step–hops (make a half turn on each step–hop, with the arms in first position). The legs are turned out

at the hips. Point the knee of the free leg, slightly bent, into the line of direction, with the toes almost touching the ankle bone of the supporting leg. Focus into the line of direction. Be sure to do the pattern on both sides so that the turns can be practiced in both directions. Dance it!

Lesson V: *Development of the Schottische and the 2/4 Polka*

OBJECTIVES:

1. To develop kinesthetic sensitivity and intellectual understanding of step pattern, quality, and rhythmic organization of the schottische and the 2/4 polka and how these steps can be evolved from fundamental steps.
2. To provide experience in varying the movement through change of direction and change of movement style.
3. To provide experience in combining these steps with each other and with some of the fundamental steps.
4. To provide creative experience in composing a short study relating two people spatially.
5. To give the students an enjoyable dance experience.

PROCEDURE:

1. General preparatory techniques.
2. Do, in moderate tempo, three walks and a hop, swinging the leg forward on the hop. Make the movement very smooth.
3. Now change the step pattern to step–close–step–hop, still keeping the movement smooth and gliding.

This is called a schottische.

4. Do three schottisches forward and one schottische moving backward.
5. Do two schottisches and four even step–hops forward:

   a. Do the pattern very smoothly, with extended ankles.
   b. Do the pattern in country style, with flexed ankles.
6. Do one schottische and four step–hops, making the step–hops twice as fast:

Make the schottische smooth and the step–hops gay and perky. Be sure the step–hops are even.

7. Now make the rhythm of the schottische twice as fast:

$\frac{2}{4}$ | step　close　step　hop |

8. Change the last half of the step-pattern to an uneven rhythm:

$\frac{2}{4}$ | step　close　step　hop |

Make the movement lively and bouncy. This is known as a 2/4 polka. It is sometimes begun with the hop:

$\frac{2}{4}$ hop | step　close　step |

9. Combine two schottisches and four polkas:

schottische	schottische	polka	polka	polka	polka
st　cl　st　h	st　cl　st　h	h st cl st h	st cl st h	st cl st h	st cl st

$\frac{4}{4}$

Contrast the two qualities as much as possible.

10. Do one schottische forward, one schottische backward, and the four polkas forward.

11. Combine: one schottische forward, one backward, two polkas forward and four step–hops turning:

schottische	schottische	polka	polka		
st　cl　st　h	st　cl　st　h	h st cl st h	st cl st h	st h　st h	st h　st h

$\frac{4}{4}$

Contrast the qualities of the slow and the fast movements as much as possible and be aware of the build in momentum. Dance it!

12. In couples, take the above pattern and very quickly create a little duet, using a variety of directions and relating to each other in various ways.

Lesson VI: *Development of the 6/8 Polka; the Slide-and-Lift Variation Combined with Skips; and the Cross-Polka.*

This is a long lesson, and, for some students, might have to be extended over two class periods.

OBJECTIVES:

1. To give the students an understanding of the step pattern, rhythmic organization, and quality of the 6/8 polka and of how it is related to the slide and the skip.

2. To provide an opportunity to experience the polka with various directional changes.

3. To develop an awareness of two possible movement variations of the 6/8 polka.

4. To provide experience in combining these steps with the fundamental steps.

5. To provide the students with an enjoyable dance experience.

PROCEDURE:

1. General preparatory techniques, including No. 13 and also the following:
   Lying on the floor with the arms extended sideward, keeping the shoulders on the floor, lift one leg straight into the air, placing the foot on the floor as far to the other side of the body as possible. Touch the heel to the floor and point the toes downward. Return it to position and repeat with the other leg.

2. Slide the length of the room and back again.

3. Slide, turning on every fourth slide to face the other side of the room, but continue sliding in the same direction. Always make the turn toward the line of direction.

4. Do the same, turning on every second slide.

5. Discuss with the class the fact that, in the process of turning, a hop has been substituted for the close of the second slide, so that the second slide has now become a skip. Thus, the step pattern is really a slide and a skip, which is known as the 6/8 polka.

6. Do the pattern in pairs, facing each other, with inside hands joined. Perform the first polka face-to-face, the second one back-to-back. Let the joined arms swing down and through on the change from face-to-face to back-to-back and vice versa.

7. Singly, face the line of direction and take the same step pattern as before, but do not turn the *body* from side to side.

8. Do one polka forward, one backward, two forward, and four into alternate diagonals.

9. Do the polka forward, only on the hop, extend the free leg to the rear with the knee straight and the ankle extended. Go forward on the slide, and directly upward on the skip, with the chest lifted and the head back.

10. Use the arms to help increase the elevation.
    a. Swing the arms out to each side on the slide; swing them forward and upward on the skip.

b. Now try swinging the arms across in front on the slide (*a*), and upward and backward on the skip with the arms in back of the ears, the elbows rounded and palms forward. Arch the whole upper body, and lift the head, but keep the abdominal muscles firm so that the lower back does not hyperextend. Make the whole body as long as possible while it is in the air (*b*).

a   *b*

11. Combine this version of the polka, which is called a "slide-and-lift," with two skips in which the free leg is carried forward. On the skips, the arms can be held quietly at the sides, can swing in opposition to the legs, or can swing across the body and out to the sides. Choose any one of these, but make the movement definite.

12. Now do the original basic 6/8 polka; but on the hop, whip the free leg, in a big arc, up and across to the other side of the body. Press the heel forward, turning the foot out, as you step. Keep the arms quiet, and the shoulders parallel to the front of the room. When the leg swings across the body lean to the opposite side, but keep the shoulders parallel to the floor.

13. In lines of three or four people abreast, rest your hands lightly on the shoulders of the adjacent people. Take this step, which is called the "cross-polka" down the floor, moving as a team. Adjust your steps to those of the other people so that you progress for-

ward at the same rate of speed. Exaggerate the sideward body lean and the size of the leg whip.

14. Progressing individually, again, repeat the cross-polka with the arms softly extended sideward.

Lesson VII: *Development of the Hip-Turn Polka and Review of Previous Material*

OBJECTIVES:

1. To provide additional experience in varying the 6/8 polka.
2. To review the movement material of previous lessons.
3. To give the students an enjoyable dance experience.

PROCEDURE:

1. General preparatory techniques, with emphasis on feet and legs, including No. 10.
2. Stand, facing the barre (stall bars or other objects can substitute for a barre), and rest the foot of one leg, completely extended, upon it. With a hop, turn directly away from the barre, keeping the free leg straight and still on the barre. With another hop turn back to face the barre again. Be especially conscious of the rotation that takes place in the hip joint.
3. Review the 6/8 polka moving forward down the floor.
4. Do the step–close–step forward, and swing the free leg straight forward so that on the hop you can turn away from it as you did at the barre. You are now facing the rear of the room. Do a step–close–step backward and swing the free leg back so that on the hop you can turn toward it to face forward again. Thus a forward polka with a swing forward and a backward polka with a swing backward will be alternated. On the backward leg swing, the body may tilt forward slightly, but keep the head and shoulders up. Always be sure to swing the leg completely through before turning, and for safety's sake, land on a turned out foot. Be sure that a complete half-turn is made each time.
5. Elevation can be increased by using the arms to help. One way is to swing the arms forward on the slide and sideward and upward on the hop turn.

6. Review the cross-polka (Lesson VI, Procedure 14).
7. Review the slide-and-lift and two skips (Lesson VI, Procedure 11).
8. Review the schottische, 2/4 polka, and step–hop (turn) pattern (Lesson V, Procedure 11).
9. Divide into groups of 3, 4, 5, or 6 people and choose one of the following problems to work on as a group during the next class period.

a. Using the schottische, 2/4 polka, step–hops, and any other combination of fundamental steps that fit together pleasingly, compose a group study to 32 measures of 4/4 meter.

b. Using skips, slides, or any combinations of fundamental steps, such as step–hop–hop, and any of the 6/8 polka variations, compose a group study to 32 measures of 6/8 meter.

Work for consistency in the style and general quality of movement.

Lesson VIII (and possibly IX): Composition of a Dance Study Based Upon the Polka, Schottische, and Combinations of Fundamental Steps

The lesson will take one or two class periods, depending upon the rate of speed at which the students work.

OBJECTIVES:

1. To provide an opportunity for students to utilize the movement materials they have previously experienced, in creating and dancing a simple group composition.

2. To give the students experience in the use of democratic procedures in solving a group problem cooperatively.

3. To provide an opportunity for the students to perform for each other and to experience a sense of achievement.

4. To help students to develop stage presence and the ability to project their feelings to others by means of movement.

5. To help students to enjoy sharing creative experiences with each other, both actively and vicariously.

6. To help students to evaluate their choreographic efforts intelligently and constructively.

PROCEDURE:

1. Review the compositional assignment and help the students get organized with a minimum waste of time.

2. Offer suggestions to the groups where help is needed.

3. When the majority of the groups are ready, present the studies for the remainder of the class to evaluate as to interesting floor pattern, step combinations, group relationships, pleasing transitions, and consistency of movement style.

4. Comment on the portions of the dance studies that were especially successful, discussing reasons for the success. Then suggest how the studies might be improved.

If circumstances are such that eight or ten lessons are not available for a unit on fundamental steps, this unit can be shortened in a number of ways:

1. It would be possible to make a four lesson unit, ending with Lesson IV, by omitting Procedures 6 and 7 from Lesson III

and making Lesson IV consist of (1) warm-ups; (2) Procedure 7 from Lesson III; (3) Procedures 1 and 2 from Lesson IV; (4) Procedure 6 from Lesson III.

2. It would also be possible to make a six-lesson unit by extending Lesson III over two lessons and by ending the unit with Lesson V.

3. The material beginning with Lesson VI and extending through the end of the unit could be offered as a separate unit on the 6/8 polka by omitting Procedure 8 and limiting the compositional assignment to Procedure 9b of Lesson VII.

The material is very flexible and can be re-arranged in a number of ways, provided each lesson is given a unifying idea, and a climax, and provided the lessons follow each other in a logical progression.

Unit Two: Swinging Movement

Lesson I: *Swinging Movement with Emphasis on Arm Swings*

OBJECTIVES:

1. To provide experience with and understanding of the swing and its structural organization.

2. To develop kinesthetic sensitivity and awareness of feelings evoked by swinging movement.

3. To offer a variety of experiences with swinging movement, particularly the arm swing.

4. To develop technical proficiency in the performance of these movements.

5. To provide an enjoyable movement experience.

PROCEDURE:

1. General preparatory techniques, including Nos. 22 (first version), 4, 28 (first and second positions), and 35.

2. Begin by swinging the arms back and forth and then discuss the characteristics of a swing. A swing consists of: (1) an initial downward impulse of the swinging part; (2) a continuation and gathering of momentum (with the aid of gravity) as the part moves on and up, (3) a momentary suspension of the swinging part as the upward force of the momentum and downward pull of gravity are equalized. Each of these three parts requires one count, so a swing falls into a three-beat rhythm. In performing the following swinging activities, try to be aware of the help that gravity gives to the movement; of the easy, relaxed feeling that characterizes swinging quality; and of the moment of rest that

occurs at the end of each movement arc. Make the movements large and free, but, at the same time, keep them under control.

3. Swing both arms in a downward arc across the body to the right, shifting the weight to the right foot; swing both arms back to the left side, shifting the weight to the left foot; swing the arms in a complete circle to the right ending with both arms to the right. As the arms circle, take a step–close–step (R–L–R) sideward with the feet. Make all the movements very large, reaching so far to the side with the body and arms at the end of each swing that the free leg is lifted, fully extended, off the floor. Focus on the hands. Enlarge the movement still further by taking a hop after the last step at the end of the arm circle.

4. Do the same pattern as in 3 above but without the hop, and making the horizontal range smaller and concentrating on height. When the arms circle overhead, turn the body completely around. The step pattern changes from a step–close–step to a small step–leap–step, almost in place, as the body turns around.

5. Do the same pattern as in 3 but in a forward and backward direction instead of sideward. The foot pattern is the same as in 3 but done in a forward and backward direction. Make the swings very large, arching the body as the arms swing forward and up, and tucking the body as the arms swing back. Add a hop, to the end of each arm circle.

6. Standing in second position and using the side of the forefinger to cut the air, swing the right arm in a free circle in front of the body, circling down under first, and then up over (a) and make another circle, as far out to the side as possible (b), so that the entire pattern is a horizontal figure-8. Shift the body weight to the left and then to the right as the two circles are made. Initiate the movement in the shoulder and upper back; keep the elbow easy, letting it bend where needed to make the circles round; cut the air with the side of the forefinger in making both circles; and focus on the hand. Exaggerate the sideward reach. Let the body, as well as the arm, become a part of the movement. Practice the movement on the other side also.

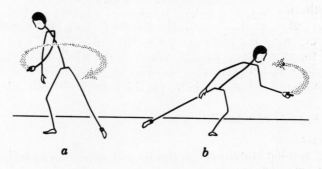

a   b

7. Now, with the right arm, draw a vertical figure-8, by circling the arm overhead, as if drawing a halo, or shouting "hurrah!" (*a*), and then circling it down in back of the body, as if cutting a seat behind you with the side of the forefinger (*b*). The feet are close together, with the left one slightly ahead. When making the circle overhead, rise on the toes; stay there, as the circle is made behind, but bend the knees forward and push the hips forward also, without hyperextending the lower back (keeping abdominal muscles firm), and twist the upper body around to the right to look at the hand.

Practice this pattern on both sides.

8. Combine the horizontal and vertical figure-8 patterns, circling across in front, out to the side, up above the head, and down behind. Give a slight whip-like impulse to the beginning of each circle. Focus on the hand. Use the body as well as the arm to make the movement very large.

9. Moving down the floor, do a running-waltz using all open, running steps, accenting the first of every three by stepping onto the whole foot with the knee bent and by taking the other two steps on the half-toe. Make the movement very smooth, and drive it forward continuously. Accent the first count with a slight body impulse as well.

10. Now, using the running-waltz as a base, add the double figure-8 with the arm, one running-waltz for each arm circle. If using the right arm, begin with the left foot. Make the movement very large, using the body as well as the arm and make the directions of the four circles definite. Focus on the hand. Drive the running-waltz forward even when the arm circles in back. Try to give the movement a dance feeling. Do the pattern on both side.

Lesson II: *Leg and Arm Swings*

OBJECTIVES:

1. To develop kinesthetic sensitivity and awareness of feelings evoked by swinging movement.

2. To provide a variety of experiences with swinging movement, especially arm and leg swings.

3. To develop technical skill in the performance of these swings.

4. To provide an enjoyable movement experience.

PROCEDURE:

1. Preparatory techniques, including those recommended for Lesson I, with special emphasis on forward and backward leg-swings (No. 35). Alternate sides with leg-swings after every 4, then 2, then 1, and again 1. (4, 4, 2, 2, 1, 1, 1, 1). Begin each part of the series by swinging the leg to the rear first.

2. Now, starting at one end of the room, progress forward with the leg-swings, changing sides after each forward swing. Start by stepping forward with the right foot. Lift the left foot, which is already back, to its full height in back and then brush it forward. Step forward on the left foot, lift the right foot in back, brush it forward, and so forth. To make the balance more secure, step onto a slightly turned out foot and keep the free leg equally turned outward. Extend the ankle of the free leg completely at each end of the leg-swing. The arms may be held quietly in first position, shoulders down, or if the class is experienced with movement, may be swung oppositionally.

Make the leg-swings large, but keep the body under control by tightening in the abdomen. Point the toes, and add a smile!

3. In place on the floor, and with plenty of room to move, review the horizontal figure-8 pattern of Lesson I, 6. Make the movements large and free.

4. Now reverse the figure-8 pattern. Draw the top of each circle first and then the under-curve, cutting the air with the side of the little finger. Notice that the arm is less free to move, and more body movement is required in order to make the movement large. Exaggerate this body movement and give the entire pattern a true swinging quality.

5. Do this reverse figure-8 pattern, progressing down the floor, using three little steps for each circle. Start with opposite arm and foot. The pattern does not carry one straight forward, but into alternate diagonals.

6. Now return to the original horizontal figure-8 pattern, progressing forward with a running-waltz base.

7. Change the step pattern so that it is now:

The free leg, on the step–hop is not brought forward, but is extended in back. Change the direction of the figure-8 slightly also, so that the first circle is made in front of the body and the second circle is made diagonally backward and upward. Start with the opposite hand and foot. Twist the upper body and reach back as completely as possible when the arm circles in back. Try to get as much elevation as possible, and enjoy the movement!

Lesson III: *Leg-Swing Variations*

Students who are not very well coordinated may find that leg-swings are difficult for them because of the problem of balance involved. If so, it may be advisable to postpone this lesson until a later time when they have had more dance experience and are capable of controlling and enjoying the movements. Well-coordinated students, however, even if beginners in dance, can profit from the movement experience and find it both challenging and enjoyable.

OBJECTIVES:

1. To develop kinesthetic sensitivity and awareness of feelings evoked by swinging movement.
2. To provide a variety of experiences with swinging movement, especially leg-swings.
3. To develop technical proficiency in the performance of these swings.
4. To provide an enjoyable movement experience.

PROCEDURE:

1. Preparatory techniques, including Nos. 22 (first version), 10, 4, 28 (first and second position), and 35.
2. Review the leg-swing sequence that progresses down the floor (Lesson II, 2).

```
          step   lift        brush
          (fd)   (bk)        (fd)
       6 |___    ___    ___  ___  ___|
       8
```

3. Now add a slight lift off the floor, actually a hop, at the end of the forward brush or swing of the free leg.

```
          step   lift        brush
          (fd)   (bk)        (fd)        hop
       6 |___    ___    ___  ___  ___    ___|
       8
```

4. Finally, when the previous pattern has been mastered, add another hop at the end of the backward leg lift.

```
          step   lift             brush
          (fd)   (bk)   hop       (fd)         hop
       6 |___    ___    ___  ___  ___    ___|
       8
```

Make the leg-swings large, but keep the body under control. Arms may be held quietly or may be swung oppositionally. Point the toes and add a smile!

5. Review, or teach for the first time, the hip rotation at the barre of Unit One, Lesson VII, 2.

6. Away from the barre, for practice: Swing the free leg directly forward and, with a hop (*a*), rotate the leg at the hip joint, turning the body away from it to face the opposite direction; be sure the hip-turn is made in mid-air. Keep the free leg fully extended and land in a lunge position, the supporting foot turned out. The lunge may be quite small at first (*b*), but gradually extend it so that the body is elongated quite close to the floor and the hips are as low as possible (*c*); stretch the free leg back as far as possible, but keep the head and chest up. The hands may reach forward or the fingertips touch the floor.

a   *b*   *c*

7. Precede the hip-turn lunge with six runs forward, in the form of two running-waltzes:

							(hop)	
run	run	run	run	run	run	step	swing turn	lunge

6/8

8. Now precede the entire pattern with two leg-swings with hops, as described in 4 above.

	(back)		(forward)			(back)		(forward)	
step	lift	hop	brush		hop	step	lift	hop	brush	hop

6/8

							(hop)	
run	run	run	run	run	run	step	swing turn	lunge

6/8

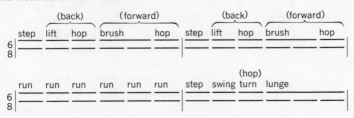

Do the pattern with vigor, but also with control.

Lesson IV: *Review of Several Swinging Movement Patterns which are then Combined into a Movement Sequence.*

If the material included here from Unit One is not already a part of the students' experience, these activities can be introduced to the students at this time.

OBJECTIVES:

1. To review familiar movement material that is also based on swinging movement in order to enlarge the students' conscious vocabulary.
2. To develop kinesthetic sensitivity and awareness of the feeling-states evoked by swinging movement.
3. To further the students' technical proficiency in the performance of these techniques.
4. To develop an awareness of one's relationship to a group in the performance of the movement sequence.
5. To provide an enjoyable dance experience through the performance of familiar movement sequences as a group activity.

PROCEDURE:

1. Preparatory techniques, including Nos. 22 (second version), 13, 4(e) or 25, and 35.
2. Unless Lesson III was omitted, review the leg-swing pattern, progressing down the floor, starting with the simple leg-swing, without hops, then adding the hops. (Lesson III, Procedures 2, 3, and 4).
3. Review the slide-and-lift variation of the 6/8 polka (Unit One, Lesson VI, Procedures 9, 10b).
4. Review the figure-8 arm-swing with the run–run–run–step–hop base (Lesson II, Procedure 7). Change the arm pattern slightly. The arm still circles in front of the body, but instead of making a second circle, diagonally backward, to complete the figure-8, the arm reaches diagonally forward and upward during the step–hop. Be sure to begin the pattern with the opposite arm and foot, and remember to leave the free leg behind on the step–hop.
5. Review the hip-turn and lunge (Lesson III, Procedure 6).
6. Review the swing combination (Lesson III, Procedure 8). Then substitute a run–run–run–step–hop pattern, using the arm-swing pattern described in Procedure 4, for the leg-swing in the first measure, so that the pattern is performed as follows. Starting with the right arm and left foot, do one run–run–run–step–hop pattern; continue with one leg-swing pattern, backward and forward, stepping on the left foot, lifting the right leg backward, and then brushing it forward; add two running-waltzes forward; and finish with a hip-turn and lunge. Practice the pattern on both sides. Practice the pattern, moving down the floor, one line at a time.

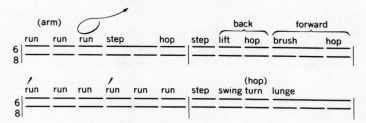

If Lesson III was omitted from the previous lessons, substitute two skips forward, or turning, for the leg-swing pattern in the second measure, and substitute a slide-and-lift for the hip-turn and lunge in the last measure.

7. Vary the pattern by taking the first running-waltz in a forward direction and the second running-waltz facing backward, but continue to move into the line of direction. Also try substituting a slide-and-lift for the hip-turn and lunge, if you have not done so already.

8. Choose the variation preferred by the majority of the class and perform the pattern, using the following class organization. Divide the class into four equal groups, placed at the four corners of the room. Have two, three, or four people at a time, depending on the size of the class, perform the pattern, moving toward each other from two of the diagonally opposite corners of the room, passing through each other on the running-waltzes. After two measures, the groups from the other two corners begin the pattern, and pass through each other also. Continue, each time with new groups moving diagonally across the room until all have had a turn. Make the movements large and free, and recognize the opposite group through which you are passing, by directing your focus and arm movements toward them.

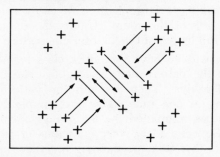

Lesson V: *The Development of Another Movement Sequence Combining Swing-Activities*

OBJECTIVES: The same as those of Lesson IV.

PROCEDURE:

1. Preparatory techniques, including Nos. 22 (second version), 4 (*e*) or 25, 28 (first and second positions), and 35.

2. Review the leg-swings, progressing down the floor, with hops added (Lesson III, Procedure 4), unless Lesson III was omitted from the previous lessons.

3. Review the double figure-8 swing with arms, using a running-waltz base (Lesson I, Procedure 10). Make the tempo quite fast.

4. Review the slide and skip combination, turning around on the skips (Unit One, Lesson I, Procedure 4).

5. Combine these swinging movements in the following fashion: start, by stepping on the right foot, and do two complete leg-swings forward (with hops); continue, with two slides, directly sideward, and two skips, turning once around in place to the right; do a double figure-8 arm-swing pattern with the left arm, accompanied by four running-waltzes forward, commencing with the right foot; and continue forward with four more running-waltzes, without arm swings, but with the arms or body subtly responding to the accent of the waltz. Practice this pattern on both sides.

   If Lesson III was omitted, four skips forward, or two slide-and-lifts, or one slide-and-lift and two skips can be substituted for the two leg-swings.

6. Now, in couples, starting side-by-side from the center of one end of the room, do the same pattern in opposition to each other. Start the leg-swings forward by stepping on the outside foot, and progress forward as much as possible during their performance. Do the slides directly sideward, away from your partner, focusing on him at the same time. Turn around once, in place, away from your partner, on the skips. Commencing with the outside foot and inside arm, take the first four running-waltzes (with the arm pattern), moving diagonally forward toward the center, so that partners meet. Complete the pattern with the last four running-waltzes by making a large half-circle away from your partner toward your side of the room. Unless the dance space is very large, use the full length of the floor for one pattern.

   It is probably wise to have the entire class together, in partners, walk through the pattern first, to establish the floor pattern and partner relationships. Then perform the pattern with only one couple starting at one time. The next couple begins when the couple ahead has completed the leg swings and is beginning the slides. Partners need to be very conscious of each other, establishing the fact that they are dancing together through focus and proper space relationships; and partners need, also, to be aware of the fact that they are a part of the larger whole—when four couples are dancing, one couple is moving forward, one to the side, one diagonally in, and one curving out. Make the movements large and free and, above all, endeavor to enjoy the sensation of movement.

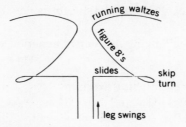

Lesson VI: *Culmination of the Previous Swing Sequence*

OBJECTIVES:

1. To review and polish the dance sequence learned in the previous lesson so that it can now be enjoyed as a dance.
2. To experience a simple variation of the previous sequence.
3. To develop kinesthetic sensitivity and awareness of feelings evoked by swinging movement.

PROCEDURE:

1. Preparatory techniques, including those suggested for Lesson V.
2. Review the dance sequence given in Lesson V, Procedure 5.
3. Now change the pattern slightly. On the double figure-8 arm-swing, when the arm circles overhead "drawing a halo," turn the body completely around with it; when the left arm circles overhead, the body turns to the right. Keep the running-waltz step going, even while turning around. Add this variation to the pattern as it is performed in couples. Continue doing the movement sequence, one couple after the other, until the pattern becomes easy and fun to perform.

As was true of Unit One, Unit Two can also be shortened in a number of ways to adapt it to specific requirements. In certain situations, Lesson III could be omitted; or the Unit could end with Lesson IV; or Lesson IV could be omitted; or the Unit could end with Lessons V and VI. In this way, the Unit could consist of three, four, five, or six lessons. An additional lesson may be needed in which to evaluate student progress. Any of the movement combinations described in the Unit could be used as a basis for testing technical skills.

Unit Three: Accent and Rhythmic Pattern

Lesson I: *Accent in Movement*

OBJECTIVES:

1. To enlarge the students' understanding of and experience with ways of creating accent by means of movement.

2. To develop accuracy in the performance of a given rhythmic problem.
3. To provide a challenging movement experience.

PROCEDURE:

1. A few general conditioning exercises.
2. Discuss with the class and list various ways in which accent can be established by means of movement. Among these ways are stamping, clapping, changing direction, changing level, changing locomotor activity—hopping, jumping, etc.—or performing a strong movement with some body part such as the head, the hips, or the arms.
3. Do the following pattern in the following ways:

a. Clap it, intensifying the sound of the claps on the accented beats.
b. Walk the pattern, changing direction on the accents.
c. Walk the pattern, changing level on the accents.
d. Walk the pattern and replace the walk with a hop, leap, or jump on the accents.
e. Walk the pattern and create the accents by performing a movement with some other part of the body.
f. Take the remaining part of the period and work out a movement sequence to this same pattern using at least three of the above ways of creating accent; guard against accenting any unaccented beats. Do these patterns with one quarter of the class performing at a time.

Lesson II: Counter-Accents in Movement

OBJECTIVES:

1. To develop the creative powers of the students in evolving movement appropriate to given patterns in accent.
2. To demonstrate the choreographic possibilities of presenting different accent patterns simultaneously as counter-rhythms.
3. To develop awareness of one's rhythmic and spatial relationship to other performers.

4. To develop students' discriminative powers in choosing two or more movement patterns that have pleasing relationships to each other.

5. To provide an enjoyable dance experience.

PROCEDURE:

1. A few general conditioning exercises.

2. Divide the class into groups of three, four, or possibly five people. Instruct one-third of the groups, i.e., three of the groups if there are nine groups altogether, to create a movement pattern to four measures of 4/4 meter, accenting the second beat of each measure; another third of the groups to do the same thing but accenting the third beat of each measure, and the last third of the groups to proceed similarly but accenting the fourth beat. The movement is to be performed in unison by the several people within a group, with everyone facing the same direction. While the patterns need not be completely stationary they should be confined to a relatively small floor area without progressing very far in any direction. The accents should be definite and the movement made as interesting as possible. Try to complete the assignment very quickly.

3. When the patterns are finished, have all groups practice performing them to 4/4 accompaniment that emphasizes the metrical accent (the first beat of the measure).

4. Choose one group that is accenting beat 2, one group that is accenting beat 4, and one group that is accenting beat 3, and so arrange them that they can perform at the same time.

Where it is possible to make the movements relate to other groups, try to do so through slight adjustments in direction and focus. Now replace one or two of the groups with other groups that are accenting the same beats. Shift the groups around spatially so that they relate to each other differently, if better space relationships can be made. Continue to experiment until all groups have had a turn. Discuss, with the members of the class who are watching, the choreographic effects created by the performance of accents in counterpoint; and point out particularly interesting group relationships as they occur.

Lesson III: *The Development of Movement in Response to an Accent Pattern, Using Drum Beaters*

OBJECTIVES:

1. To develop kinesthetic sensitivity and movement response to rhythm.
2. To show how dance movement can result from a simple, familiar activity—drum beating.
3. To develop an awareness of the effect of accent on a movement pattern, giving it interest, form, and clarity.
4. To provide an enjoyable movement experience.

PROCEDURE:

1. Sit in a comfortable position with a drumstick (plain sticks can be substituted) in each hand. Demonstrate how a drumstick is held between the thumb and forefinger with the end of the handle touching the fleshy pad of the palm. The students then beat the floor in front of them, using alternate drumsticks.
2. Beating the floor very softly, accent the first beat in every four by applying greater force to the beat. Then repeat, accenting the first of every three beats; then the first of every two beats.
3. In 4/4 meter, accent the first beat in every four, hitting the floor far out from the body. Let the whole body, as well as the arm, reach out. Make the arm and drumstick move in an arc, by reaching up, over, out, and down to the floor in any direction. Execute the unaccented beats close to the body.
4. Now beat the following pattern, executing the accented and unaccented beats as in Procedure 3. Make the accents in as many different directions as possible. Repeat the whole pattern several times.

   |/— — — —|/— — —|/— —|/—|

5. Beat the following pattern, executing the accented and unaccented beats as in Procedure 3. Get as much twist and stretch into the body as possible.

   8/4|— /— — /— — — /— /—|

6. For the remainder of the lesson, use the following rhythmic pattern:

   8/4|/— — — /— — — /— — —|

   Beat the above pattern, executing the accented and unaccented beats as in Procedure 3. Use the whole body in making the accents, and work for maximum stretch. Repeat the activity many times, gradually setting the directions in which the accented beats are made. Always execute the unaccented beats in front of the body.

7. Repeat Procedure 6, only do not touch the floor with the beaters. Become very aware of the directions in which the accents are made.

8. Stand and mark out with the feet the pattern made by the drumsticks by stepping out with the feet on the accented beats, always returning to "home base" to move the feet in place on the unaccented beats. Make the accented steps as large as possible.

9. Execute the arm pattern and the foot pattern together. Then, eliminate any arm movement on the unaccented beats, returning the arms to the sides after each accent. Reach out with the drumsticks, making the accented movements as large as possible. Aim for rhythmic accuracy.

10. Repeat Procedure 9, only do not hold the drumsticks. Try to maintain the same feeling of reaching out on the accents. Gradually increase the tempo until the movement can be performed no faster.

11. Now repeat the pattern, changing the foot pattern in some way so that a progression is made forward; retain the accented beats backward, if there were any in the pattern.

12. Change the arm pattern on one of the accented beats by moving it under and up and over toward the body, rather than up, over, and down.

13. Add a turn on one group of unaccented beats. Still make the accented beats very clear.

14. Perform the patterns, moving one after the other, progressing down the floor. Try to execute the pattern with controlled abandon.

Lessons IV and V: *Accents in Counterpoint*

OBJECTIVES:

1. To further the development of rhythmic accuracy through responding to accent.

2. To develop kinesthetic sensitivity and movement response to rhythm.

3. To develop an awareness of the effect rhythmic organization has on a movement pattern in giving it clarity of form and heightened interest.

4. To develop awareness of a partner relationship.

5. To develop the ability to perform a rhythmic activity accurately against other rhythmic distractions.

6. To develop an understanding of the importance of effective choice of movement, quality, tempo, range, directional emphasis, and bodily tension in communicating moods or ideas.

PROCEDURE:

1. Clap and memorize the following rhythmic pattern:

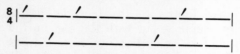

2. Translate the pattern into locomotor movement, walking, in any direction, on each beat and accenting the strong beats in any manner desired, with arms, body, or with locomotor or directional changes.

3. In pairs, relating to a partner, set a movement pattern to the rhythm. One person in each couple begins with measure 1 and progresses to measure 2, while his partner begins with measure 2 and then performs measure 1. The two people do not do the same movement pattern but create movements that relate to each other. On the accents, be sure to use the whole body rather than confine the movement to step pattern alone, and continue to step on the unaccented beats. Execute the rhythm only once.

4. Present the pattern, two or three couples at a time, for the rest of the class.

5. Now use these same movement patterns to express the idea of an angry dispute between two individuals. Take a few minutes to rework the movement pattern. Try not to change the original movement structure, but modify, in quality, dynamics, range of movement, etc., the manner in which it is performed. Choose several of the most successful patterns to be presented to the rest of the class. Discuss with the entire class the effect the dramatic context had upon their original movement patterns; in that movement, in most cases, was intensified and sharpened; the range, in some instances, was increased; and much of the movement was either directed toward the adversary, or performed in opposition to him.

6. Now, use the original movement sequence to express the idea of persuasion. Again, choose several patterns to be presented, and discuss how the movement was modified by the change in dramatic concept. Students will probably notice that the movement is less strong and percussive than in the previous situation.

7. Change the dramatic element to terror, either of one's partner, or of some outside force of which both participants are afraid. Present several of the couple patterns and notice how the emphasis in the movement direction is changed from out-going to in-coming, and how the range of the movement is reduced al-

though the intensity remains strong. Focus, normally, is in the direction of the object of terror.

8. As a final variation, give the movement pattern the dramatic connotation of showing off—a friendly rivalry between partners for attention. Present the results, as in the previous situations. The dramatic idea may call for an increase of tempo. Movement, again, becomes out-going, and focus will probably be toward one's partner or an imaginary audience, depending upon whom it is that the performer is trying to impress.

9. Conclude the lesson with a discussion of the fact that while the basic movement structure remained constant, it was the change in quality, tempo, intensity, range, or directional emphasis of the movement that conveyed the dramatic meaning. Although not all of the movement patterns were always completely adaptable to the expression of all four of these dramatic concepts, almost any movement can be given more than one interpretation, depending upon how it is performed.

Lessons VI and VII: *Cumulative Rhythm*

OBJECTIVES:

1. To develop understanding and appreciation of the spatial and dynamic effects of cumulative rhythms upon movement.
2. To develop rhythmic accuracy in the creation and performance of movement that is related to a given rhythmic structure.
3. To provide creative experience and an opportunity for democratic cooperation in solving a compositional problem.
4. To give the students a sense of enjoyment and achievement in the presentation of their compositional studies.

PROCEDURE:

1. Discuss the fact that a cumulative rhythm is a rhythmic arrangement in which the number of beats in the successive measures is systematically augmented or decreased according to a definite pattern. Illustrate, for example, by using the following numbers to represent the number of beats in successive measures:
   a. 2–3–4–5–6–7–8–9
   b. 3–2–4–2–5–2–6–2–7
   c. 10–8–6–4–2
2. Working individually, move to the following pattern:

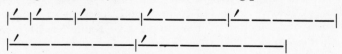

Walk on each beat, and change direction sharply from R to L, or L to R, at the beginning of each measure. Cover as much space as one can do comfortably on each step. Do this pattern several times and notice how the movement expands, spatially, as the measures are lengthened.

3. Now move to the following pattern:

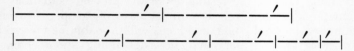

Accent the *last* beat of each measure with some strong body movement, of arms, legs, or torso. Be sure to accent only those beats that are indicated. It is not necessary to walk on all of the beats, though it is quite permissible to do so. Do this pattern several times and notice how dynamic excitement grows as the accents occur in increasingly closer proximity.

4. In couples, use the following rhythmic structure for another experiment with cumulative rhythm:

a. Partners clap alternate measures, in question and answer fashion, as if carrying on a conversation, clapping each underlying beat.

b. Now clap only the first beat of each measure, letting the hands rebound and continue to move away from each other during the rest of the measure. Notice how the size of the movement is reduced as the measures grow shorter. Let the whole body be brought into the movement. Experiment with expanding the movement of the arms (after the clap) in different directions.

c. Now try to find other ways of making the sound on the accent, in addition to clapping the hands together. Strike the floor or the body with both hands or only one, or strike the floor with the foot, and so forth. Continue to extend the movement as described in b above, so that the body responds to the percussive movement also.

d. Do the pattern once again; this time, not all of the accents have to be sounded, but they must be seen and felt. Try to find as interesting movements as possible, and set the pattern. Then perform these patterns, a few at a time, for the others in the class. Observe, especially, how both movement range and tension are affected by the progressive reduction of beats in each measure.

5. Divide the class into groups of from three to six people. Assign the following problem to half of the groups: Compose a movement pattern in which the emphasis is upon the expansion and

contraction of *space*. The rhythmic organization consists of the following number of quarter-notes in each measure:

1–3–5–7–9–7–5–3–1

Make the 9-count measure the climax of the movement study. Make the groupings of beats definite; for example, don't change direction in the middle of the longer measures, but use the flow of the lengthened phrase to extend the range of the movement.

To the other half of the groups assign the following problem: Compose a movement pattern in which the emphasis is upon increasing and decreasing the *dynamic excitement* of the movement. The rhythmic organization contains the following number of quarter-notes in each measure:

5–4–3–2–1–1–1–2–3–4–5

Make the three 1-count measures the climax of the study. Accent the last rather than the first beat in of the measures.

The time required for the completion of these studies will undoubtedly extend into a second period. The teacher will have to observe the progress of the groups carefully to be sure that they are not digressing from the movement assignments, and to re-direct them if they do.

6. When the studies are completed, present them, one group at a time, for class evaluation. Judge the compositions, not only for pleasing choice of movement, but especially as to whether the compositions have achieved the specified spatial and dynamic effects.

Lesson VIII: *Rhythmic Patterns Evolved from the Rhythm of Names*

OBJECTIVES:

1. To help students to become conscious of the rhythm of speech and to respond motorly to these rhythmic patterns.

2. To develop accuracy of rhythmic response.

3. To provide an opportunity for creative experimentation in finding movements that can be performed in accordance with specified rhythmic patterns.

4. To provide an opportunity for students to work together democratically in solving group problems.

5. To give the students a sense of enjoyment and achievement in the presentation of their compositional studies.

PROCEDURE:

1. Discuss the meaning of the term "rhythmic pattern," which refers to the orderly arrangement of beats and combinations and divisions of beats relative to the underlying pulse or beat. Most rhythms have identifiable rhythmic patterns; and rhythm can be found in nearly everything. There is rhythm in names.

2. Have the class clap the rhythmic patterns of the names of two or three of the class members. Diagram these rhythms on the black-board. Try to choose names that are rhythmically interesting. For example:

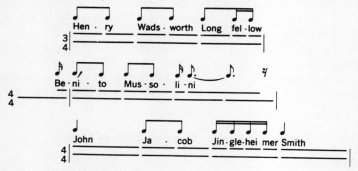

Rhythms will vary, of course, according to the way the name is said. Every syllable, if pronounced, should be accounted for in the rhythmic pattern.

3. Now divide the class into groups of moderate sizes (3, 4, 5, or 6 people). Assign to each group an interesting name pattern to be used as the rhythmic base for their movement problem. Examples of name patterns that might be used are the following:

Each group is to present a movement study in which the rhythmic pattern of the assigned name pattern is performed four times, using a different movement pattern each time. Be sure that each syllable of the name pattern is represented by a movement. Make the relationship of the performers to each other as interesting as possible. The movement does not have to be in unison. At times, parts of the rhythmic pattern could be performed by some of the participants, and other parts performed by others in the group.

4. Present these studies, one group at a time, for the other members of the class. Evaluate the results as to rhythmic accuracy and pleasing compositional form.

Lesson IX: *Syncopation*

OBJECTIVES:

1. To discover, kinesthetically, the effect that syncopation has upon bodily tension.

2. To increase rhythmic perception.

3. To develop rhythmic accuracy in responding to syncopated rhythmic patterns.

4. To give the students opportunity to discover various ways in which syncopated patterns can be interpreted in movement.

5. To provide an enjoyable movement experience.

PROCEDURE:

1. Beat a steady 4/4 rhythm on the drum and ask the students to clap the middle, or "-&," of each beat. Ask the students what kind of rhythmic effect is being created by this means. Some of them may recognize the results as "syncopation." Discuss syncopation; explain that it is created by the placement of accent on a normally unaccented beat, or on a portion of a beat. Normally, a metrical accent occurs on the first beat of a measure, and sometimes a secondary metrical accent occurs on a middle beat, or in other regular places. A metrical accent is designed to group the beats. There is also a *slight* accent on the first of every beat. When accents occur elsewhere in opposition to these normal metrical accents, the result is syncopation.

2. Walk, stepping high on the ball of the foot on the first half of the beat; and forcing the heel down, with a sudden movement, on the second half of the beat. Exaggerate this syncopation by adding some movement with the arms, body, or head on the last half of the beat.

3. Divide the class into two groups facing each other. Group one walks forward to 4/4 rhythm, accenting the first and third beats with a step forward and some sharp arm or body movement on each of them. Do not step on the unaccented beats. Use two measures or four steps in all.

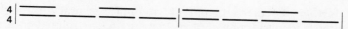

4. At the same time, group two walks backward to the 4/4 rhythm, stepping backward, with some sharp arm or body movement on counts two and four.

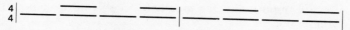

5. At the end of four measures the two groups reverse directions and exchange accents. Give the movement pattern the dramatic connotation of attack and retreat.

6. Students clap the following rhythmic pattern, counting the rhythm aloud while the teacher beats the underlying beat:

Discuss the fact that if the silent or unaccented beats are whispered or beaten outward in the air, with no sound, rhythmic accuracy is more likely to be assured than if these beats are not accounted for.

7. Clap the rhythm with the eyes closed.

8. Stand, and lightly stamp the pattern in place.

9. Walk in the rhythm of the pattern, moving forward.

10. Use some changes of direction; i.e., backward, sideward, etc.

11. Occasionally change the type of weight transfer; instead of walking, on some of the intervals use a hop or a leap or a jump.

12. Substitute body movement for that of the feet for parts of the pattern; i.e., clapping, or doing a movement with the head, hips, shoulders, elbow, etc.

13. Change level in some portion of the movement pattern. All changes must relate to the designated rhythmic pattern.

14. So far, this has been a problem of improvisation as the rhythm is beaten by the teacher on the drum. Now, allow the students a few minutes to set their patterns. Try to give the pattern some particular quality or mood.

15. Without crowding, arrange the members of the class in an informal circle or semi-circle, numbering them off consecutively. As the class claps the rhythm softly, each member of the class, in consecutive order, performs his movement pattern; it may be desirable for the teacher to beat the underlying beat on the drum. One performance should continue immediately after another so there is no break in the rhythm.

Lesson X and XI: *Rhythmic Pattern Performed as a Round*

OBJECTIVES:

1. To further the development of rhythmic accuracy through the creation and performance of movement that is related to a given rhythmic structure.

2. To develop the ability to perform a rhythmic activity accurately against other rhythmic distractions.

3. To provide opportunity for creativity in solving a compositional problem.

4. To develop awareness of the relationship of one moment sequence to another, in terms of rhythmic and spatial contrast; and the ability to design movements that both harmonize and contrast pleasingly with each other.

5. To develop sensitivity to the spatial relationships of one group of dancers to another, and aesthetic judgment in establishing relationships that are satisfying.

PROCEDURE:

1. A few general conditioning exercises.

2. Diagram the following rhythmic pattern on the blackboard for the students to clap and learn.

$$\begin{array}{c}\text{1}\quad\text{2}\quad\text{3}\quad\text{4}\quad\mid\quad\text{1}\quad\text{(2)}\ \&\ \text{3}\quad\text{(4)}\ \&\\ \frac{4}{4}\end{array}$$

$$\text{1}\ \&\ \text{2}\ \&\ \text{3}\ \&\ \text{4}\ \&\quad\mid\quad\text{1}\ \&\ \text{(2)}\quad\text{(3)}\ \&\ \text{4}$$

3. Divide the class into four sections and clap the pattern as a round, the groups commencing one measure apart.

4. Discuss the fact that a round is made interesting by the rhythmic contrast that occurs between the measures; i.e., slow rhythms in contrast to fast rhythms, or broken intervals occurring against unbroken ones. In movement, that contrast can be established spatially, as well as rhythmically. Since all four measures will eventually occur simultaneously, each measure should contrast in some definite way with the other three measures so that all four parts are readily distinguishable. High movement can be contrasted with low, a stationary base against a moving base, curving or turning movement against straight, and so forth. Further contrast can be established by differences in movement quality, such as percussive movement against sustained; or claps could be used against movement that is silent. At the same time, in working out movement for the rhythmic pattern, a feeling of continuity must be established between the measures and a unity of style and general quality should govern the whole.

5. Divide the class into small groups to work out a movement pattern designed to be performed as a round. Remember that the complexity of a round is established by the interplay of "voices," so the movement pattern, itself, can be kept very simple. It is usually wise to see that the floor pattern covers space in several directions to permit increased spatial interplay between the voice parts when the pattern is performed as a round.

6. At the end of the first class period, if possible, or the beginning of the following one, let each group show its movement pattern to the rest of the class. Choose the patterns that are most pleasing as movement forms and are most likely to become interesting rounds. Assign eight or nine class members to work with each chosen pattern; include the original creators of that pattern.

7. The problem for each group is, first, to learn the pattern perfectly, and then to perform it as a four-voice round, with each voice doing the pattern three times. Much experimentation will need

to be done with the spatial arrangement of the four groups in relation to each other. For example, each group might start successively from the same spot on the floor (or off-stage) and progress over the floor along the same path. Or, the groups might start from different positions on the floor. It might be desirable to have all the groups start by facing in a given direction; or spatial interest might be increased by arranging the groups so that they face in different directions. The groups should try to keep the floor pattern consistent with the original plan, regardless of the direction that the group is facing. Try out several plans and choose the one that seems best suited to the particular movement pattern of the group. Spatial relationships may have to be adjusted slightly. Try to avoid having the movement of one group cover that of another, and try, whenever possible, to relate the movement of one group to that of another by means of focus.

  8. Present these rounds for class evaluation.

This unit, like the others, can be sub-divided into two or several short units if such an arrangement seems desirable. A unit on accent alone could be made of Lessons I through V, or the unit could be still further shortened by omitting some of the lessons. A unit on rhythmic pattern could be made of Lessons VIII through XI.

Unit Four: Direction, Focus, and Change of Level

Lesson I: Direction and Focus in a Straight Path

OBJECTIVES:

  1. To develop an awareness of the concept of space as a dynamic substance through which the dancer moves.
  2. To develop awareness of the directional relationship of the mover to the surrounding space through which he moves.
  3. To introduce movement in all possible straight-line directions.
  4. To increase awareness of the importance of focus in establishing direction and in giving meaning to movement, generally. To increase the students' control of focus.
  5. To teach correct foot placement for the performance of clear-cut directional patterns, including forward, backward, sideward, and diagonal directions.
  6. To increase kinesthetic sensitivity and awareness of the feelings aroused by moving in straight line patterns and by the use of specific dynamics, qualities, or styles of movement.
  7. To provide an enjoyable movement experience.

PROCEDURE:

  1. Vigorous general preparatory techniques, including No. 28 (pliés in all six positions, without the arm patterns, except in first and

second positions). Be sure to explain the relationship of the foot positions to directions in space.

2. Begin by demonstrating three different uses of focus while walking forward: (a) focusing downward; (b) focusing sideward; (c) focusing straight ahead. Ask the students to state their impressions of these three different walks as to movement meaning. Normally, the impressions received are the following: (a) someone absorbed in thought or, if the head is bent forward, sad; (b) someone interested in an outside object; (c) someone moving forward, with purpose and determination. Obviously, the use of a forward focus did the most to establish the forward direction of the movement. In this lesson, focus will therefore be used in the direction of the movement in order to reinforce the movement.

3. Practice walking forward by stepping forward, toes first, on a single line, pressing the heel forward across the line so that the feet are slightly turned out. This gives the walk a slightly broader base than if the toes were straight ahead, and, together with the turn-out in the hip joint, gives the dancer greater balance and security. Do the same, moving backward.

4. Now take four steps forward, focusing directly forward, and four steps back, unfocusing the eyes and dropping the eyelids slightly but not the head. Alternate these two directions, concentrating on making the change in focus very definite.

5. Now try moving sideward without turning the hips. It will be discovered that there are two possibilities. The movement can be made either by taking a step and a close alternately or by stepping and crossing alternately in front and in back. Using the latter method, move sideward five steps: step side, cross in front, step side, cross in back, step side. Place the feet very precisely. When crossing over, be sure to lead across with the heel of the foot, so the hips remain forward; in contrast, the students could also do a grapevine step in which the hips are permitted to turn to their maximum range. Focus sideward, directly over the shoulder, establishing that focus on the "-&" preceding the first step. Alternate moving right, then left.

focus	step (side)	step (cross front)	step (side)	step (cross back)	step (side) focus

6. Now put all of these directions together, making a square (forward, sideward, backward and sideward). Take 4 steps in each direction and change focus just *before* stepping in each new direction. If the square is to be made to the right, start on the right foot. It will be noticed that on the second sideward series, the *first* step is a cross-over step. Be sure to establish the focus definitely in all directions on the proper count. When the square has been com-

pleted on one side, change feet quickly and make the same square on the other side without losing a count. This exercise is in the nature of a precision drill. The challenge of performing the focus change and foot pattern with clockwork precision can be fun.

7. Do the same floor pattern as above, only turn the whole body to face each of the directions and focus forward into the line of direction at all times. Be sure to start with the right foot when making the square to the right, and with the left foot when making a square to the left. Make the steps large.

8. Do the same as in Procedure 7, but run, kicking the feet up in back, toes pointed. Keep the tempo moderate and make the corners sharp.

9. Now discuss the problem of moving diagonally. Experiment to see how the feet must be placed in order to keep the hips from turning into the diagonal. The first step is taken in fourth position, directly out from the instep of the turned-out supporting foot. The second step crosses over, leading with the heel, and is placed so the imaginary diagonal line passes exactly across the instep. Alternate these two foot placements and then try this on the other side. Don't let either the hips or the shoulders turn. Make the steps very smooth and gliding with knees bent. Focus directly into the diagonal.

10. Now alternate five low, gliding steps into the right diagonal, facing front, with three sprightly, running steps into the left diagonal, and three into the right diagonal, facing the diagonals, kicking the toes up behind as in Procedure 8. The runs are a faster tempo than the walks. Repeat, starting the glides to the left. Contrast the two movement qualities.

11. Facing each of the diagonals, starting with the right foot, take five steps into the right diagonal, one step into the left diagonal, one into the right diagonal, and then repeat all, starting left.

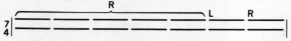

Take large steps and drive the movement forward with real urgency. Turn completely into each diagonal with the whole body. Have the movement pattern give the effect of someone trying frantically to make up his mind.

12. Facing the diagonal, take four light running steps into the right diagonal starting with the right foot, and a step–touch–step to check the momentum and change to the other foot. Repeat all, into the left diagonal, and continue in this fashion. Make the movement lively, but light.

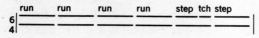

13. As a final challenge, do the following pattern, walking forward into each direction:

Beginning with the right foot, take five steps facing forward; pivot half left and take two steps facing the starting point; pivot a quarter left and take three steps facing the right side of the room; pivot half right and take four steps facing the left side of the room. Pivot a quarter right, and repeat the entire pattern an indefinite number of times. Start slowly, and gradually accelerate the tempo.

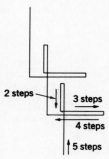

Lesson II: *Directional Variations of a Given Movement Pattern*

OBJECTIVES:

1. To develop awareness of the directional relationship of the mover to the surrounding space through which he moves.
2. To provide an intellectual challenge by introducing simple problems involving direction and focus, and to develop skill in the performance of them.
3. To develop awareness of some of the possible variations in direction that can be applied to a given step pattern and floor pattern.
4. To increase sensitivity to moving with a partner and enjoyment in performing as a team.

PROCEDURE:

1. Vigorous general preparatory techniques, including No. 28 (all positions, with arms).
2. Place the following pattern on the blackboard:

| step | step | step | step | step | cl | step | step | step |

3. Clap the pattern. Do the pattern accordingly: move forward on the first four steps, move sideward on the step–close–step, and backward on the last two steps. Face the front of the room throughout the pattern. Work out the pattern individually. Then, with a partner, start shoulder-to-shoulder from one end of the

room and perform the pattern in opposition to your partner. Commence with the outside foot. Partners will move away from each other on the step–close–step the first time, and toward each other the next time. Focus forward when moving forward; sideward when moving sideward; and unfocus when moving backward. The next couple begins when the first couple has completed one pattern (8 counts).

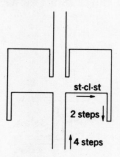

4. Let two couples start at the same time. The two inside people (one from each couple) will move toward each other on the step–close–step and become partners when the pattern is repeated. The next two couples begin 8 counts later. If partners always move forward shoulder-to-shoulder, an interesting floor pattern is created.

5. Now, using the same step pattern and floor pattern, change the directional relationship of the body to the path. Face the direction of the *path* throughout the pattern instead of facing one end of the room. When turning to face the back of the room for the last two steps, the outside, rather than the inside foot is free. Flip the outside leg backward from the knee, as if kicking the train or ruffled flounce of a skirt, when making this turn. When turning to face forward again for the repetition of the pattern, turn toward the foot that is back. Focus in the direction of the movement. Couples commence 8 counts apart. Work out the pattern without accompaniment first. Then perform it in fours, as described—Procedure 4.

6. Let each couple create their own variation. The floor pattern, step pattern, and rhythmic pattern are *not* to be changed, but the dancers may change their body facings in relation to the path, such as by moving backward on the sideward path and so forth. Have the couples perform their patterns one after the other for the rest of the class.

Give the students plenty of time to think through and practice these patterns informally before expecting them to do them in relationship to

other people. The enjoyment comes when the students are able to perform the patterns with precision.

Lesson III: *A Simple Round Based on Directional Changes, Performed in Different Styles* *

OBJECTIVES:

1. To illustrate how a simple directional pattern can be made interesting by the interrelationship of people.
2. To provide experience with various styles of moving and develop kinesthetic sensitivity and awareness of the feelings evoked by those styles.
3. To develop ability to concentrate on one's own part without becoming distracted by what others are doing.
4. To provide an enjoyable dance experience.

PROCEDURE:

1. General conditioning exercises.
2. Organize into groups of four people. The four people stand side-by-side, facing front with sufficient free space in front of them to equal an oversized square for a square dance set. Some foursomes may have to sit out and take their turns later. They number off 1 to 4 starting from the left. Number one commences the action by moving forward four steps, backward four steps, and forward eight steps, turning around on the eighth step to face the others, and repeats the pattern from the other side of the square (*a*).

a

Number two starts the same pattern 8 counts after number one has begun; number three starts 8 counts after that; and number four starts 8 counts after number three. They continue to move in this fashion until the end of the 8th measure of 4/4 meter. At this point the two outside people (numbers one and four) are ready to approach the center of the square from one side of it, and the two inside people (numbers two and three) are ready to approach the center of the square from the opposite side (*b*).

* The following movement pattern was devised by Margaret H'Doubler, Professor Emeritus at the University of Wisconsin.

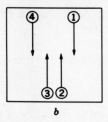

b

All move forward to the center to form a single line (4 cts., meas. 9). On the fourth step forward, the two center people turn around quickly so that all are facing in the original direction. All four join hands in a line, and the outside people also join hands, forming a circle that moves around to the left (8 cts., meas. 10–11). The circle opens into a line again, but with dancer number two in the lead, and backs up to the edge of the left side of the square, facing the center of it (*c*) (4 cts., meas. 12).

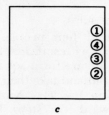

c

They continue three more times, each time finishing on the side of the square that is immediately to the left of where they stood before, until all are back "home." The second time, after circling, number three dancer is placed at the head of the line (on the extreme left) and the third time, number four dancer takes that position. Walk through the pattern slowly at first, making sure that all transitions are understood, particularly the formation of the line in the center before the circle is made. Be sure that the center two people turn around before joining hands with the others; otherwise the order of numbering of people is thrown off for the successive parts of the dance. Also be sure that each person takes his turn in the lead position.

3. Now that the pattern has been learned, it can be pointed out that the first part (meas. 1–8) of the dance pattern is a round, spatially, at least. The last part (meas. 9–12) is a unison transition.

4. Do the entire pattern, all four times, in a brisk, marching style, focusing on the people dancing on either side or across from you.

5. Now, do the pattern in a slow, stately manner that might characterize a court dance such as a pavane. Take the hands of the people who dance beside you, but in a courtly fashion. Try to be completely aware of all the changing couple relationships.

6. Finally, do the pattern vigorously, with skips, in the style of a rollicking folk dance, joining hands with the dancers who are moving forward or backward with you.

Lesson IV: *Direction and Focus, Moving in Curves*

OBJECTIVES

1. To acquaint the student with centripetal force and its effect upon the body.

2. To acquaint the student with the need for adjusting the body alignment when moving on a curved path.

3. To develop an awareness of the sensation of moving in a curved path.

4. To acquaint the student with variations that are possible when moving in curves.

5. To provide an enjoyable movement experience.

PROCEDURE:

1. General conditioning exercises, including vigorous ones.

2. In groups of 6 or 7 people, form a moderately small circle and move around it with long, low gliding steps taken very quickly. Try to keep the body in a vertical position over the feet. It will soon be noticed that centripetal force causes the body to lean toward the center of the circle.

3. Now that the effect of this force upon the body has been recognized, consciously incorporate it into the body movement pattern. Standing with the side of the body toward the center of the circle, shift the entire upper body in toward the center of the circle and shift the hips away from the center to compensate. (Don't bend sideward, shift the body parts sideward horizontally. Shoulders should be parallel to the floor.) Focus on the center of the circle and hold the arms quietly at the sides or slightly behind the body; move with long, low gliding steps, knees bent, around the circle. Keep the tempo fast and the accompaniment very smooth. On signal, change and go the other way, shifting the body parts to the opposite side. Change several times.

4. With everyone spaced so that he has room to move individually, make a six-step circle to the right and then a similar circle to the left (a figure-8 pattern) with long, low gliding steps. Make each circle as large as it is possible to do and still return to the starting point by the sixth step. Start each circle with the inside foot. In order to do so, a quick change of feet will have to be made between the two circles. Do not let this change step become bouncy or jerky; keep it smooth. Shift the upper body to the inside of the circle as much as possible, and the hips to the outside.

Focus on the center point. Arms are slightly behind the body. Practice the pattern until it becomes smooth and well timed.

5. Repeat the figure-8 pattern, but use the inside arm to indicate softly the direction of the center point of the circle around which you are moving.

6. Repeat the figure-8 pattern, but use the inside arm to indicate the direction of the path in front of the body. Remember that the path is a curved one and that the line of the arm should follow the curve. The outside arm is probably most comfortable if held slightly away from the body. Focus on the center of the circle. Change the movement pattern so that the circle to the right is made with five fast, low gliding steps; then rise on the toes and pivot once around to the right with two more steps. When on the toes, establish a feeling of suspension. Shift the focus and the body-lean to the other side, and perform the entire pattern to the left; during the turn the leading arm comes down to the side while the other arm is raised ready to repeat the activity in a counter-clockwise direction. Emphasize the contrast between the long, low gliding steps and the high pivot turn.

$$\begin{array}{c} \overbrace{\qquad\qquad glide \qquad\qquad}\quad \overbrace{pivot\ turn} \\ \text{step}\quad\text{step}\quad\text{step}\quad\text{step}\quad\text{step}\quad\text{step}\quad\text{step} \\ \frac{7}{8}\ | \quad\rule{0pt}{0pt} \quad\quad\quad\quad\quad | \end{array}$$

7. Try one additional variation in the use of the inside arm. Extend that arm forward and rotate it out; bend the elbow so that the fingertips are toward the ceiling. Hold the outside arm slightly away from the body. Focus over the shoulder at the center point of the circle as the body moves on the figure-8 path described in Procedure 4.

8. Try moving backward around the figure-8 path, using the arms as in Procedure 6 to indicate the path that one has already taken. Make the first step, with the inside foot, directly backward and very large; do not cut in toward the center of the circle. Lean sideward toward the center of the circle, not forward, and focus on the center of the circle. Keep all the steps low, gliding, and fairly fast. The backward circle will be slightly smaller in circumference than the forward circle.

9. Now, moving across the width of the room, make a series of large half-circles, using five very fast, gliding steps for each half-circle. Make the curves deep. Do not cross the mid-line until time to make the next curve. Use 5 fast counts to make each half-circle; and use 3 more counts to pause at the junction of the semi-circles, suspended on half-toes, shifting the body alignment and the focus to relate to the new focal point. Keep the body continually facing the direction of the curved path, with the side of the body toward the focal point; and keep the focus on the center point around which you are moving. Try to exaggerate the drop into

the next curve and make the first step directly away from the center line. Use the arms in any way that seems comfortable.

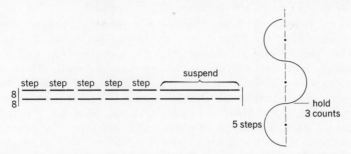

10. Take the same pattern as that given in Procedure 9, but eliminate the 3-count suspension, shifting the body alignment immediately, at the end of the fifth step, as the first step in the new curve is begun. Make the whole action across the room very smooth and continuous, exaggerating the depth of each curve and the body lean by making the steps very long and low. Use the arms in any way that is comfortable.

11. Alternate one curve moving forward with one moving backward, using five steps for each. The curves now are on the same side of the dividing line, and the floor pattern becomes a scallop. Exaggerate the depth of each scallop. Make the first step of each curve, especially the backward ones, directly away from the imaginary line. Be sure to focus on the center point of each curve.

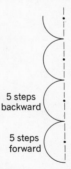

In practicing curves, it is extremely important to remember to keep the tempo of the gliding steps fast at all times, so that the effect of the centripetal force can be felt by the body.

Lesson V: *Direction and Focus, Moving in Curves* (Continued)

OBJECTIVES: The same as those for Lesson IV, with one additional objective—

1. To contrast the kinesthetic sensation of the body leaning in, with that of the body leaning out in relation to the curve.

Procedure:

1. General preparatory techniques.
2. Review Lesson IV, Procedures 4, 5, 6, 7, and 8.
3. Now, reverse the body alignment in relation to the center of the circle. Shift the hips in and the upper body out. Focus out on the horizon and reach out with the outside arm, extending the reach with the aid of the upper body as well. Make a circle clockwise, reaching out with the left arm, as if trying to touch the edge of the horizon all the way around. The focus moves around with the arm. Make the circular path taken by the feet quite small, using five steps to get around, keeping low in the legs in order to reach out farther. Use 3 counts to hold, facing forward, suspended high on the half toes, ready to drop to the other side with the other arm extended. The reach is taken to the opposite side, directly away from the center of the circle.
4. Moving across the width of the room, review Lesson IV, Procedure 9.
5. Now make five-step half-circles, with the body reach and the focus *outward,* moving around with you. Start with the side of the body toward the focal point and on the first count reach with the outside arm directly away from the focal point. Make the half-circles with five low, gliding steps and use two additional counts to pivot once around with two steps taken up on the toes. Make the pivot toward the center of the half-circle with the body held high and leaning slightly in. Then drop low and reach out as you begin the next half-circle.

pivot

pivot

6. Alternate a five-step half-circle with the focus and the upper body shifted out, with a three-step half-circle with the focus and body leaning in. Reach out with the arm and take low gliding steps on the five-step curve, and reach toward the focal point, stepping high on the half-toes on the three-step curve. Be sure to make a complete half-circle on those three steps. It will be noticed that the body does not have to shift its alignment now, and the same arm is used for both curves. Only the use of focus and of the direction of arm reach changes.

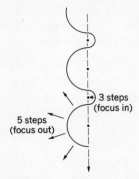

3 steps
(focus in)

5 steps
(focus out)

7. Review Lesson IV, Procedure 11.

8. Now change the pattern of Procedure 11 so that the backward curve is taken on the other side of the imaginary line. Move forward with five steps in a half-circle, focusing in; on the sixth count step across in front of the body with the free foot, rise onto the balls of the feet and pivot, toward the focal point, halfway around. The body is now facing the opposite direction, ready to step backward with the inside foot. Make a five-step curve moving backward, focusing in. The entire pattern requires eleven counts. Repeat the pattern, starting the next forward curve on the same side of the line on which backward curve was made. Contrast the high suspension on the pivot with the drop into the backward curve.

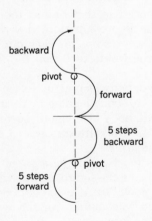

backward

pivot

forward

5 steps
backward

pivot

5 steps
forward

This pattern appears to be confusing at first and may need to be walked through slowly a few times before taking it up to tempo.

Lesson VI (alternate plan): *Culminating Lesson on Straight Lines and Curves*

If the instructor prefers to omit the lesson on hexagons and the following material on change of level, this lesson could be used effectively as a culminating experience for the study of straight lines and curves. Ideally, it should be followed by a lesson in which the students compose their own group patterns using straight lines, or curves, as described in Lesson IX (omitting the consideration of level change).

OBJECTIVES:

1. To review the kinesthetic feeling of moving in a straight line.
2. To review the kinesthetic feeling of moving in a curved path with the body leaning in, and with the body leaning out.
3. To contrast the manner of execution of moving in straight lines with that of moving in curves.
4. To provide opportunity for the students to be creative in their use of arms in connection with the performance of directional patterns and in their choice of body movement in the performance of curvilinear patterns.
5. To provide a challenge in the mastery of a given floor pattern that involves straight lines and curves.
6. To provide pleasure in the performance of the pattern as a group activity.

PROCEDURE:

1. Preparatory exercises, including several vigorous activities.
2. Progressing down the floor, take five steps forward and two steps backward. In body posture and use of focus, try to reflect the difference in the feeling of moving forward and backward. Add an arm pattern of your own to the movement.
3. With everyone spaced so that he has room to move individually, review quickly the figure-8 pattern described in Lesson IV, Procedure 4, but use seven steps for each circle so that one can begin each circle with the inside foot. Do the figure-8 in the following ways:
   a. Moving forward, body leaning in, focus in.
   b. Moving backward, body leaning in, focus in.
   c. Moving forward, body leaning out, focus out.
   For each of the above patterns, try to find an interesting and different use of the arms.
   d. Now combine any two of these three ways of moving, while continuing to make the figure-8. Use whatever number of steps you need. A pivot turn may be added as a transitional movement if desired. Be definite in the way in which you relate your body to the curved path. Again, experiment with the use of your arms until you find a pattern that pleases you.
4. In groups of 3 to 8 people, with everyone in the group moving around a single focal point, walk through the following pattern:
   a. Move around the circle for 6 steps with the focus and body-lean toward the center, pivoting on the 6th step to face the opposite direction.

b. Continue in the same line of direction, moving backward around the circle for 6 steps, still leaning in, and focusing toward the center.
c. Take 6 steps, moving in a straight line directly away from the center of the circle, focusing forward.
d. Take 6 steps backward, toward the center of the circle.
e. Moving around the circle again, take 6 steps with the body-lean and focus away from the center, pivoting on the 6th step to face the opposite direction.
f. Continue in the same line of direction, moving backward, still leaning and focusing out. Pivot on the 6th step in order to . . .
g. Move backward, with 6 steps, in a straight line directly away from the center of the circle.
h. Move forward with 6 steps, directly toward the center of the circle.

As a group, decide how the arms are to be used for each part of the above pattern. Practice the pattern until you can perform it smoothly, paying special attention to making the transitions a part of the dance movement. Perform the pattern with awareness of the contrast in kinesthetic feeling between moving in straight lines and in curves. Also, be aware of the expansion and contraction of space in the group pattern.

Lesson VI: *Hexagons*

OBJECTIVES:

1. To acquaint the students with the hexagon as a floor pattern and with its relationship both to curves and to straight lines.
2. To heighten kinesthetic sensitivity to the difference in the movement feeling when a hexagon is performed as a curve, and when it is performed as a straight line.
3. To develop rhythmic accuracy in the correct performance of a given rhythmic pattern "against" the rhythm of the musical accompaniment.
4. To provide an enjoyable movement experience.

PROCEDURE:

1. General preparatory techniques.
2. Review Lesson IV, Procedure 5, and Lesson V, Procedure 3.
3. Now, make a six-step circle, but keep the entire body facing the front of the room instead of turning it to face the path of the curve; it will be discovered that a hexagon design is made on the floor.
4. Now make this hexagon, by stepping sideward right, crossing backward into the right diagonal with the left foot, crossing backward into the left diagonal with the right foot, stepping sideward

left, crossing forward into the left diagonal with the right foot, and crossing forward into the right diagonal with the left foot. Lead with the toes on the sideward steps, and with the heel on the cross-over steps.

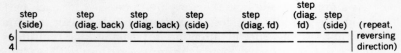

Take a quick step sideward, and reverse the direction of the hexagon. Pick the feet up high, and place them very definitely in their respective positions. Make each angle of the hexagon very clear by exaggerating the direction of each step. Do not allow the body to turn.

	step (side)	step (diag. back)	step (diag. back)	step (side)	step (diag. fd)	step (diag. fd)	step (side)	(repeat, reversing direction)
6/4								

5. Now do the same step pattern; still face the front of the room, but keep the head almost in the center of the hexagon and let the feet and hips move around beneath it. Give the pattern a feeling of curve, even though the body, itself, does not turn. Use the arms in such a way that they, too, emphasize the feeling of curve.

6. Make one hexagon, without reversing direction. On the sideward steps, keep the body facing front; but on each of the diagonals swing the free leg around to the back or front in a large arc, allowing the hips and body to turn with the leg movement. Make these steps deep, bending both knees. When taking the backward diagonals, bend the body slightly forward from the hips as though bowing graciously. Use the arms in any way that adds to the majesty of the movement. Do the pattern in a slow tempo and give the whole activity a courtly quality.

7. Do the pattern once more as in Procedure 4 (reversing direction), but change the rhythm. Hold the first step in the backward diagonal and the first step in the forward diagonal for two counts instead of one. Exaggerate these held steps, lifting the foot high, and placing it on the floor with a slight accent. Perform the pattern to a highly syncopated jazz accompaniment.

	step	step		step	step	step	st	st	(repeat, reversing direction)
8/4									

Change the holds to the first two steps.

	step		step		step	step	step	st	st	(repeat, reversing direction)
8/4										

Combine the two patterns. Use the arms in any fashion that seems appropriate to the jazz quality of the movement.

8. In lines, starting from one end of the room with several people abreast, make a series of half-hexagons to alternate sides, moving forward continuously. Keep the movement large and smooth. On the sideward step, reach directly sideward with both arms; then bring the arms horizontally around to the front and in to the body on the two diagonal steps. Let the large, sweeping curve of the arm pattern emphasize the curvilinear quality of the movement as a whole. The second people in line wait six counts before commencing the pattern.

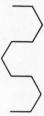

9. Do the same moving backward, but reach forward with both arms on the sideward step, and bring the arms horizontally around to the side and in to the body on the backward diagonal steps.

10. Combine one forward half-hexagon with one backward half-hexagon. Four steps will now be needed for each half-hexagon in order to make a smooth transition from forward to backward, and vice versa. Make the pivot turn forward into the line of direction. Combine the two arm patterns described above.

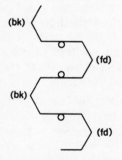

11. Repeat Procedure 10, but change the rhythm. Make the first step on an up-beat preceding count one (count "-a"); make the first cross-over step on count –1; make the second cross-over step on on count 2 and hold count 3; step side on count 4. Repeat the same rhythm on the backward half-hexagon.

&	1	2	(3)	4
side	cross	cross		side

Make the movement as jazzy in quality as possible. Use the arms in any way that will emphasize the jazz quality. Numerous other rhythmic variations can be made with any of these hexagon patterns.

Lesson VII: *Change of Level*

OBJECTIVES:

1. To introduce the students to some of the possibilities for level change in body movement.
2. To develop awareness of the effects of variations in tension and tempo upon movement.
3. To teach the student to initiate movement with various parts of his body and to observe the effect of this action on other body parts.
4. To give an opportunity for guided improvisation.
5. To provide an enjoyable movement experience.

In this lesson, it may be wise to condition students to explore movement effectively by urging them to concentrate each on his own movement and solve movement problems individually without watching to see what others are doing. Often there is more than one right way of performing a movement sequence, and watching others, who are performing differently, may make one feel confused and insecure.

PROCEDURE:

1. Preparatory exercises, including No. 17 and several vigorous body swings.
2. From a kneel-sit position, curl the body forward over the knees so that the body is in a position of complete flexion. Stay in this position and try to think of parts of the body that could lead in moving to a standing position of complete extension. Some possibilities are: the small of the back, the shoulders or shoulder, the head, the elbows, and the hands.
3. Experiment with using the small of the back to lead. From the flexed position, see how far it is possible to go toward a standing position of complete extension without allowing the small of the back to relinquish the lead to some other part of the body. It will be discovered that it is possible to get to one's feet, with the upper body relaxed forward from the waist; but from here on, other parts of the spine must unroll sequentially until the head, at last, is on top. Complete the extension by bringing the arms up sideward to overhead with a slight elbow lead, shoulders down. Stretch from the tips of the toes to the fingertips, keeping the shoulders down, and focus up. Now reverse the pattern. Bring the arms smoothly down again to the sides, elbows leading; and,

with a head lead down, return to the flexed position on the floor. The arms are relaxed. When getting onto the feet from the knees or down to the knees again, step through with one leg at a time. Try the entire pattern again, making it very smooth, observing the sequential organization of the movement. Start the movement by arching and lifting in the small of the back. Step through onto a turned out foot, which will help with balance. Keep the arms and shoulders relaxed when not in use.

4. Now, starting from the same position on the floor, make the head lead up to standing, using the face as the part of the head that leads. Turn the face up to the ceiling before any other part of the body moves. Continue to focus on the ceiling, rising upward until the body is completely extended on half-toe, the arms down at the sides. It may be discovered that the face can turn upward from a forward direction or from the side; either way has interesting and very different possibilities; try them both.

5. a. From the original position of flexion, use one shoulder to lead
to the feet. Lift the shoulder and look under the arm, which
is hanging relaxed, with the elbow very slightly bent and below
shoulder level. The asymmetrical pull will cause the body to
twist toward the side that is pulling. Continue lifting the
shoulder, and step through, coming up to the feet. When the
force of the shoulder pull finally lifts the arm above shoulder
height, the body should be twisted so that one is looking under
the arm toward the back of the room.

b. Lead down with the shoulder and elbow. Start the movement
by rotating the arm, twisting the elbow forward. Pull forward
and downward with the shoulder and elbow until the body is
once again on the floor. The final position will be a twisted one.

6. In a regular kneel-sit position, experiment with using the palms
of the hands, fingertips, wrists or elbows to lead up or down in
various ways. Go only from knee-sit to kneeling and down again,
while experimenting. Remember the hands or arms can be forward
or sideward in relation to the body. One arm or both may be
used, and if both are used, they do not have to move in the same
way; it is possible, for example, to combine a fingertip lead with
one arm and an elbow lead with the other. Notice that a wrist
lead is a weak lead which may be used delicately to produce a
lyrical effect, or with exaggeration to produce an effect of comedy.
Find an interesting way of using the arms, or parts thereof, to go
from complete flexion to complete extension; find another interesting arm lead to return to the floor again. Do the chosen pattern

several times until you are sure of the degree of energy, the timing, and the movement style needed to make the movement effective. Perform the pattern for the rest of the class, a half or a quarter of the class performing at one time. When you have finished, hold the last movement until everyone else in your group has finished, too.

7. Vary the amount of *energy* used for different parts of a movement sequence. Start from the original flexed position on the floor as in Procedure 2. Slowly, with as little energy as possible, extend the arms softly sideward, the arms not completely straight. Try to feel as though some outside force were supporting and lifting you by holding you under your upper arms. Rise to your feet with a feeling of weightlessness and let the arms "float" up to overhead. Use 16 counts for this. On the last 4 counts of the 16, gradually increase the tension in the whole body, especially the arms, making fists of the hands; and now with an elbow lead, pull the body quickly and forcefully, down to the floor onto one knee (1 count); avoid allowing the knee to bang against the floor.

8. Combine several body leads. Moving from a position of flexion on the floor to standing, use a shoulder lead upward for 4 counts, shift to a head lead for 4 counts, and again shift to a fingertip lead

by one arm, extending the arm completely overhead (4 counts).
Return to the floor (8 counts), using a face lead down, turning the
head down sideward, away from the arm that is extended overhead. Make all of the pattern very strong and the leads very
definite.

9. Complete the lesson by running very lightly around the room
changing direction on cue.

Lesson VIII: *Change of Level with Emphasis on Falls*

OBJECTIVES: Similar to those of Lesson VII.

PROCEDURE:

1. General conditioning exercises, including Nos. 16 and 17.
2. Standing, use the same pelvic tilt as in warm-up exercise No. 16
   to carry the body to the floor. With the feet slightly apart, rise
   on the toes and tilt the pelvis, bending the knees and pressing
   them forward. As the knees continue to bend and press forward,
   tilt the body back in counterbalance. Slide the knees gently into
   the floor without dropping the hips. Step through, and come back
   up to standing. Until the movement is mastered, it may be wise

to use another dancer for support so that there is no danger of banging the knees into the floor.

3. Take any position on the floor, lying down or sitting or partially lying down. From that position find an interesting way of rising from the floor to complete extension and returning to any position on the floor again. You may go directly to your feet or go part of the way up, change position, and go partially down before rising completely. Make use of an intermediate level, either on the way up or the way down. Don't be an "elevator," merely moving up and down between "floors"; somewhere along the way, "get off" on one of the floors and find something to do on that level. Be aware of the body leads and the sequence of movements that you are using. Try to make the pattern as interesting as possible. Choose your own tempo and intensity and perform the movement pattern with conviction. Let a half or a quarter of the class perform at once.

4. Controlled falls may be performed in many different ways: forward, sideward, backward, turning, or rolling onto the floor. In learning a *backward* fall the following procedure might be used: Start from a standing position; reach forward with both arms and lean forward with the weight on the left foot. Cross the right foot behind the left with the toes straight. Lower the body onto the side of the right leg; then sit, and roll the spine down to the floor, one segment at a time; let the arms fall naturally to the sides, the right leg bent beneath you and the left leg straight.

There are several possibilities for recovery. One is to fling the the left leg straight overhead, tuck the body forward as the leg swings down, and, using this forward impetus, shift the weight onto the left foot, coming up to standing or to a modified "arabesque" position, with the lifted leg bent in back. The hands may be used to help by pushing on the floor, if necessary.

Now begin the fall with a step–hop on the left foot, swinging the arms forward and upward; roll down to the floor sequentially, as described above, as quickly as possible. Finally, add a preliminary run to the step–hop and fall. Run forward three steps, beginning with the right foot; step–hop, on the left, and fall; swing the leg overhead; and come to standing. Practice the fall on both sides.

5. Begin a *sideward* fall from a kneeling position. Reach upward to the left side with both arms as far as possible, reaching with the body as well as the arms. Shift the hips to the right; and as the arms swing down and out to the right, the hips and the hands touch the floor simultaneously. Slide the hands on the floor to the right and extend the body completely, except for the right leg, which is still bent. Pull up to kneeling, with the side of the torso leading, circle the arms in front of the body and fall to the other side.

From a standing position, reach to the left side with arms and body, as before. Tuck the right leg behind, keeping it off the floor. Simultaneously, swing the arms down and through to the right, and lower the body toward the floor by bending the supporting left knee until the body is almost sitting on the floor. Catch the weight on the hands and the side of the right leg, and slide the arms and body completely out to the right. Keep the focus and the body-lean to the left, away from the direction of fall, as long as possible. Recover by rolling over onto the back, swinging the extended leg into the air, and coming up in the same manner as that used for the back fall, and step forward into a modified "arabesque," facing sideward. Now precede the fall by a step–hop on the left foot, swinging the arms and body vigorously to the left at the same time. Add three preliminary runs forward as in the back fall, starting with the right foot. Practice the fall on both sides.

run run run step	hop	fall	roll over	kick	rise

6/8

6. Divide the class in thirds and do the pattern as a round, with each group starting 6 counts after the one preceding it.

Lesson IX: *Composition Based on Focus, Direction and Level Change*

OBJECTIVES:

1. To give the students an opportunity to discover movement and movement combinations for themselves.

2. To give students an opportunity to develop interesting space relationships in the specific use of straight lines, curves, and change of level in group composition.

3. To help students to differentiate the feelings associated with moving in straight lines and in curves and to project those feelings ⸰ through their own movement.

4. To help students become conscious of and skillful in their use of focus to give clarity and meaning to movement.

5. To help students apply principles of good design to dance composition.

6. To develop democratic attitudes in the solving of a group problem.

PROCEDURE:

1. Divide the class into groups of from 3 to 7 people of their own choosing. Let each group choose one of the following compositional problems. Encourage groups to select different problems.

   a. Compose a dance study, involving the use of straight lines in both floor pattern and body movement. Concentrate especially on making interesting floor patterns and on the interrelationships of people as they move among each other. Bring some change of level into the composition also, contrasting one level with another, or contrasting stationary movement with locomotor movement. Limit the locomotor activity to walking or running. Remember that movement in straight lines is not necessarily performed in a jerky, percussive manner. Give the dance study a consistent feeling quality or mood, but don't use it to tell a story.

   b. Compose a dance study involving the use of curves in floor pattern and body movement. Bring in some level change, but for the most part keep the action on a moving base. Use a single circle, around which everyone moves, no more than once in your pattern. Move in different kinds of curves and try to establish compositional interest by the changing of the spatial relationships of people and the configurations of the floor plan. Limit the locomotor activity to a fast, gliding walk. Be aware of the difference between the feeling of moving in curves and in straight lines, and establish the "feeling" you associate with curves in your composition.

   Hexagons may be used in either of the above studies, provided they are performed in the appropriate manner.

   c. Compose a dance study in which contrast of level is your primary concern. Try to have each participant use at least three different levels, but do not have everyone use the same level at the same time. Remember that contrast of level usually enhances the compositional interest. Use some floor pattern too, so that the dancers do not become rooted to one spot, but change their relationships to each other. Remember that falls are very dramatic, and should be used sparingly as a convincing outgrowth of the rest of the movement. Do not become involved with a story, but try to establish a movement quality and mood.

The length of these compositions must be determined by the length of time that can be devoted to the assignment; one and a half class periods are recommended.

2. After the groups have chosen their compositional problems, the teacher can offer assistance by answering questions and by further explanation or illustration to clarify issues that are misunderstood. Principles of good compositional form can be brought to mind as the need arises.

Lesson X: *Evaluation of Compositions*

OBJECTIVES:

1. To develop stage presence and the ability to project feelings to others through movement.
2. To develop a sense of enjoyment in sharing creative experiences with others, both actively and vicariously.
3. To give the students a sense of achievement.
4. To develop a refined sense of evaluation.
5. To develop the ability to give constructive criticism.
6. To develop the ability to accept criticism graciously.

PROCEDURE:

1. Completion of compositional studies begun in Lesson IX.
2. Each group, in turn, presents its study to the remainder of the class for their enjoyment and evaluation. The following points might serve as criteria for evaluation:
    a. Were the floor pattern and group relationships interesting? What parts did you especially enjoy?
    b. Was good use made of focus?
    c. Were the uses of level pleasing and was there interesting contrast of level among the dancers or groups of dancers?
    d. Were the transitions between the various movements satisfactorily achieved?
    e. Did the curved line and straight line studies really establish a feeling appropriate to the linear design?

As was true of the previous units, this unit on space could be shortened or subdivided in several ways. The unit could be limited to experiences with (1) straight lines, (2) curves lines, (3) change of level. The performance of hexagons could be taught as a part of a unit on straight lines or a unit on curves. The important thing is for students to be exposed to a variety of experiences pertaining to a given movement concept. If time is limited, it is better to cover one area thoroughly than many areas superficially. There are other days and other years, and if students' interest is sufficiently piqued they will be eager to extend their dance experiences.

Unit Five: Jumps and Leaps

In this unit considerable repetition of activity is deemed necessary in order to establish correct habits of movement and to strengthen the muscles that control the action. Some students will need even more practice than has ben allowed in these five lessons in order to become proficient at jumping and leaping.

Lesson I: *Preparatory Techniques for Jumps and Leaps*

OBJECTIVES:

1. To develop intellectual and kinesthetic awareness of certain movement controls involved in jumping.
2. To develop correct movement habits for jumping, particularly in reference to the feet and legs.
3. To warm and strengthen muscles needed for jumps.
4. To provide exercise that is physically stimulating and enjoyable to perform.

PROCEDURE:

1. Begin with two or three familiar preparatory techniques involving the whole body.
2. Continue with the following preparatory techniques involving the use of the feet and legs, to be performed in consecutive order: Nos. 5, 6, 28 (in at least first, second, and sixth positions), 29, 31, 34, and 35.
3. Complete the lesson with the special techniques in preparation for jumps and simple jumping activities (first and second positions only) described in detail in Chapter 2. Take great care that all activities are performed correctly.

Lesson II: *Jump Variations*

OBJECTIVES: The same as those in Lesson I, with one addition.

1. To acquaint the students with jump variation possibilities.

PROCEDURE:

1. Review quickly, but carefully, all of the general and special preparatory techniques listed in Lesson I.
2. With a partner of approximately the same height, stand one in front of the other, both facing the front of the room. The person

in front is the "ball"; the person behind is the "bouncer." The ball commences jumping, with feet in first position. As he jumps, the bouncer presses down on his shoulders with both hands, releasing his hands immediately as the "ball" rebounds into the air. Try to sense the correct timing of pressure and release to help, not hinder, the efforts of the jumper. Notice how the increased pressure against the floor causes the jumper to bounce higher than he could do previously on his own. Change parts.

3. Without a partner, do jumps in first position, pushing against the floor and trying to achieve as much elevation as possible, while staying with the established beat of the music or drum.

4. Do four jumps in first position and four in second position, alternately (32 jumps in all).

5. At the ballet barre or stall bars, face the barre and rest both hands on it (about waist height). Do four jumps in first position, but between the third and fourth jumps, while in the air, extend both legs sideward as far as they will go in a wide stride position (a). The count will be 1–2–3–&–4; the wide stride extension in the air is taken on count "–&." Use the barre to help, but don't lean on it. Do the series four times. Be sure to plié and bring the heels down to the floor on all landings; and keep the body vertical at all times.

6. Do the same as in Procedure 5, only on the big jump (with the legs turned out at the hips) bend the knees in a "frog" position, the toes of the two feet nearly touching each other directly underneath the body (d).

7. Away from the barre, standing on one foot, attempt a jackknife position using one leg and both arms. Keep the back very straight so the forward bend comes entirely from the hips. With legs and arms straight, attempt to touch the hands and toes of the free foot, in front of the body, and quickly return to a vertical position.

8. Now do the series of four jumps (away from the barre) and on the big jump do a jackknife, using *both* legs (c). Practice several times.

9. Standing on one foot, fling the arms forward and upward to overhead, and arch the *upper* back, at the same time extending the free leg straight backward. Protect the lower back from hyperextending by tightening the abdominal muscles. Return the arms forward and down to the sides as quickly as possible after flinging them overhead.

10. Now do the same series of four jumps, arching the upper body, with both legs back on the high jump (b).

11. Divide the class in half.
    a. Group I does the four jumps, with the big jump in wide stride position. Group II does the same, while Group I waits in place.

b. Group I does the four jumps, arching the back on the big jump. Group II follows.

c. Group I does the four jumps with the big jump a jackknife. Group II follows.

d. Group I does the four jumps with the big jump in frog position. Group II follows.

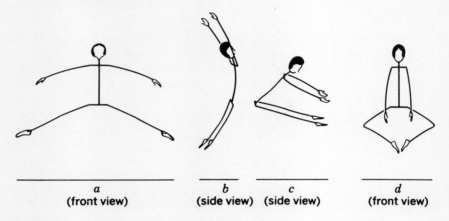

a	*b*	*c*	*d*
(front view)	(side view)	(side view)	(front view)

Lesson III: *Leaps*

OBJECTIVES:

1. To develop intellectual and kinesthetic awareness of the movement controls necessary in leaping.
2. To develop correct movement habits in leaping.
3. To warm thoroughly and strengthen the muscles involved in leaping.
4. To provide an exhilarating movement experience.

PROCEDURE:

1. Commence with the same general preparatory exercises as for Lesson I.
2. Continue with the special techniques in preparation for leaps described in Chapter 2.
3. Conclude the lesson with simple leaps for distance, also described in Chapter 2.

Lesson IV: *Leap Variations*

OBJECTIVES:

1. To develop intellectual and kinesthetic awareness of the movement controls involved in leaping.
2. To develop correct habits of movement in leaping.
3. To strengthen muscles involved in leaping.

4. To acquaint the students with leap variation possibilities.

5. To provide an enjoyable dance experience.

PROCEDURE:

1. Review all of Lesson III, re-stressing the technical controls in each activity.

2. Combine a walking step and a leap in an uneven rhythm. Practice, first, stepping on the right foot and reaching forward with the left foot; suspend the movement momentarily, and then drop lightly onto the left foot. Continue forward in this fashion, with the arms swinging in opposition.

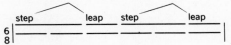

When the rhythm and coordination are established, substitute a leap for the suspension. Lead with the chest, driving the movement forward horizontally, so that the leaps are done for distance and not for height; keep both legs turned out at the hip joint. Then practice stepping with the left foot, leaping onto the right foot.

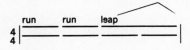

In this pattern, as indicated in the diagram, the leap is identified with the landing, and the aerial suspension has already taken place.

3. Do the above pattern but now try to attain height on the leaps instead of distance. Be careful to control the landings by keeping the body lifted and the leg muscles firm, but elastic.

4. Combine two runs and a leap, giving the leap twice the time value of the run, and using the time to get up into the air as high as possible. The runs should be used as a preparation for the leap. Repeat the pattern continuously down the floor.

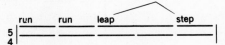

In this pattern, as indicated in its diagram, the leap is now identified with the push-off, and the aerial suspension follows it.

5. Now, change the rhythm to a five count, and add a step on the fifth count.

    a. Do the pattern, stressing distance on the leap, rather than height; continue the length of the floor; then, practice again, beginning with the other foot.

    b. Do the leap for height in the same manner.

    c. Now, while suspended in the air on the leap, bend the front leg, quickly, at the knee, so that the leap becomes what is known as a "Bambi," or "stag" leap. Direct the energies so that both height and distance are covered on the leap.

    d. This time, bring both legs forward, successively, on the leap, keeping them straight, and swinging them as high as possible; a movement pattern that is sometimes called a "hitch-kick."

    e. Do the same action, but kick the legs backward on the leaps.

    f. Alternate Procedures c and d.

Lesson V: *Leap Variations (Continuation of Lesson IV)*

OBJECTIVES: Similar to those of Lesson IV.

PROCEDURE:

1. Review the preparatory exercises given for Lesson I.
2. Review prances down the floor.
3. Review continuous leaps forward (for distance).
4. Review step–leaps, first for distance and then for height.
5. Combine runs with step–leaps in the following pattern:

    run   run   run   step   leap   step   leap

(slow) $\frac{9}{8}$

On repetition of the pattern, the leaps will occur on the other foot. Do the leaps first for distance; then for height; and then as stag leaps. Now do the first leap for distance and the second leap for height or as a stag leap.

6. In place on the floor, review the jump series from Lesson II.

Unit Six: Qualities of Movement

Lesson I: *Swinging and Sustained Movement Qualities*

OBJECTIVES:

1. To provide experience with a variety of swinging and sustained movements.
2. To develop both kinesthetic and intellectual awareness of the characteristics of swinging and sustained movement.
3. To enable students, in movement performance, to differentiate between the two qualities.

4. To provide experience in giving the different qualities to the same movement.

5. To give the students an enjoyable dance experience.

PROCEDURE:

1. Commence with preparatory techniques including swinging movement, such as Nos. 22, 25 and 35; and sustained, such as Nos. 15, 16, 17, or 33.

2. Explain that the quality of a movement is determined by the *way* in which the energy for its performance is released; i.e., suddenly or gradually; at the beginning of a movement, or in the middle, or at the end. The *amount* of energy is not the determining factor because a swing, for example, may be forceful, or weak, but it is still a swing.

3. Review quickly two or three of the swinging movement sequences that the students have experienced in previous lessons, such as one of the arm swing patterns given in Unit Two, Lessons I and II, and the leg swing variation of Unit Two, Lesson III, or a 6/8 polka variation, Unit One, Lessons VI and VII, or any other familiar swinging movement patterns.

4. Through discussion during the performance of these swings, review the principal characteristics of swinging movement—previously described in Unit Two, Lesson I. Try to elicit as much of this information as possible from the students themselves. Call to the attention of the class the fact that most free bodily actions such as throwing, catching, running, skipping, sliding, waltzing, and variations of the 6/8 polka are basically swinging movements.

5. Improvise upon swinging movement quality. Begin by gently swinging the torso, keeping the arms quiet; add an arm swing, one arm or both; add a leg swing, gradually increasing the force and range of the swinging movement until locomotion results; lift off the floor completely; gradually decrease the range and force of the movement and change level, without stopping the swinging movement, until one is sitting or lying on the floor, still swinging some part of the body; return to standing position and quickly bring the movement to a climax again; then reduce the movement until the body is completely quiet. While improvising in this manner, be experimental; try to find as many ways as possible of performing swinging movement with this complex instrument, the human body.

6. Review the slide-and-lift with two skips of Unit One, Lesson VI, Procedure 11.

7. Discuss the nature of "sustained" movement; explain that it is characterized by a continuous, even release of energy, that the movement can be forceful or weak but must be smooth.

8. Now repeat the bodily action of the slide-and-lift and skip pattern, but give the movement a sustained quality and change the under-lying rhythm from 6/8 to 8/8; do not come off the floor; remember to include the arm pattern as well. Be sure to remove all of the swinging quality from the movement. Perform the pattern with smoothness and control.

9. Divide the class into approximately six groups. Each group is to to choose a swinging movement sequence—such as one of the sequences given at the first of this lesson, or a movement pattern found in tennis, or in softball—that the group members have all experienced, and translate it into sustained movement. Make the derived pattern something more than a literal translation of the swinging activity into the sustained. Adjust the movement slightly as necessary to make the sustained movement pattern interesting in its own right.

10. Progressing quickly from one group to another, let each group present first the original swinging movement sequence, and then its sustained derivative.

Lesson II: *Sustained and Percussive Movement Qualities*

OBJECTIVES:

1. To provide experience with a variety of sustained and percussive movements.

2. To develop both kinesthetic and intellectual awareness of the characteristics of sustained and percussive movements.

3. To enable students in the performance of movement to differen-tiate between these two qualities, and between these qualities and the swinging quality.

4. To provide experience in improvising within a given quality or qualities.

5. To give the students an enjoyable dance experience.

PROCEDURE:

1. Begin with a few familiar conditioning activities, including No. 17. Perform this exercise first as described, using four slow counts for each of the four sustained movements. Now do the same move-ment pattern, but complete the lateral extension (*a*) in *one* count, holding the position for one more count. Perform parts *b* and *c* in a sustained quality, using four counts for each part, but perform *d* quickly, on one count, as in *a*, holding the position for an additional count. Make the quick movements very strong.

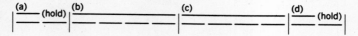

2. Discuss the nature of "percussive" movement; explain that it is characterized by a sudden, forceful release of energy. The movement is completed as quickly as possible and may consist of one full-range "explosive" action, or it may consist of one or more incomplete, or broken, movements, which are called "staccato." The fast movements performed in the previous exercise were examples of explosive movement.

3. Experiment with explosive movement. In any explosion there must be tension or pressure build-up from within the object, and this tension causes the explosion to take place. Stand with the feet close together, knees slightly bent, arms close to the sides, and the entire body contracted and tense, especially in the abdominal area. On a drum beat, move explosively forward, sideward, or diagonally into a deep lunge, thrusting the arms forcefully in any direction. The arms may move in a parallel fashion or in different directions. Freeze the movement in its final position. Then on the drum beat return with another percussive movement to the original position. Experiment with different directions, twists of the body, and levels on the explosion.

4. Repeat Procedure 3, only make the recovery to the original position a very sustained movement using eight counts. On the sustained movement gather in energy to be used for the next lunge.

5. Experiment with staccato movement. Take any position on the floor: sitting, lying down, kneeling. Now on the drum beat change position as quickly as possible with strong staccato movement, holding the new position with tension until the next drum beat. Gradually, by a series of position changes, rise to the feet and then return in the same manner to a new position on the floor. Use as many position changes as are necessary, but move only on the drum beats. Allow time for each position to be completely frozen before sounding the next accent. The drum beats should be sounded at regular intervals, but with a pause after each beat.

6. Review sustained movement quality by the following procedure. The instructor performs four large sustained movements, with his arms, legs, and body, using eight counts per movement. Bring in change of level and twisting of the body; but never face completely away from the students. Commence each of the four movements with a slight breath-like impulse to emphasize the beginning of the movement. At the same time, the members of the class mirror the movements of the teacher. After the teacher has directed the class in four sustained movements, the students continue to perform four more sustained movements, each improvising his own pattern, commencing wherever the teacher's fourth movement ended. After trying this problem a couple of times, the leadership role can be given to one of the members of the class,

or it can be passed from student to student, each one doing two movements of eight counts. Each new leader carries on where the last left off, and there is no pause between leaders.

7. Progressing down the floor with a smooth, gliding walk, perform with the arms the following pattern in sustained movement: on the first two walks bring the arms forward to shoulder height; on the next two steps, extend them horizontally sideward with elbows leading slightly; on the two following steps raise the arms directly overhead; and on the last two steps, which are taken moving backward, bring the arms forward and downward to the side; then repeat all. Keep the movement very smooth and continuous. Try to regulate the speed of the arm movements so that the arms never arrive in any position too soon and thus cause the movement to stop even momentarily. Initiate the arm movements from shoulder joint and shoulder blades, making the action strong and commanding. Try the same pattern using one arm only then the other arm.

arms move forward		arms move sideward		arms move upward		arms forward and down	
step	step	step	step	step	step	step	step
forward						backward	

8. Spaced informally on the floor, improvise individually the following pattern in sustained and percussive movement:

```
8 / perc (hold) / perc (hold) / perc   ── (hold) ──
4 |_____|

  sustained ──▶
  |_____ ____ ____ ____ ____ ____ ____ ____|

  / perc (hold) / perc / perc      ── (hold)──
  |_____|

  sustained ──▶
  |_____ ____ ____ ____ ____ ____ ____ / perc / perc |
```

Clap and say the pattern in rhythm several times before trying it in movement. The pattern may be done either on a stationary base or with steps or lunges on the percussive movement and/or gliding walks on the sustained movement. Level change might also be included where it feels appropriate. Exaggerate the contrast in the two movement qualities as much as possible.

Lesson III: *Pulsating Movement Quality in Duple Rhythm—"Vibration"*

The term "vibration" is perhaps more correctly applied to a very fast oscillation of body parts, but through common usage it has also come to be associated with the pulsating movement in *duple* rhythm that is the subject of this lesson. The term "duple rhythm" is used here to mean a rhythm that consists of two equal intervals of time. Pulsating movement can also be related to a *triple* or ternary rhythm and is so presented in Lesson VI.

OBJECTIVES:

1. To familiarize the students, both intellectually and kinesthetically, with pulsating movement in duple rhythm.
2. To develop skill in the performance of pulsating movement.
3. To introduce variations of pulsating movement and combinations with other movement qualities.
4. To provide an enjoyable dance experience.

PROCEDURE:

Best results are achieved if the "vibration" is never stopped, once it is started. With this unbroken repetition, the movement becomes so natural to the dancer, like his heartbeat, that he is sustained by it, and can continue dancing, as in certain primitive dances, for hours or even days. It sometimes happens in such a lesson that the students feel themselves lighter, with more endurance and greater ability to do high elevations with ease than they could under ordinary circumstances.

1. Begin the lesson by discussing with the student the nature of pulsation. As a form of movement, a pulsation is a movement impulse that returns on itself. Usually, the impulse is small and rapid like a heartbeat. When it is related to a binary or duple rhythm, the impulse and return are of equal duration and there is no rest period between them.
2. Stand in first position. Lock the knees and then release them slightly. Become aware of this unlocked position, and never completely straighten the legs again during the lesson. Bend the knees about an inch more, and return them to the slightly bent position. Alternate these two positions with a gentle bouncing movement and keep this action going until it becomes easy.
3. Do eight bounces or pulsations with the weight on the right leg, and then eight with the weight on the left; four right, four left; two right and two left. Continue the two pulsations right and two left; this, now, is the basic vibration, called a "double vibration." There are two vibrations (down-up, down-up) on each beat of the music. The beat is moderately fast.
4. Do four double vibrations, stepping forward, and four backward, and continue in this fashion.
5. Move toward one end of the room, taking double vibrations with each step. Tempo is very important. It may be necessary to increase the speed of the movement gradually until an ideal tempo is established. The class should continue the pulsating movement even while waiting. In order to keep going, the body should be lifted out of the legs, and the bounce should be easy and effortless;

this is very important. The weight should be distributed through-out the whole foot; placing weight on only the ball of the foot causes one to tire quickly.

6. Move forward across the floor with a double vibration.

7. Move backward across the floor with a double vibration.

8. Move sideward right.

9. Move sideward left.

10. Do three double vibrations forward. In place of the fourth double vibration, pause; on the pause, the body seems quiet, but the vibration should still be going on inside.

11. Now, in place of the fourth double vibration, substitute a jump in second position. The emphasis is down and there is no rebound after the jump; but there is still a feeling of lightness; the thighs go out instead of down.

12. Do the same pattern as in Procedure 10, but face the side wall on the jump (double R, double L, double R, jump, facing R). Alternate sides.

13. Speed the tempo so that the movement becomes jazzy. Do doubles down the floor again.

14. Now do singles down the floor, bouncing the knees only once on each step, so that the movement becomes a little "leapy" run. Two singles are done on each beat.

15. Do four doubles and eight singles.

16. Do four doubles moving straight ahead, then change direction on the singles, using any direction—backward, sideward, around in a circle, et cetera—so long as you are ready to go forward again on the doubles. Make the singles large, strong steps, and the directional changes sharp.

17. Do four doubles, and somewhere in the eight singles add a high level—up on the toes, perhaps one arm or both arms up, chest up, focus up.

18. Do four doubles, and on the singles add direction change and occasional low levels—bent knees, focus down, et cetera.

19. Do four doubles, and improvise on the singles, using change of direction, high or low level changes, or occasional pauses, as in Procedure 10.

20. Do the same as Procedure 19 but add some elevation, coming completely off the floor somewhere in the pattern. Let yourself go with the movement as much as possible, and don't be afraid to experiment.

21. End the lesson with singles taken down the floor in very fast tempo so that they become a very light, skimming run.

Lesson IV: *The Application of Various Movement Qualities to a Given Space Pattern*

OBJECTIVES:

1. To provide students with the opportunity to create definite movement patterns for the purpose of communication within specified limitations in spatial design and movement quality.
2. To acquaint students with the changes in dramatic effect that different movement qualities can have upon a given movement theme.
3. To give the students an enjoyable dance experience.

PROCEDURE:

1. Choose a few preparatory exercises in which movement quality can be stressed.
2. Review sustained movement quality. Starting in twos from one corner of the room, take five smooth, gliding steps forward and four steps turning once around in a sustained quality. Continue forward in this manner, alternating the direction of the turn. Establish a movement pattern with the arms that is organically satisfying in relation to the floor pattern. Make all of the movement smooth and sustained, in a lyrical style, with moderate tension.
3. Do the same floor pattern but make the sustained movement as strong as possible.
4. Review swinging movement quality. Take running waltzes down the floor (Unit Two, Lesson I), using the arms and body to establish the quality of the waltz. Keep the tempo quite fast.
5. Using a moderate 4/4 meter as a base, progress forward taking a firm step and a percussive movement with the body or arms on each beat of the music. Keep the knees slightly bent and the whole body very tight so that the movement is strong and percussive and is felt not just in the arms, but by the body as a whole.
6. Progress down the floor combining Procedures 4 and 5 in the following syncopated pattern: two running waltzes forward followed by three steps with percussive body and arm movements, using two counts for each step. Clap the rhythm before doing the movement pattern.

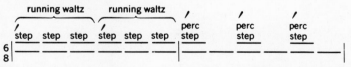

Make the waltzes very light and free and the percussive movements strong and earthy.

7. Starting on a low level anywhere in the room, improvise individually upon the following space pattern, using *swinging or
sustained movement* qualities, performed in a *lyrical style* in *moderate tempo*. Rise, run forward, turn around, establish two new
directions, move to a new low level. After improvising the movement several times, try to set it, and give it some specific mood or
dramatic meaning. Divide the class in halves or thirds or quarters,
depending on the size of the class, and perform the patterns for
the rest to see. Remember that timing and mood may be
different for each individual. Do the pattern without accompaniment, but feel the accompaniment inside your own body; or else
use accompaniment that does not establish a definite beat or
mood but merely provides a sort of "moral" support for the dancers.
Discuss the various moods and dramatic ideas communicated by
the dancers.

8. Using the same basic pattern as in Procedure 7, do the pattern in
a *slow tempo* with *powerful, sustained movement*. The exact
choice of movement will not necessarily be the same as that of
Procedure 7. Improvise upon the problem first and then set the
movements with a definite mood or dramatic meaning in mind.
Present the studies, one group at a time, for the others to see; then
discuss the moods and dramatic ideas projected by the various
patterns.

9. Using *fast, sharp, flashy, percussive movements*, follow the same
procedure as in Procedures 7 and 8.

**Lesson V: Couple Improvisation in Antiphonal Form with Different Movement
Qualities**

OBJECTIVES:

1. To provide a stimulus for the discovery of fresh movement forms
through the process of improvisation.

2. To increase kinesthetic and intellectual awareness of the characteristics of swinging, sustained, and percussive movement and
their expressive potentials.

3. To develop sensitivity and responsiveness to the movement of
another dancer.

4. To provide pleasure through the experience of relating one's
movement to that of another dancer.

PROCEDURE:

1. Begin with a few preparatory exercises in which swinging, sustained, or percussive movements are stressed.

2. Divide into couples. One person in each couple is "number one,"
the other person is "number two." Using swinging movement

quality only, number one improvises for two measures of 6/8 meter. Number two then responds with his own swinging movement during the next two measures of 6/8 meter. Number one "speaks" again with a two-measure phrase of swinging movement; and once more, number two responds. The active dancer should try to be as ingenious as possible in finding interesting swinging movement. A locomotor base can be used for some of the movement. Try arm swings, body swings, leg swings with turns, and so forth. Use change of level in some part of the pattern. Each person should be very conscious of his partner, and when taking the passive role, he should be responsive to his partner's movement through focus and through very small movements of his own. Try to establish a real "conversational" feeling between partners, without being pantomimic. Improvise in this fashion several times, allowing the other person to be "first speaker" some of the time. Try to remember and set the movements that are most satisfying. Show the movement patterns, a few couples at a time, to the rest of the class.

3. Do the same as in Procedure 2 only with sustained movement and using two measures of 8/4 as the compositional phrase.

4. Using one measure of 4/4 meter as the rhythmic base, start at one end of the room and have each person, in succession, clap a simple rhythm of two, three, or four accents related to the underlying beat. The accents may occur either on the beat or on the off-beat. Try to make each rhythmic pattern different, e.g.:

This rhythmic exercise is merely to illustrate some of the variations of accent patterns that are possible in 4/4 meter.

5. Now return to the movement "conversation" problem. Number one improvises with percussive movement to one measure of 4/4 meter, placing the percussive movements (any number) wherever he chooses within the measure. Number two responds in the next measure of 4/4, making his own rhythm. Number one "speaks" again, and number two responds. Don't try to plan the rhythmic patterns in advance. Let the rhythm and the movement be spontaneously determined. Make the movement very strong, perhaps with a feeling that the "conversation" has turned into an argument. The dynamic intensity of the movement can be further augmented if the musical or percussion accompaniment is syncopated, once the beat has been established for the dancers. After improvising the movement problem several times, proceed as in Procedure 2.

Lessons VI and VII: *Pulsating Movement in Ternary Rhythm; Collapsing Movement; and Combining of Movement Qualities*

OBJECTIVES:

1. To familiarize the students, both intellectually and kinesthetically, with pulsating movement related to a ternary or triple rhythm, as distinguished from pulsating movement related to binary, or duple, rhythm.

2. To familiarize or re-familiarize students with collapsing movement.

3. To challenge student creativity in composing a movement pattern that utilizes all of the movement qualities studied in this unit.

4. To sharpen student ability to differentiate movement qualities through the performance of a movement pattern in which these qualities are combined.

5. To provide an enjoyable movement experience.

PROCEDURE:

1. Begin by swinging one arm back and forth, from shoulder height, in an easy, natural swing. Gradually reduce the size of the movement and increase the speed slightly until the movement becomes pulse-like in quality. The movement is a very small "down–up," and the body is still somewhat relaxed, as it was in the original swing. The timing is like a swing, too, only slightly faster as the range of movement is decreased. The "down" phase and the "up" phase of the movement are of equal duration, but there is a pause between pulsations, so that the movement is related to three beats instead of two.

Now, try to recall the pulsation in duple rhythm, experienced in Lesson II, by bouncing the knees in a duple rhythm ("down–up, down–up" to a very fast count of 1–2, 1–2). Now, add an extra count, in which the movement in the knees is suspended momentarily, after each pulse ("down–up–rest, down–up–rest" to a fast count of 1–2–3, 1–2–3). Note how much more relaxed the movement is when done to the triple rhythm.

2. Continue the triple rhythm pulse in the knees, then extend the pulse to one arm, and finally, to both arms. Try using different parts of the body to pulsate, such as the hands only, or the foot and ankle, and also the whole body. Try changing levels, while maintaining the pulsation in some portion of the body.

3. Discuss the fact that pulsating movement of either type, duple or triple rhythm, can suggest a hypnotic state that is lethargic, or

frenzied, depending upon how it is performed; or can suggest a state of waiting, or anticipation of something else that is expected to follow.

4. The last movement quality to be explored is collapsing movement, which is movement caused by draining the body or a portion of it, of all energy, thus causing it to succumb to the force of gravity; this type of movement and a teaching approach to it have been discussed in detail in the section on falling under Posture in Chapter 2. Practice a collapsing fall.

5. Divide into groups of 3 to 7 people and work out a group study that is based on the following movement pattern.

sustained		pulse	pulse

6/8

swing	swing	sustained	

swing	explode	sustained	

sustained	stac stac	collapse	(hold)

Try to make each movement quality a necessary outgrowth of the movement quality that preceded it, so that the entire composition has a feeling of unity, and can be performed convincingly. Concentrate also, on making each movement quality distinctive in its particular manner of energy release; that is, don't allow sustained movement to become swinging; or collapsing movement, sustained. The pattern may be done as abstract movement, or may take on dramatic connotations; but if a dramatic idea is used, it may be wise to let the idea develop as an outgrowth of movement experimentation, rather than start with the dramatic idea; thus, the tendency to become pantomimic will be avoided. The dancers do not have to perform the pattern in unison, but may organize themselves any way they like, as long as they do not digress from the assignment. Use the rest of the class period and part of the next one to complete the compositions; then show them, one group at a time, for class evaluation. Evaluation should be based upon whether the assignment was successfully fulfilled. Other points that might be discussed are these: unusual and ingenious movements; interesting group relationships and how they were established or might be established by making minor changes in the present pattern; dramatic meanings that may have been implied by the movement and particular aspects of the movement, such as body tension or use of focus that helped to convey these meanings.

Unit Seven: Further Exploration of Movement as a Means to Composition

Lessons I and II: *Central and Peripheral Movement* *

OBJECTIVES:

1. To increase kinesthetic sensitivity to body movement generally and awareness of the areas of the body from which a movement is initiated.

2. To develop the ability to differentiate between the characteristics of movements that are initiated peripherally and those that are initiated from the center of the body.

3. To develop the ability to control the amount of force used in the performance of a movement.

4. To develop the ability to differentiate between the characteristics of movements that are performed with great force and those that are performed with little force.

5. To help students to identify the characteristics of their own natural manner of moving, and to experience other ways of moving in order to enlarge their movement vocabularies.

PROCEDURE:

1. Pantomime the following actions, taking sufficient time to become acutely aware of precisely how the body is moving.
   a. You are in a field where stalks of milkweed are growing. It is autumn; the milkweed pods are open and the little feathery seeds are floating about. You reach around you to pluck them out of the air as they float by; some of them are high and some are low; some are close and some are far away. If you move too quickly you will stir the air and they will be wafted away.
   b. Someone has presented you with some saris from India from which you are to choose one. The fabrics are silks of the most sheer and gossamer quality. One at a time, you unfold them, hold them to the light in various ways, drape them over your arm or over a leg, and cast them aside, until you select the one that you want.
   c. You are sewing on a coarse rug with a long rope thread and a rusty needle. Both the needle and the thread are difficult to pull through the carpeting.
   d. You are using a chisel on a wall that is barely within reach, on the other side of a ditch. Using one or both hands, you attempt to chip the wall surface.
   e. You are playing soccer, running and kicking the ball. Sometimes you kick directly forward and sometimes sideward in relation to your body.

* The concept for this lesson and several of the examples presented here were originated by Lucas Hoving, professional dancer and teacher.

f. You are a prisoner. Your arms have been tied behind your back and you are struggling to free yourself from these bonds. After much effort, you finally succeed. Now, your outstretched arms have been shackled to a wall. People are throwing stones at you and you are trying to dodge them with your body.

g. You are trying to lift some large, heavy rocks from the ground; they are difficult to pick up, and you must get down close to the ground in order to lift them. There is a three foot wall beside you, and when you have lifted each rock, you throw it over the wall. You find a huge boulder, and with great effort, you push it out of the way.

2. Discuss the differences and similarities in the movement that took place in the previous activities. The most obvious difference was in the amount of force used in Procedures a and b in contrast to the other activities; but Procedures a, b, c, d, and e shared one important element: in these five activities, most of the movement was both initiated and carried out by the peripheral portions of the body, the arms and the legs, and although the torso may have been indirectly involved its action was secondary. In Procedures f and g, however, it is probable that movement was initiated in the torso and was transferred later to the extremities. Most strong work movements are centrally controlled; that is, they begin in the torso and are projected outward. But it is also possible to perform strong peripheral movement, as in Procedures c, d and e. The form and the resulting kinesthetic sensation of any movement will change perceptibly, depending upon whether it is centrally or peripherally motivated, and whether it is executed with maximum or minimum force. Speed of movement is another influential factor, but one with which we shall not concern ourselves at this time.

3. Create a movement phrase of about four measures; then perform it in the following ways:

a. Strong movement, initiated peripherally.
b. Gentle movement, initiated peripherally.
c. Strong movement, initiated centrally.
d. Gentle movement, initiated centrally.

Do not alter the basic structure of the original movement pattern. Present these patterns for the class to witness and evaluate. Be sure to check the results for accuracy in fulfilling the assignment. Observe how the effect created by the movement is changed in each of the four presentations. Notice that some people are naturally inclined to initiate most of their movement peripherally, while others prefer to initiate movement centrally. Some people, also, move habitually with little body tension, while others, particularly boys, normally prefer strong movement. It is important for dancers to familiarize themselves with all movement possibilities, if they are to become versatile performers.

Lessons III and IV: *The Use of Ropes in Choreography*

OBJECTIVES:

1. By means of improvisation, to explore the use of a rope as an aid in establishing spatial design in movement.
2. To explore the use of a rope as a prop in conveying a dramatic idea.
3. To increase awareness of the importance of linear design, directional forces, and bodily tension as a means of imparting dramatic concepts through movement.
4. To provide a creative challenge to the students.

PROCEDURE:

1. Begin with a few general preparatory exercises.
2. In pairs, work with a rope about the size and texture of a jumping rope, and about 6 to 8 feet long. Experiment freely with the rope at first, to see what different relationships can be established between two people with the aid of a rope. Concentrate upon the spatial designs that can be made by the dancers' bodies and the rope. Try to remember the most interesting patterns so they can be repeated later.
3. Continue the improvisation, but now be very conscious of the kind of design that is being created. Some designs will be symmetrical; that is, the movement design of one dancer will be the mirror image of the other (*a*). Some designs will be asymmetrical; the movement design of one dancer will complement rather than duplicate that of his partner (*b* and *c*). Some designs will be sequential in their movement line; the movement design created by one dancer continues and completes the linear pattern established by his partner (*b*). And some designs will be oppositional; the movement design of one dancer is antagonistic to that of his partner (*c*). In symmetrical and asymmetrical patterns the lines of action may be either sequential or oppositional.
4. Utilizing any of the movement material and spatial patterns discovered thus far, compose a very short study that is interesting purely in its spatial design, without reference to any dramatic content. Include at least one symmetrical pattern of either kind, sequential or oppositional; one asymmetrical–sequential; and one asymmetrical–oppositional relationship. Concentrate also, on the movement involved in getting to those positions; don't allow the positions themselves to become a series of static tableaus.
5. When most of the groups have finished, view the results, one couple at a time, and discuss (1) whether the conditions of the

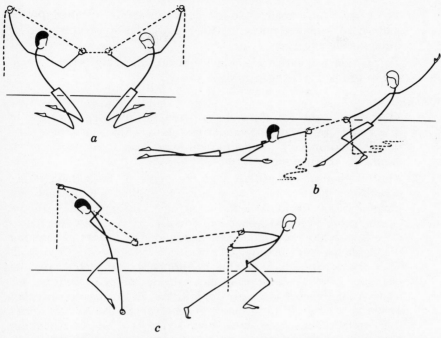

a

b

c

assignment have been met and (2) the relationships that were particularly pleasing and original.

6. Again in pairs, improvise with the rope, this time using the rope to relate the two people in some dramatic fashion. The rope may be used either in a literal sense, or it may be given a symbolic significance; it might be used as a force that emphasizes the antagonism between two individuals, or that symbolizes their dependence upon each other, and so forth. After improvising, set a pattern that is designed to convey whatever idea the partners have agreed upon.

7. Present these studies, one at a time. See if the members of the class, by observing the movement pattern without the aid of a preliminary explanation, can interpret correctly the idea that the dancers wished to convey. Discuss the aspects of the movement that were responsible for their success or failure.

Lessons V, VI, and VII: *Abstraction of Everyday Movement*

OBJECTIVES:

1. To increase intellectual and kinesthetic perception of practical, everyday movements, as distinguished from movements chosen exclusively for dance.

2. To discover within these everyday activities, aesthetically pleasing patterns of movement that, with slight alterations, can be used for dance expression.

3. To discover how to alter the movement elements within a specific pattern in order to endow it with a particular style, character, or dramatic significance.

4. To provide a creative challenge and an enjoyable experience in group problem solving.

PROCEDURE:

1. Discuss the term "to abstract" as it is used in dance to mean: to select and exaggerate movement essentials, eliminate unnecessary details, and modify the movement when necessary in order to emphasize its meaning or form.

2. Most students have experienced the game of basketball, either actually or vicariously; if they haven't, another activity that employs a variety of movements involving many parts of the body, can be substituted. Working individually, try to recall and reproduce in a pantomimic movement sequence the actions of catching the basketball, dribbling it, pivoting, and throwing the ball. There is no actual ball, but the performer should pretend that he has one. Try to bring into the pattern contrast of level; for example, if the ball is caught high in the air, make the throwing action low, close to the ground; or vice versa. Use several directions in performing the movement sequence. Try to make the pattern as interesting as possible in terms of pure movement. Set the pattern so that it can be repeated.

3. Now, do the entire pattern in very slow motion, so slow that you are hardly moving at all. If there were jumps or leaps in the original pattern, you must now remain in contact with the floor. Become extremely conscious of the spatial designs being made by all parts of the body.

4. Reconstruct the pattern slightly, eliminating any movement or movement repetitions, that are not especially satisfying. Now, dispense with the idea of actually holding a ball, but do the movement in terms of itself, with no pantomimic reference to the game of basketball. Exaggerate some of the movements and minimize others if necessary, experimenting until a satisfying movement sequence is established. Continue to perform the movement in slow motion.

5. Now, add one or two percussive movements to the slow, sustained movement quality already established. Put these percussive movements anywhere in the pattern, not necessarily where they would ordinarily have been found in the original movement. Give the pattern an interesting rhythmic structure, related to a moderately slow 4/4 meter.

6. In groups of 3 or 4 people, each person performs his own pattern for the other members of his group. Each group chooses the most satisfying pattern of those shown; then all of the group members

learn the pattern so they can perform it in unison with all of the group members facing in the same direction.

7. Arrange the groups around the edges of the room, facing the center of the room, and show these patterns, one group at a time, in immediate succession, for the rest of the class to see. Discuss the aspects of the movement patterns that were especially delightful, and try to determine what made them so. Observe also, the variety of movement material that has been distilled from a simple sequence of basketball activities. This is usually as much as can be accomplished in an average class period.

8. Remain in the groups formed in Procedure 6 and now relate the movement sequence to 3/4 meter and perform it in the quality and style of a Viennese waltz. Take a few minutes to make whatever adjustments are necessary in the performance of the original pattern. Again, give the movement a definite rhythmic structure so that it can be performed the same way every time. Know exactly the number of measures that are used, and be conscious of the rhythmic phrases. Try not to digress from the original *movement* structure, but at the same time give all of the movement in the pattern a consistent quality and style. Using the same class organization as described in Procedure 7, present these patterns, one group after another, without pausing, or stopping the musical accompaniment.

9. Continue as in Procedure 8, only this time give the movement a jazz quality that can be performed to a highly syncopated jazz accompaniment. When the groups are ready, show these patterns as before, and notice in what ways the movement has been changed to give it different quality and style. Discuss the fact that the movements used in these dance sequences were, for the most part, already a part of the students' experience and needed only to be recalled and modified to become usable as dance.

10. Now in pairs, pantomime the following actions of a forward and a guard: the forward moves into position to catch the ball, he catches it, then moves around to the other side of the guard to throw the ball; the guard can move anywhere. Make the movement sequence and the partner relationships as interesting as possible. Follow the step-by-step procedure described in Procedures 3, 4, and 5, allowing sufficient time for the accomplishment of each portion of the development: (a) do the pattern in slow motion; (b) discard the idea of basketball, and eliminate undesirable movements and exaggerate others; (c) add some percussive movement, and give the whole movement pattern a definite rhythmic structure.

11. From the following list of "feeling states," partners choose the one that seems most appropriate to their movement pattern: consolation, gaiety, ritual, aggression, aspiration, grief, companion-

ship. Modify the movement *slightly*, when necessary to express the chosen mood, but never depart from its original structure.

12. When everyone is ready, partners perform their patterns, one pair at a time, doing first the original movement pattern of Procedure 10, and then the variation expressing a feeling state. See if the chosen mood is communicated and can be guessed by those who are observing, and then discuss what aspects of the movement—force, tempo, movement quality, use of focus, and so forth—were changed in order to give the movement its specific meaning.

Lessons VIII and IX: *Dancing to Poetry—Japanese Haiku*

OBJECTIVES:

1. To develop understanding of the proper relationship of dance and poetry to each other when they are used together.
2. To develop appreciation for the beauty, simplicity, and economy of statement in the Japanese haiku.
3. To develop ability to understand the word imagery of the haiku and to be able to use this imagery as inspiration for dance.
4. To develop ability to translate verbal imagery into movement overtones that will intensify the sensory impression of the poetic idea.
5. To develop ability to find movement that portrays the feeling aroused by the poem rather than movement that is a literal or pantomimic interpretation of it.
6. To develop sensitivity to appropriate timing in relating the reading of the poetry to the dance movement.
7. To provide a satisfying dance experience.

PROCEDURE:

1. Read two or three of the Japanese haiku to the class and discuss the characteristics of this form of poetry. According to description given in the haiku collections published by the Peter Pauper Press, the haiku, a seventeen syllable poetic form, is a "lightly-sketched picture" that is not expected to be a complete statement; the reader is supposed to add to the words his own imagery, and to become a co-creator. There is almost always, in a good haiku, more than a mere statement of feeling; there is a switch to a different viewpoint in the course of the poem, which makes the poem an implied metaphor.
2. Read the following haiku and use it as a basis for discussion and choreographic experimentation:

> The floating heron
> Pecks at it till it shatters . . .
> Full moon on the water.
>   Zuiryu *

* *The Four Seasons* (Mount Vernon, New York: The Peter Pauper Press, 1958).

The problem might be approached in the following manner.

How many verbal images does the poem disclose? What movement quality is suggested to you by the image of a floating heron? The dancer's task is not to represent a heron, but to express the movement feeling suggested by a heron, floating on water. Perhaps it is the calm of a summer evening that the word-picture recalls to you. See if you can find some movement that has the quality of the word image, as you perceive it. Experiment with using different body parts in various ways to express the idea. Try, also, using different levels, and locomotor as well as stationary movement.

What movement characteristics are suggested to you by the words "pecks" and "shatters"? Would the action be large or small; rapid or slow; strong or weak? How do the two images differ in shape and in movement quality? What emotional overtones are suggested by these words and how could they be expressed in movement? Try to find movements that are appropriate to these ideas, again remembering that it is not the dancer's role to pantomime the poem. Don't use just the hands or arms. Experiment with other body parts.

Now consider the moon. How can the imagery of the moon, or moonlight on the water, be given movement form without resorting to the obvious? Here, the movements that are chosen must do more than express the dancer's feelings about the moon; they must also be the resolution of the dance.

3. In creating the form, decide first what feelings or images suggested by the poem you wish to express through movement. Remember that you should not try to duplicate what the poet has so beautifully expressed in words, but should add something with movement that entitles you to be a "co-creator." Try to find as many ways as possible of expressing your ideas through movement, and then select the ones that are the most fresh and satisfying. Be aware of the elements of contrast in the poem and make use of them.

While you are composing, try to decide how you want to relate the words and the movement. There are several possibilities. The poem could be read before the dancer commences to move, as a sort of program note to the dance; or it might be spoken by the dancer, or by a reader, during the dancing. If the poem and the dance are to be presented together, then the timing has to be regulated so that the two sensory stimuli complement, but do not compete with each other. Certainly, the dancer will need more time to express, in movement, what he has to say than the length of the poem (if read without pause) will allow. The problem, then, is to decide how to space the movement and the poetry so that the meaning of neither is lost. It is often effective to set the mood with movement first, before introducing the verbal stimulus, but there is no rule that requires the dancer to do so. Probably, the dancer will want to phrase the poem in some way to allow the dance movement to be extended as long as is necessary before introducing a new thought or visual image. Although meaning is sometimes heightened by the simultaneous presentation of the verbal image and its counterpart in movement; at other times, a momentary suspension (but not cessation) of movement, while the words are being spoken, is more effective. Whatever the temporal relationship between the movement and the words is to be, each art form should appear to be the mutual inspiration for the other, and the interplay of the two art languages should create a true marriage of the arts.

4. Use the above haiku, or choose another one from those that are quoted below, to create a short dance composition. Relate the words to the movement in whatever way seems most satisfying to you.

Haiku

Energetic ant . . .
Silhouetted on the still
Snowflake-peony.
        Buson *

Ah, I intended
Never, never to grow old . . .
Alas, the New Year's bell.
        Jokun †

Dewdrops, let me cleanse
In your brief sweet waters
These dark hands of life.
        Basho †

Raging winter storm
Roaring to its utmost end . . .
Ever-sounding sea.
        Consui †

Three loveliest things:
Moonlight . . . cherry blossom
  . . . Now I go
Seeking silent snow.
        Rippo †

Yellow autumn moon
Unimpressed the scarecrow stands
Simply looking bored.
        Yahu †

My very bone-ends
Make contact with the icy quilt
of deep December.
        Buson *

Oh dark sleepy pool
Green unexpected frog
Goes plop! Watersplash!
        Basho †

5. Present these compositions for class evaluation, using the points that have been discussed in class as a basis for this evaluation.

* *The Four Seasons* (Mount Vernon, New York: The Peter Pauper Press, 1958).
† *Japanese Haiku* (Mount Vernon, New York: The Peter Pauper Press, 1955).

The dance units described in this chapter should be looked upon as a beginning and not as an end of the approaches that can be made to dance. Techniques that are centered in the torso, as opposed to locomotor activities, have been especially neglected in this presentation of dance units, primarily because they are difficult to describe simply and to interpret correctly when presented in print. It should be assumed that these facets of students' dance education would not be omitted or minimized in actual practice.

SELECTED BIBLIOGRAPHY

Lockhart, Aileene. *Modern Dance—Building and Teaching Lessons,* rev. ed. Dubuque, Iowa: W. C. Brown Company, 1957.

Murray, Ruth. *Dance in Elementary Education,* rev. ed. New York: Harper & Row, 1963.

Turner, Margery J. *Modern Dance for High School and College.* Englewood Cliffs, N.J.: Prentice-Hall, Inc., 1957.

Turner, Margery J. *Dance Handbook.* Englewood Cliffs, N.J.: Prentice-Hall, Inc., 1959. Chapter III.

5

Teaching Ballroom Dance Creatively

Ballroom dance is primarily a social activity; it is not an art form in the sense that its chief purpose is to express and thus communicate to others ideas, feelings, or emotions. The function of ballroom dance is to give physical enjoyment to the participants through the performance of the specific rhythms and movements involved and social satisfaction through group participation. This does not mean that ballroom dance cannot be a source of aesthetic pleasure to observers and performers; on the contrary, ballroom dance should be an aesthetically as well as physically satisfying movement experience.

EDUCATIONAL OBJECTIVES

Although ballroom dance shares with modern dance some of the same educational objectives, it also possesses other important objectives of its own.

1. Along with other dance forms, ballroom dance can help to encourage good posture, improve coordination, and add to the general physical and mental alertness of the participants.

2. Kinesthetic awareness of how the body is moving, and of how such movement feels, can be intensified.

3. Rhythmic awareness can be increased, as well as the ability to give movement a particular rhythmic structure, relating it to an established beat.

4. Knowledge of specific ballroom dance steps, in terms of their movement quality and style, partner relationship, direction, step pattern, and particular rhythmic structure, can be provided; and based upon this knowledge, physical skill in the performance of these steps can be developed.

5. Awareness of the principles underlying good leading and following in ballroom dance and the ability to lead and follow successfully can be developed.

6. An opportunity can be provided also for creative expression in the devising and performing of interesting step combinations.

7. An opportunity can be provided for physical release in the enjoyment that is inherent in moving rhythmically to music.

8. Aesthetic appreciation of dance movement that is well performed can be increased; and ability to discriminate between dance that is socially and aesthetically attractive and that which is not can be developed.

9. As a social activity, ballroom dance can help to develop social skills by imparting a knowledge of social etiquette and by giving students the experience they need in order to feel at ease in social situations involving the opposite sex.

10. Finally, social enjoyment can be enhanced as the student gains confidence in his own ability to perform as a dancer and to handle himself skillfully in social situations.

ACHIEVEMENT OF OBJECTIVES

It will be noticed that in listing the benefits of ballroom dance above, it has been implied that such goals are attainable, but they are not attained merely by listing them as lesson objectives; they must be consciously worked for through the use of teaching procedures that will assure their accomplishment. The principles of good posture, for example, will need to be reviewed and consistently brought to mind if good posture is to be encouraged through ballroom dance activity. With beginners especially, bodily tensions that are the result of insecurity tend to create special postural problems, such as hunched shoulders, that need correcting.

Kinesthetic awareness of movement and its accompanying sensations can only be achieved if students are challenged to observe their own movement critically and discriminatively. Neither kinesthetic awareness nor intellectual knowledge of the various aspects of special ballroom steps can be acquired if such steps are merely imitatively taught. Each step needs to be carefully analyzed in its presentation if students are to understand what it is they are doing.

Some of the most important elements of any ballroom step are its style and movement quality. By "style" is meant the posture, carriage, and subtle body control that is necessary to make for excellence of performance; by "quality," the particular manner in which the energy of movement is released that gives to the dance its distinctive character. Movement qualities are often described by such terms as: *sustained, flowing, lingering, bouncy, undulating, swooping, sharp, staccato.* Movement quality helps to establish the style of a step. The performance of the mere mechanics of a dance step is not alone sufficient to give it identity as a recognized dance form. More than anything else, it is the quality of the movement and the styling that gives a dance step its character. Correct styling and movement quality in ballroom dance will be achieved only if they are stressed throughout the performance of all dance activities. This means that the teacher himself must understand the style and the movement qualities of the steps he teaches and must know how to instruct his students so that they can achieve these ends; he must know whether a step should be smooth and gliding, or bouncy, or free, pendular and lilting, or perhaps subtly restrained, and then be able to analyze and teach the specific body controls that contribute to these desired results. A good demonstration can be tremendously helpful at this point.

Ballroom dance of the 20th century, unlike the forms of previous eras, permits the dancer to improvise his own step combinations instead of following prescribed routines; it encourages creativity and individuality on the part of the performer and allows the imaginative dancer freedom to dance as he chooses. On the other hand, without the security of several combinations upon which to rely, the person who lacks the imagination and courage to be experimental is likely to dance one step monotonously for an entire evening unless he is taught *how* to invent his own dance sequences and is given sufficient self-confidence to do so. As soon as the student has learned two or three basic steps and has been taught a few examples of how they might be combined, he should be encouraged to create combinations of his own—combinations that can be made interesting by change of step, rhythm, direction, and partner relationships. By being made aware of the variables that are at his disposal, the student is given the tools with which to create, and with continued practice in doing so, he eventually develops self-assurance in his ability to improvise.

Aesthetic standards are cultivated through teacher guidance in helping students to make critical evaluations of the dancing they see. Demonstrations by students who are accomplished performers, and when necessary, by the instructor himself, can help to set standards of excellence that can be emulated by the rest of the class. Ungainly dance postures may need to be illustrated also, but never by pointing an accusing finger at some hapless couple in the class. A clever, exaggerated demonstration on the part of an instructor and generalized comments that are not directed to any one person can often help to make a point, enabling the student to evaluate his own performance, and when necessary, to make the needed corrections.

Social skills are developed not only by discussing rules of ballroom dance etiquette, but most of all by consistently putting into practice those rules that are applicable to the classroom situation. Ballroom dance will not become a social experience until the student has learned to consider himself as part of a group rather than merely as the partner of a single individual. Social behavior will be developed when students learn to mingle with others, to exchange partners, and to enjoy doing so.

Social enjoyment will be a natural outcome of the students' increased experience with ballroom dance as a social activity if a pleasant, relaxed atmosphere has been established; if the teaching material has been successfully assimilated and students have been given enough practice to enable them to feel really comfortable in what they do; and if students have been given the necessary encouragement during the learning process to build their confidence.

SUGGESTED TEACHING MATERIAL

Fundamentals

Before attempting to learn any ballroom dance step, it is first necessary to gain command of the two basic fundamentals of ballroom dancing which are (1) maintenance of a faultless dance posture and (2) mastery of the dance walk.

Dance Posture

Good posture in ballroom dance is not unlike good posture generally, which has been described in Chapter 2. The body weight, however, is moved slightly forward over the balls of the feet in a position of readiness to move. The feet are pointed straight ahead and the knees are unlocked to allow one to move quickly and easily. There should be no break at the hips—no bending forward or leaning backward. Hips that are allowed to protrude not only present an ungainly appearance when viewed from the side but upset the total body alignment. The chest and diaphragm should be lifted, but not pushed forward, an important point to remember since the diaphragm is used as a lead indicator; the shoulders are level and relaxed; and the head held erect over the spine. It is important to remember not to look down at the feet while dancing, but to depend upon the kinesthetic sense, rather than the eye, to report their location.

The Dance Walk

The basic step for all ballroom dancing is the dance walk. While the ballroom dance walk is similar to a normal, everyday walk, there are certain important aspects that need to be emphasized:

1. Point the toes straight ahead, and keep the weight directly over the balls of the feet; they are always the last part of the feet to leave the floor and the first to touch it.

2. Maintain a narrow base, so that the legs are close together, never in a wide straddle, except when moving sideward. A wide base tends to stabilize the body, making rapid movement changes difficult, and when stepping forward or backward, causes the body to lurch from side to side.

3. In stepping, move the leg from the hip joint, not from the knee. Reach with the toes, keeping the foot as close to the floor as possible without touching it.

4. When first learning to dance, make all steps directly forward, backward, or sideward—never on the diagonal unless required in the step pattern—so that the direction of movement can be clearly perceived by the follower.

5. Take long steps on the slow rhythms when moving forward and backward, and shorter steps on the quick rhythms and when moving sideward. When the leader is moving forward, it is of particular importance for the follower to make her backward step as long as possible, so she does not hamper his movement. The leader is then free to take any length step he desires.

6. In a forward walk, make the body weight precede the stepping foot; in a backward walk, reach with the leg before shifting the body weight.

7. When stepping backward, move the leg independently of any movement in the torso, and reach with the toes.

Dance Positions

Conventional or Closed Position

Partners are facing each other, with the follower very slightly to the leader's R, so that her feet will dovetail with those of her partner. The heads of both dancers are turned slightly to the L in order to look over each other's R shoulder. The follower's L hand is placed lightly on the leader's R shoulder, with her forearm in contact with his upper arm. It is important for the follower to maintain a firm, but not heavy pressure with her L hand on the leader's shoulder to enable her to sense her partner's lead. The leader's R hand, with the fingers together, is placed flat against the follower's back, either in the center of her back or just below her L shoulder blade with the fingers crossing her spine, depending upon the relative anatomic structures of the two people involved. His R elbow is held high so that there is support for the follower's forearm (of which she never takes advantage). The leader's L arm and the follower's R are extended to the side, just below shoulder level, with the elbows slightly bent. The follower places her fingers in the palm of the leader's hand and his fingers are curled over her fingertips so that moist palms are not together. An alternative is for both dancers to extend their hands, palms toward each other, the leader then grasping the follower's fingers lightly between his fingers and thumb. In the lindy and cha cha cha, the palms of both partners are down, with the man's hand on top to expedite a change of hands from one side to the other.

Semi-open and Open Positions

Partners are turned to face partially, or completely, in the direction of their extended arms. To assume this position from closed position, the leader turns to his L, the follower to her R. The leader's R side and the follower's L side are touching. The relative position of the arms is the same as for closed position. To assume a semi-open position, an eighth turn is made; for the open position, a quarter turn is made so that partners are standing side by side, facing the line of direction*; the arms may remain extended or be dropped to the sides.

Reverse Open Position

Partners are turned in the opposite direction from open position, or toward their bent arms. To assume this position from closed position or from open position, the leader turns to his R, the follower to her L. The extended arms are lowered.

Side Position

In right side position, partners are facing in opposite directions, with R sides touching. The position of the arms, described for closed position, is adjusted slightly to accommodate this change in body relationship, but basically it remains the same. In left side position, partners are facing in opposite directions, with L sides touching.

Varsouvienne Position

Partners are facing the same direction, the lady to the R and slightly in front of her partner. The lady raises her arms a little above shoulder height. The man holds her R hand in his R, and her L hand in his L.

Shine Position

Partners are facing each other with no contact.

* For ballroom dance, "line of direction" refers to the counterclockwise progression of movement on the dance floor.

Leading and Following

Ballroom dance is a cooperative activity in which each partner must be able to perform his role if the endeavor is to be successful. No amount of knowledge of dance steps will result in good dancing if the leader is unable to lead with confidence or the follower unable to follow. The experienced dancer will give lead indications naturally and automatically, often without being aware that he is doing so, and the experienced follower will respond automatically to a feather-touch lead. Most beginners, however, need to be given instruction and practice in the performance and correct timing of lead indications or in following these precisely and gracefully. The requisite strength or subtlety of the lead will depend to a large extent upon the experience and responsiveness of the follower.

Essentials for Good Leading

1. Maintain good posture, especially in the upper body, making sure that the shoulders are relaxed and that there is as long a space as possible between the lower ribs and the hip bones.
2. Dance on the balls of the feet, with the weight definitely on one foot or the other.
3. Keep the R arm firm; do not allow it to move independently of the body.
4. Know a step thoroughly before attempting to lead it, and dance it with assurance so that the follower will have confidence in you and not become tense and try to anticipate your moves.
5. Know the proper lead indications for each change of position, direction, or step; give them inconspicuously, but make them strong and definite.
6. Hold the follower firmly to give her a sense of security, but not in a way that will restrict her movement.
7. When leading, always begin dancing with the L foot.
8. As a general rule, make steps directly sideward, forward, or backward, not somewhere in between.
9. Dance in time with the music and in proper relationship to the accented beat.
10. Know what you intend to do sufficiently far ahead to be able to act with assurance, and give the necessary lead indications in advance of the movement.
11. Except when going backward, move the body in the desired direction before moving the feet.
12. Know a variety of steps and rhythms, but when dancing with a strange partner, use only the simple basic steps until you have ascertained her ability to follow.

13. When the partner is not an apt follower, hold her closer and more firmly than usual in order to give a more definite lead, and increase the strength of the lead indications. Repeat a step several times before changing steps.

14. Practice alone often, since practice makes perfect.

15. Remember that the three most important essentials to successful leading are (1) adequate knowledge of the steps and rhythms; (2) correct lead indications, and (3) control of their timing.

Lead Indications

Parts of the body that are used generally to give lead indications are as follows:

1. The diaphragm—which in closed position is in continuous contact with the follower so that she can feel any intended direction change, and is used especially to press against the follower when the leader wishes to move forward.

2. The R elbow—which is raised when the leader wishes to move forward.

3. The palm of the R hand—which is pressed more firmly than usual against the back of the follower when the leader wishes to move backward, and released to move forward or to indicate a series of quick steps in a forward direction.

4. The fingers of the R hand—which are used to turn the follower to the L.

5. The heel of the R hand—which is used to turn the follower to the R.

6. The shoulder—which is used for turns, twisting and dropping in the direction of the turn.

7. The L hand—which is used to move the follower to the left or right of the leader. This lead is used only for exaggerated changes and when absolutely necessary.

Specific leads that are used to indicate particular changes in direction and dance position are as follows:

From	To	Lead Indications
Closed position	Move forward	Move forward with the body—diaphragm lead—lifting the R elbow and releasing the pressure of the palm of the R hand.
Closed position	Move backward	Press the R palm against the follower's back, pulling her toward you as you prepare to step backward.
Closed position	Move sideward	Lean very slightly into the direction of the movement, making sure

From	*To*	*Lead Indications*
		that the R arm and hand move with the body.
Closed position	Turn right	Twist the R shoulder back, lowering it slightly, while pressing lightly with the heel of the R hand.
Closed position	Turn left	Twist the R shoulder forward, lowering the L shoulder slightly, while pressing with the fingers of the R hand.
Closed position	Open position	Press with the heel of the R hand, turning the follower to face the line of direction so that the leader's R side and the follower's L side are together. Begin when the L foot is free.
Open position	Closed position	Lift the R elbow; press with the fingers of the R hand; and pull the L shoulder back. Begin when the L foot is free.
Closed position Open position	} Reverse open position *	Press with the fingers of the R hand; lower the extended arm and turn to face away from the line of direction. Begin when the R foot is free.
Closed position	Right side position	Lift the R elbow slightly and press with the fingers of the R hand, turning slightly to the L, while moving your partner to your R side. Begin when the L foot is free.
Reverse open position	Open position	Press with the heel of the R hand; raise the extended L arm and return to face the line of direction. Begin when the L foot is free.
Right side position	Closed position	Press with the heel of the R hand, moving the follower into closed position. Begin when the R foot is free.
Closed position	Left side position	Press with the heel of the R hand, moving the follower to your L side. Begin when the R foot is free.
Left side position	Closed position	Lift the R elbow and press with the fingers of the R hand, moving the follower into closed position. Begin when the L foot is free.
Alternating between right and left side positions †		Use the above leads, twisting slightly into alternate diagonals.

* The change from semi-open position to reverse open is sometimes called a junior cross.

† Sometimes called a senior cross.

Essentials for Good Following

1. Know a variety of ballroom steps and practice them alone.
2. Know the leads for each change of direction, position, and step.
3. Maintain good posture and proper balance over the balls of the feet.
4. Keep the L hand on top of the leader's R shoulder, and the L forearm against his R upperarm, but don't clutch him frantically, or lean on or against him. Support you own weight.
5. In closed position, keep your shoulders parallel to those of your partner.
6. Be relaxed, but not limp.
7. Begin dancing with the R foot.
8. Always have one foot free for an immediate step; never stand with the weight equally divided between both feet.
9. Wait for the leader to move first. This wait creates a slight resistance that enables the leader to use pressure, which is your lead indication.
10. Never anticipate a dance step or try to out-guess the leader. Your movement should lag slightly behind that of your partner.
11. Learn to be responsive to the slightest pressure from your partner and to take the line of least resistance.
12. Remember to move the leg from the hip joint, and develop a long, free step, especially when moving backward.
13. Reach with the toes.
14. Never lean forward or backward from the hips or look down at your feet.
15. If your partner makes a mistake in a step, or rhythm, follow him anyway.
16. Never criticize or attempt to lead your partner.
17. Dance with as many different partners as possible.

Dance Etiquette

Etiquette on the dance floor, as everywhere else, is simply a matter of courtesy and consideration for the feelings of others. Because ballroom dance is a social activity, the participants need to be able to mingle easily with others and to perform graciously the social amenities that make for comfortable human relationships. Ease of behavior in a social situation depends to a large extent upon knowing the right thing to do at the right time.

While a lecture on rules of social etiquette may be too large a dosage to be swallowed at one time, suggestions regarding social courtesies can be given during a dance class as the need arises with opportunities for practicing these courtesies. With practice, such courtesies become natural and the person finds himself socially at ease in any situation. Here are some rules to good form in social conduct that may be helpful to the student:

1. When inviting a lady to dance, the gentleman might phrase his invitation as follows: "May I have this dance?" or "Would you care to dance?" or "May I have the pleasure of this dance?"; but not, "Do you have this dance taken?" which moves away from *invitation* toward *interrogation*, and might embarrass the lady if she does not.

2. The lady's response might be: "Certainly" or "Yes, thank you" or "I'd be delighted" or she might simply nod and smile.

3. The lady never refuses to dance without having a very good reason; she may have promised the dance to someone else, or she may be tired and prefer to sit out the dance. If she refuses an invitation, she does not accept another partner for the same dance.

4. When moving across a crowded dance floor, the lady precedes the gentleman.

5. At the end of the dance, the gentleman thanks the lady and she makes some gracious response, such as "I enjoyed it," or "The pleasure was mine."

6. A gentleman does not leave a lady unaccompanied on the dance floor. At the end of a dance, he might introduce her to another gentleman or escort her to a group of her friends or sit with her until the music begins when he may excuse himself.

7. When introductions are made, the gentleman is presented to the lady, and a younger person to an older one; the name of the lady or the older person is given first. The procedure might be: "Jane, I'd like you to meet Phillip Scott. Phil, this is Jane Rogers."

8. A gentleman always rises when a lady is standing or when she enters a room.

9. A gentleman, when "cutting-in," touches the shoulder of the partner of the lady with whom he wishes to dance. If he is not acquainted with the couple, he introduces himself to the gentleman, who in turn presents him to the lady.

10. When cutting-in is permissible, it is improper for either the gentleman or the lady to refuse to change partners.

11. A gentleman should not cut-in on a gentleman who has taken his partner, but should wait until another gentleman has cut-in.

12. A gentleman should never stand on the sidelines or cut-in when there is a lady without a partner.

13. All dancers should always accept graciously the partners with whom they have been paired in a mixer.

14. Partners should not dance together continuously for an entire evening. A gentleman dances the first and last dances with his

partner of the evening, but he also arranges to exchange partners frequently so that the evening may become a social occasion.

15. Couples should dance inconspicuously, without showing off, or taking more than their share of the dance floor. On a crowded dance floor, the lindy and other vigorous dances that might cause the couple to collide with other dancers are inappropriate.

16. When colliding with one's partner or with other dancers an apology should be made by the offender.

17. One should dress appropriately for the occasion (which includes the use of a deodorant).

18. One should also remember to bring along a smile.

Selection of Dance Steps

With new dance fads appearing almost semi-annually, it is difficult for a teacher to know what steps to include in his teaching program. Just about the time he has mastered the intricacies of the latest craze, it is already passé and another step has usurped its position of supremacy. Although the popular steps of the day are always the ones that students are most interested in learning, development of any real proficiency in ballroom dancing cannot be achieved without first mastering its fundamentals. Probably the three most important fundamentals of ballroom dance for the beginner are (1) mastery of the dance walk, (2) command of the principles of leading and following, and (3) the development of accurate rhythmic response.

Practice in performing the dance walk does not need to be a boring experience. Such practice can be made both interesting and challenging by changing the meter and the speed of the music; by varying the rhythm of the step relative to the music; by altering the direction of the step; and by changing the dance position of the partners performing it. In fact, it is from these variations of the dance walk that such steps as the fox trot, the waltz, and the tango have been derived.

No course in ballroom dance is complete without study of the fox trot, including some of its many variations, and the waltz. These steps are standard, and are as basic today as they were thirty years ago. Of the succession of popular steps that have come and gone in recent years, the lindy has probably been the most durable, and it is one that satisfies the youthful craving for lively dancing. The rhumba, the samba, and the cha cha cha also show signs of a certain degree of permanency (relatively speaking), and have popular appeal. Although the tango is one of the loveliest of the dance forms, its style is so subtle and difficult to achieve that students rarely are able to grasp more than its superficial aspects. In spite of this fact, however, beginning dancers enjoy attempting to dance the tango because of its compelling rhythms.

One great mistake that is frequently made in teaching ballroom dance is that of attempting to teach too much in too short a time. A few steps and rhythms, mastered thoroughly, will be much more valuable to the student than a great many steps and rhythms covered superficially. Not only does the student perform the steps badly when this latter method is employed, but the smattering of knowledge that he has acquired is likely to increase his confusion and insecurity. With beginners, if a choice must be made, it is wise to stay with the basic steps, the fox trot and the waltz, and to select one or two currently popular steps such as the lindy or the cha cha cha to satisfy the students' immediate interests. When variations of these forms have been explored and proficiency of form and style in the performance of these steps has been achieved, then the student is ready to add to his dance repertory. If the teacher is in doubt regarding the ability level and interests of his students, helpful information can be obtained through the use of a check list by which students can indicate (1) the steps in which they feel reasonably well skilled and (2) the steps in which they would like some instruction.

TEACHING A DANCE STEP

Much has been said about the relative merits of the "whole" and "part" methods in teaching. In the whole method the step is presented in its entirety to the learners rather than by breaking it into its component parts and developing it one part at a time. Results of experimental studies have shown that the whole method is a much faster way to teach a movement skill than the part method since many learners are capable of grasping an activity immediately once they are given the visual picture of it by demonstration.

If learning of skills were the only objective with which a teacher were concerned, then unquestionably, the whole method would be the one to use; but we, as educators, are concerned with much more than this. The educator is also concerned with developing rhythmic understandings; with helping students to explore movement and to discover relationships between movements that are familiar and those that they are learning; with developing their powers of kinesthetic discrimination and sensitivity regarding their own movement; and with helping them to learn by using their own creative resources. These are aspects of motor learning that are usually by-passed for the sake of efficiency when students are taught merely to imitate the teacher. For this reason (although occasionally it may be advisable to teach a movement pattern as a whole and to break it down afterwards) generally speaking, a teaching approach that begins with movement that is familiar to the student and progresses, step by step, toward the movement pattern that is to be learned will prove to be more rewarding educationally than the results of the whole method.

The exact order of progression in teaching ballroom dance steps will vary according to individual preference and also according to what the teacher may wish, at that time, to emphasize in the learning process. Sometimes it is good to begin with a blackboard analysis of the step to be learned, while at other times it may seem better to delay this analysis until after the step has been experienced; more often, one may wish to diagram the step a little at a time as each new aspect of the movement is presented. Sometimes one may choose to establish the floor pattern and the foot relationship first, adding the rhythmic considerations later; at other times, one may prefer to commence with the rhythm. To a large degree, the order of progression will be determined by the relationship of the familiar movement used as the point of departure to the step that is being developed.

Here is a suggested progression for teaching a dance step:

1. Clap the underlying beat of the music, emphasizing the metrical accent. (This procedure can eventually be omitted.)
2. Clap the rhythm of the step without the music.
3. Clap the rhythm of the step in relation to the music.
4. Step in place, saying the rhythm at the same time (i.e. "quick, quick, slow"), first without, and then with the music.
5. Walk the rhythm with the music, moving forward and backward.
6. Give the step its proper foot relationship and directional pattern.
7. Do the step, paying particular attention to quality, style, and other movement details.
8. Do the step both forward and backward, practicing the lead indications with an imaginary partner.
9. Do the step with a partner, concentrating on lead indications.
10. Continue dancing with a partner for a period of directed practice. During this period it is often advisable to concentrate upon a particular aspect of ballroom dancing that can add variety to the dance step, such as change of dance position or change of direction. At first the teacher may need to set the dance pattern for the class, calling the change of position or direction just ahead of the action itself; for example, if the dancers start in closed position, the

call might be "One, two, three, four, five, six, *semi-open*, one, two, three, four, five, six, *reverse-open*," et cetera. Later, when all positions have become sufficiently familiar, the dancers may be given a free choice, and the call becomes, "one, two, three, four, five, six, *change position*." The same procedure can be used with directional changes and with other variational possibilities.

11. Change partners several times.

12. Combine the step with other familiar ballroom steps that possess the same style and quality and can be danced to the same music. The form of the step combination may be set by the teacher or may be created by the students themselves. Here again, the students may need to be given some directed practice in combining steps before attempting to create combinations of their own. Emphasis is placed upon the techniques of "getting into" a step or "getting out of" it .and upon making smooth transitions from one step to another. Good practice combinations can be constructed by putting the new step between steps the students already know, such as a rock, a chassé or a pivot turn, using the same number of counts for each step in order to keep the phrasing as simple as possible. As soon as students have had adequate experience combining a new step with others in their repertory, they should then be encouraged to make interesting combinations of their own.

A ballroom dance step might be analyzed as follows:

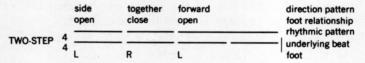

In teaching a dance step, it is wise to eliminate whenever possible any reference to R or L feet and to talk instead in terms of weight transfer. The use of "left" and "right" tends only to confuse students, especially since men and ladies are dancing with opposite feet. When saying the rhythm, the terms "quick" and "slow" seem to be more effective than "short" and "long," because the latter terms are likely to be interpreted to mean the length of the step instead of its relative timing.

The most effective teaching results are obtained when the class is taught to respond to verbal directions rather than merely to imitate what they see. Directions should be concise and easy to follow, given in a way that will cause students to think about what they are doing. This does not mean, of course, that one should never demonstrate, but rather that demonstrations should not become substitutes for verbal teaching. Complicated steps and partner relationships, such as those used in the lindy, that are difficult to describe in a way that can be visualized mentally need to be demonstrated. And once the mechanics of a step have been worked out, an excellent performance of the step in its appropriate style and quality provides a necessary model for students to emulate, as well as a source of inspiration.

When learning a new step, students should dance it alone before trying it with a partner. In so doing, a person is able to concentrate on its timing, direction and step pattern without the additional concern for keeping out of the way of his partner's feet. Furthermore, each person learns to become self-sufficient in working out a dance movement, which contributes to his growth as a dancer and as an individual. If she is to become a good dancer, it is just as necessary for the follower to know the steps she will be doing as it is for the leader.

The directional pattern of a ballroom dance step often influences the foot relationship, and it is important for a teacher to realize this fact in planning his teaching procedure. For example, if a step is taken to the side, it is natural for the feet to be brought together, or "closed," on the step that follows it. In learning the two-step, in which a close occurs on the second step of the pattern, the first step should be taken to the side, so that the directional pattern will cause the close to take place naturally. The directional pattern thus becomes "side, close, forward." Later, after the students have become familiar with the pattern, the first step can be taken in any direction. In the waltz, however, the close is on the third step, hence the first step should be taken either forward or backward, but not to the side, and the pattern becomes "forward, side, close" or "backward, side, close." Such awareness on the part of the instructor will help the students to by-pass many common errors in dancing.

Lead indications should be discussed each time a new dance step is taught no matter how many times these points have been mentioned before in reference to other steps. Regardless of how well a student can perform a step individually, it is of no use to him if he is unable to lead or to follow it when he has a partner. In a step sequence, likewise, the transitions from one step to another or from one dance position to another need to be examined with the students and the lead indications clarified. It is this ability to make smooth transitions from one step or position to another that is the mark of an accomplished dancer.

Because "keeping the rhythm" is often a serious problem with beginners, it is essential that a part of each lesson be devoted to rhythmic perception. The practice of clapping the underlying beat, stressing the metrical accent, should be continued as long as students are still having difficulty starting on the proper beat and staying with the music. A device that helps to sharpen awareness of musical phrasing is that of alternately dancing for one phrase of the music and waiting during the next phrase. This procedure is especially valuable because it gives the student much needed practice in coordinating his initial movements with the accent at the beginning of a phrase. Verbal reminders of changes in step pattern and direction given in advance of the action can help students who are still uncertain of the movement sequence. Simultaneous calling of the action of a dance step while it is being performed by the students, can help to reinforce the rhythmic pattern, provided these cue words are spoken in correct rhythmic relationship to the music. However, it is also important for students to dance without this help, so that they may learn to think for themselves and can concentrate on their own movement without any outside distraction.

When students continue to have difficulty with rhythm, two reasons are possible: it may be that they are still unable to feel the rhythm of the music; or they may be lacking the necessary coordination to execute the step in time with the music. In the first instance, the students need extended training in rhythmic perception; in the latter instance, they need additional time and opportunity to practice the movement.

Steps should be practiced in various tempos and to different pieces of music. It is usually wise to begin practicing a step to music that is moderately slow and to progress gradually to the faster tempos. After a step has been learned in one rhythm, it is often interesting to try relating the same step to a different meter, making whatever rhythmic adjustments are necessary to adapt the pattern to the new meter. Thus, a step in waltz time can be related to 4/4 meter by prolonging one of the steps for an extra count. When students learn that such adaptations are possible, they can apply this principle to other steps that they know, changing them to fit different types of music and thus enlarging their own repertory of dance steps.

PLANNING THE LESSON

The material to be covered in a ballroom dance lesson will depend upon the ability of the class, their previous learning experiences, the objectives to be attained, and the length of the class period. An inexperienced teacher often errs by giving too much material in one lesson. Review of previously learned material is usually essential in order to reconfirm the accomplishment and to provide a starting point for further learning. When teaching beginning students in public schools and colleges where the normal class period is considerably less than an hour, it is generally wise to devote the entire lesson to a single dance rhythm, such as the fox trot. Beginners usually need that much time to establish a rhythm, to become comfortable in the performance of a new step, and to acquaint themselves with some of its variations. Furthermore, students who are not rhythmically secure often have great difficulty adjusting to frequent rhythmic changes. Advanced students, on the other hand, both need and enjoy the experience of changing quickly from the rhythm and style of one dance step to that of another, since they will be expected to do this on the dance floor. One should try to give the lesson rhythmic variety by using music that will provide contrasting tempos and by combining the basic step with other related steps that have different rhythmic patterns. One should also try to give the lesson spatial variety by introducing step variations that involve different directions, such as backward, sideward, and turning, and by using a variety of dance positions. Some of these variations can be devised through the creative efforts of the students. Sometimes the combinations created by the class members are more interesting to the students than those suggested by the teacher.

Advance Planning

Each lesson needs a climax, and the teacher should budget his class time so that it is not wasted on minor preliminaries at the expense of more important aspects of the lesson. Although a time schedule needs to be kept flexible, such advance planning prevents one from going too far astray. One should decide upon the class formations to be used and should plan methods for getting the students into these formations quickly and efficiently. For some activities a circle formation is best, for others lines, or an informal scattering about the room. In teaching a new step, the use of a circle formation with everyone facing the center can be very confusing. A line formation is preferable to a circle, especially when the step is complicated or contains several changes of direction, and the ladies' and men's parts are the same. When students are practicing individually and the lady's step is the counterpart of the man's, it is often advantageous to have the ladies on one side of the room, facing the men, so that they may practice the step backwards while the men are moving forward. Moving in a circle is appropriate for the continuous practicing of a step that proceeds mostly in a forward or backward direction. For many situations an informal scattering over the floor is very satisfactory and is less formalized and restricting than the other arrangements. When the students are ready to perform the step in couple formation, it is usually wise to have them practice it by moving counterclockwise around the room as they would do on a regular dance floor. In planning a lesson, however, one should avoid wasting time with too many formation changes. One should select in advance the musical accompaniment, making sure that it is undeviating in its adherence to a steady beat. If records are to be used, they need to be well organized and immediately available, and the record player should be checked to see that it is in working order so that no time will be lost in hunting for records or adjusting the machine.

Arranging for Partners

Another responsibility of the teacher is that of getting students into couples and arranging for frequent partner changes. While advanced dancers may need only to be told to "take a partner" or "exchange partners," beginners, in choosing a partner, often experience a moment of awkwardness that can be erased through the use of simple mixers. These mixers should not be time consuming; they should be easy to teach, simple to learn, and fun to do. Mixers are used not only to help members of a group to become acquainted but also to prevent students from dancing always with the same partner; and when there are extra ladies or men in the class, mixers eliminate the possibility of the same ones each time being left without partners. Some simple mixers that are suitable for classroom use are given at the end of Chapter 6.

Exchanging partners also provides an opportunity for students to apply their knowledge of social dance etiquette, making introductions, inviting each other to dance, accepting invitations, and so forth. At least some of the time, a lesson plan should include procedures that require the students to practice these social amenities. In very large classes, the use of name tags, in the beginning at least, can help to put the fumbling student at ease, while at the same time assisting the teacher in learning the names of his students.

As is true in all teaching, a good lesson plan is an outgrowth of the lessons preceding it and is a stepping stone for the lessons to come; the lesson material is unified and is presented with concern for meaningful progressions, economical use of time, and most of all, the maximum enrichment of student experience.

Teaching Tips

1. Remember that your own attitudes will be reflected in the attitudes of your students; if you are enthusiastic in your teaching, they will be enthusiastic learners. Try to establish in atmosphere that is controlled, but pleasant and informal—one that will be conducive both to learning and to social enjoyment.

2. Wait until you have the attention of your class before giving instructions.

3. As a general rule, face the members of the class when teaching, since it is not necessary for you to turn your back to them if you teach by verbal instruction. In demonstrating, however, face the direction in which the students will be facing when performing the step.

4. When confronted with the problem of extra men or ladies in the class, solve it by letting them dance together until it is time to change partners. Then establish the practice of having the "odd" people cut in so that a different group of students will be left out the next time. Men can dance together by using the "West Point" method of grasping each other's elbows in place of the customary dance position. Contrary to common belief, the experience of leading does not impair the lady's ability to follow, but can actually improve it by increasing her assurance in performing the step and her awareness of the lead indications.

5. Do not fall prey to the temptation to devote all your time and attention to helping one couple that is in difficulty. Give them as much help as you can without neglecting the rest of the class, but if this is not enough, and you have no assistant, ask the students with special problems to stay, if possible, for a moment at the end of the class for further instruction. Sometimes, pairing these individuals with more experienced dancers in the class will solve the difficulty.

6. Occasionally have the ladies and the men exchange roles so that each can become acquainted with the other's problems in leading and following.

7. Sometimes it may be advisable to have the class dance in a small area of the size used for dinner dancing in order to teach them to modify their movements to fit a limited space and to avoid colliding with other dancers.

RATING STUDENT ACCOMPLISHMENT

Rating student accomplishment is somewhat less difficult in ballroom dance than in modern dance; for one thing, skills are more standardized in ballroom dance; and for another, the matter of creativity, while still present, is not quite such an important factor. Ballroom dance classes are often quite large, and in schools where no provision has been made for advanced instruction, there are apt to be vast differences of level of experience among the students within a given class. In large classes, it may be possible to divide the class into two or three ability levels by means of a short pre-test or by information obtained from a check list (such as the one suggested on page 190), and by evaluating student performance during the first few class meetings. Students can then be grouped and graded in relation to other students within their classification, rather than in relation to the class as a whole.

Students can be tested individually on their knowledge and accuracy in performing ballroom steps or certain combinations that are telling in terms of technique and styling. One practical way of administering such a test is to call out four or five students at a time, having them stand on one side of the room, facing the wall. As each individual's name is called, he turns around and performs a given step or step combination across the room where he waits until each of the others has joined him. Then the action is repeated with another step combination, moving in the opposite direction. In this way one individual is not influenced by the performance of another student, yet the procedure is quick and efficient. A written test on the rhythmic analysis of steps and knowledge of leading and following techniques and ballroom etiquette can be given simultaneously in an adjoining area so that all are kept busy.

Evaluating student ability to lead or follow when dancing with a partner needs a different procedure. One method that has proved successful is that of choosing the five best dancers of each sex in the class. These ten students then dance with the members of the opposite sex in the class, grading them on their ability to lead or follow, as the case may be. Each student should be graded by at least three of the five people doing the grading. The teacher can make his own evaluations of these students at the same time, while the other members of the class are practicing elsewhere in the room.

Another method, possibly superior to the one described above, is that of giving each student a number, according to the class roll, which is printed in large numerals on a card and pinned to his back. Each student then selects a partner or is assigned one with whom to dance. The instructor may wish to give a specific step combination to be performed in order to ensure that certain variations are attempted. At the end of the short musical selection each student grades his partner, writing the grade on the card on his partner's back so that it cannot be seen by him. Then each person finds a new partner for the next dance. No one is permitted to dance with the same person twice. With frequent partner changes, each student can be graded by about ten or twelve of his classmates during the period; and music can be chosen so that a variety of ballroom steps can be covered in the test. With mature students, another rating can be obtained by asking them, after sufficient forewarning, to list names of members of the opposite sex whom they judge to be the five best dancers in the class and names of the five poorest dancers. The instructor can also make his own evaluations of the dancers as he watches them perform.

When student evaluation is used, it is wise to caution students about grading too high and whenever possible to give them certain criteria for grading. Numerical grades, e.g. numbers 5 to 1, are sometimes treated more objectively than letter grades, A, B, C et cetera, and they are also easier to average together. As in all dancing, excellence of performance consists of more than just the accurate execution of steps. The superior ballroom dancer is one who is not only rhythmically and technically accurate but also is able to lead and follow each step with assurance, adding to it that element of movement quality and style that gives to the step its particular flavor.

SELECTED BIBLIOGRAPHY

Harris, Jane; Pittman, Anne; and Waller, Marilyn S. *Dance A While,* rev. ed. Minneapolis: Burgess Publishing Company, 1955. Chapter IX.

Heaton, Alma, and Israel C. *Ballroom Dance Rhythms.* Dubuque, Iowa: W. C. Brown Company, 1961.

Heaton, Alma. *The Techniques of Teaching Ballroom Dance.* Provo, Utah: Brigham Young University, 1961.

Hostetler, L. A. *Walk Your Way to Better Dancing,* rev. ed. New York: The Ronald Press Co., 1952.

Murray, Arthur. *How to Become a Good Dancer,* rev. ed. New York: Simon and Schuster, Inc., 1954.

Turner, Margery. *Dance Handbook.* Englewood Cliffs, N.J.: Prentice-Hall, Inc., 1959. Chapters IV and IX.

Yerrington, Beverly, and Outland, Tressie A. *Social Dance.* Palo Alto, California: National Press, 1961.

6

Ballroom Dance Activities

There are many ways of teaching ballroom dance, and perhaps no one way is better than another. It is not the purpose of this book to establish the best way because that is the prerogative of the teacher to determine for himself. Regardless of the method used, however, the teaching progression should have continuity and purpose. On the following pages, examples of some teaching progressions are offered as suggestions for the beginning teacher to try; they are not presented in lesson form, but it is hoped that from this material the teacher can make selections and additions in building lessons of his own.

DANCE STEPS

Dance Walk and Side-Step

Teaching the dance walk with its many variations can easily occupy one entire lesson or more, and since this step is the basis of almost all ballroom steps, its practice will need to be continued as an introductory phase of many of the lessons that follow. Learning to move the leg from the hip joint is probably the most important consideration in its correct performance. Other characteristics of the dance walk that need to be stressed in teaching have been discussed in the previous chapter under Fundamentals. Practicing the dance walk can be made constantly interesting and challenging through the introduction of other factors of movement, such as changes of tempo, rhythm, direction, and dance position. The following activities are suggested as means of introducing the dance walk with some of its variations.

1. Stand in place, with the weight over one foot. Move the free leg forward from the hip joint, reaching slightly with the toes, and touch the ball of the foot to the floor. Now move the leg backward in the same manner. Keep the body erect and properly aligned at all times, with no movement in the upper body whatsoever. Hold the hands on the hips in order to become sensitive to the action of the hip muscles. Continue to alternate this forward and backward swing of the leg from the hip joint. Practice with the other leg also.

2. Stand with the feet together with the weight over the balls of the feet. Continue to lean forward a little bit more with the upper body until it is necessary to step forward in order to regain the body balance. Be very aware of how the forward lean in the body causes the forward step to happen.

3. Individually, practice the dance walk, moving forward, concentrating on the various points mentioned on page 182.

4. Individually, practice the dance walk, moving backward; ladies in the class should pay particular attention to the backward walk, since they will be dancing backward most of the time.

5. Partners take closed position, after a discussion and demonstration of that position, and do a dance walk into the line of direction (LOD).

6. Individually, combine forward and backward dance walks in the following pattern, to moderately fast 4/4 music.

	fd	fd	fd	fd	bk	bk	fd	bk
4/4	L	R	L	R	L	R	L	R

The last two steps in the pattern form a "rock step," which should be done smoothly by keeping the knees slightly bent during the weight transfer.

7. Discuss the leads for the direction changes; these leads consist of lifting the R elbow and pressing forward with the diaphragm when preparing to move forward, and pressing the palm of the R hand against the follower's back when preparing to move backward. Be aware of the necessity for anticipating the directional changes and for giving the lead indications *slightly* in advance of the action. Practice the step pattern individually, giving the lead indications to an imaginary partner.

8. With partners in closed position, do the same pattern. The lady's part, as is usually the case, is exactly the reverse of the man's part (bk–bk–bk–bk, fd–fd–bk–fd). (Hereafter all diagrams and descriptions will be given in terms of the man's part unless otherwise specified.)

9. Choose music with a faster tempo. Clap the musical beat; do a forward dance walk to the music individually; then do Procedure 8 to this music.

10. To moderately fast 4/4 music, clap the rhythm, half-timing it; that is, clap on every other beat; then individually, do four dance walks forward and four backward, alternately, in this half-time rhythm.

forward	forward	forward	forward	backward	backward	backward	backward
$\frac{4}{4}$ L	R	L	R	L	R	L	R

11. With partners in closed position, move forward into the LOD with a dance walk done in half-time rhythm to the music.

12. Combine half-timing with regular-timing, clapping the pattern first; then doing it individually, with the men moving forward and the ladies moving backward; and finally doing the pattern with partners in closed position. All steps are forward. The call is "slow, quick, quick." Make the slow step long, with a slight under-curve, in a gliding cat-like quality; make the quick steps shorter, and a little bit springy, with knees easy.

slow	q	q
$\frac{4}{4}$ L	R	L

Discuss the lead for the rhythm change, which involves releasing the normal pressure of the palm of the R hand on the quick steps.

13. In couples, find another way of relating the one slow and two quick steps to a measure of 4/4 meter.

14. To slow 4/4 music, double-time the rhythm, clapping twice on each beat. Do the dance walk individually to this rhythm; then do two regular-time steps and four double-time steps.

q	q	q	q	q	q	q	q
$\frac{4}{4}$ L	R	L	R	L	R	L	R

slow	slow	q	q	q	q
$\frac{4}{4}$ L	R	L	R	L	R

15. Repeat the last pattern. The two slow steps are taken forward. On the quick steps, take a short step forward L; step forward R, bringing the R foot to the instep of the L; step backward L; step backward R, bringing the R foot backward to the instep of the L. This quick pattern is called a *twinkle* and is performed with a bouncy quality. Practice the twinkle independently of the rest of the pattern first; then do the entire pattern; and finally do it with a partner. The pattern can also be done in open position.

			twinkle		
forward	forward	fd	tog.	bk	tog.
open	open	o	cl	o	cl
$\frac{4}{4}$ L	R	L	R	L	R

16. When the dance walk is done to the side as a step–close or "side–together," it is known as a *side–step* or *chassé*. Do the double-time rhythm, moving sideward so that the step pattern becomes a series of *side–steps* or *chassés*. Individually, do three side–steps and a step–hold, bringing the free foot close to the supporting foot on the hold. Repeat all to the opposite side.

	chassé		chasse		chassé		step
	side	tog.	side	tog.	side	tog.	side (hold)
	o	cl	o	cl	o	cl	open
4/4	L	R	L	R	L	R	L

17. With partners in closed position, combine four forward dance walks with the chassé or side-step pattern, given above, moving to the L on the first measure of chassé and to the R on the second measure of chassé.

forward open		open		open		open		side o	cl	o	cl	o	cl	open	
4/4 L		R		L		R		L	R	L	R	L	R	L	(repeat)

18. Discuss and demonstrate the various dance positions and the lead indications for them (see page 182).

19. To four measures of 4/4 meter, practice the following combination:

Position	Lead Indication	Action
Closed	Diaphragm and R elbow; release pressure of R hand.	4 steps forward into LOD.
Open	Heel of R hand.	3 steps forward into LOD.
Reverse open	R fingers; lower extended L arm.	5 steps forward away from LOD.
Closed	R fingers; R elbow; raise extended arm.	2 chassés and 1 step sideward into LOD.
Closed	R fingers; R elbow; twist R shoulder forward.	Turning to face LOD, 1 step backward.

20. As in Procedure 19, practice the following combination:

Position	Lead Indication	Action
Closed	Diaphragm and R elbow; release pressure of R hand.	4 steps forward into LOD.
Right side	Fingers of R hand.	3 steps into L diagonal.
Left side	Heel of R hand.	3 steps into R diagonal.
Closed	Fingers of R hand; R elbow; diaphragm.	2 steps forward.
Closed	Palm alternately with diaphragm and R elbow.	4 rock steps, beginning backward L.

21. To four measures of 4/4 meter and using the dance walk in regular time, make up your own movement combination, incorporating any three of the standard dance positions. Most of these dance walk activities could also be performed in 3/4 meter.

Fox Trot, Box Step, and Box Step Turn

Fox Trot

The fox trot, unlike a number of other popular dances such as the bunny hug and the grizzly bear, whose titles were animal inspired, was named for a musical comedy star by the name of Harry Fox, who invented the step around 1914. It originally consisted of four slow walking steps combined with eight fast trotting steps; but eventually the fox trot was changed to the present combination of one slow step and two fast ones performed, now in a smooth, gliding manner.

```
        forward          side    together
        open             open    close
     4 |_____  _____  _____  _____| (also done backward)
     4 | L                 R       L
```

Count	Call *	Lead Indication	Step Pattern
1 (–2)	sl	Diaphragm and R elbow.	Step forward L.
3	q	Slight pressure R palm.	Step side R; bringing the R foot to the L foot before placing it to the side, so that the path of the foot makes a right angle.
4	q		Close L to R.

POINTS TO EMPHASIZE:

1. Make the steps directly forward or to the side, and make the forward steps large and the sideward steps small.
2. Keep the base narrow; concentrate on having the free foot pass close to the supporting foot before stepping to the side.
3. Be sure that the lead indications are given enough in advance of the step to prepare the follower for the changes in direction.
4. When the fox trot is done in a backward direction, substitute the R palm lead for the diaphragm and R elbow lead.
5. In general, make the movement quality smooth.

SUGGESTIONS:

1. Do the step continuously in a forward direction.
2. Do the step continuously in a backward direction.
3. Do the step forward for four measures and backward for four.
4. Combine one measure of dance walk in half-time with one fox trot step:

```
     forward          forward          forward          side    together
  4 |_____  _____  _____  _____||_____  _____  _____  _____|
  4 | L                 R                | L                R       L
```

5. Using four measures of 4/4 meter, make a combination of the dance walk and the fox trot of your own; some students may discover the box step in working out their patterns.

* One may also wish to use "forward, side, together" or "open, open, close" as the call, depending upon what aspect of the dance step is being stressed at the time.

Box Step

A box step in fox trot rhythm involves two measures of music and consists of one fox trot step forward and one fox trot step backward.

POINTS TO EMPHASIZE: The same as those given for the fox trot.
SUGGESTIONS:

1. Using four measures of music, combine one box step with four half-time dance walks forward.
2. Combine one box step with two fox trot steps forward.
3. Combine one box step with a fox trot forward and two chassés to the side. The step, when repeated, will begin with the R foot and will be done to the opposite side.

forward open	side open	together close	backward open	side open	together close
4/4					
L	R	L	R	L	R

forward open	side open	together close	side open	together close	side open	together close
L	R	L	R	L	R	L

4. Using four measures of 4/4 meter, create a combination of your own, from any of the following: dance walk, chassé, fox trot, and box step.

Box Step Turn

¼ turn L (toe out)   ¼ turn L (toe in)

forward open	side open	together close	backward open	side open	together close
4/4					
L	R	L	R	L	R

¼ turn L (toe out)   ¼ turn L (toe in)

forward open	side open	together close	backward open	side open	together close
4/4					
L	R	L	R	L	R

Count	Call		Lead Indication	Step Pattern
1(–2)	sl or turn		Diaphragm and R elbow; twist R shoulder forward, dropping L one slightly; R fingertips.	Step forward L, turning the foot out to make a quarter turn (lady steps back R, turning foot in).
3	q	side	Slight pressure R palm.	Step side R.
4	q	close		Close L to R.
1(–2)	sl	turn	Twist shoulders L, dropping L one slightly; R fingertips.	Step back R, turning the foot in to make a quarter turn (lady steps forward L, turning the foot out).
3	q	side	Slight pressure R palm.	Step side L.
4	q	close		Close R to L.

The dancers have now made a half turn. To complete the turn, repeat the action described above.

POINTS TO EMPHASIZE:

1. With rare exception, always begin a turn to the L with the L foot and a turn to R with the R foot.
2. Alternate a turn-out on the forward step with a turn-in on the backward step of the box.
3. Notice that the forward and backward steps of the box step are now somewhat shortened because of the turn-out or turn-in, which keeps the turn in a relatively small area.
4. To make a smooth turn, twist the upper body slightly into the direction of the movement, "banking" the turn, so to speak, so that the upper body arrives just ahead of the feet.

SUGGESTIONS:

1. Practice turning both to the L and to the R. When making a R turn, take one fox trot step forward first, beginning L, so the R foot is then free to begin the turn to the R. The technique of turning is approximately the same as it is for the L turn, but the shoulders are twisted to the R and the heel of the R hand is used rather than the fingers.
2. When the regular four measure box turn has been mastered, experiment with using only two measures to complete the turn, exaggerating the rotation of the shoulders and the turn-out and turn-in of the stepping foot on count one, and pivoting on every step rather than on just the forward and backward steps.
3. Combine the box turn with any of the previously taught steps.

Magic Step and Pivot Turn

Magic Step

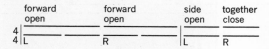

Count	Call		Lead Indication	Step Pattern
1(–2)	sl or fd		Diaphragm and R elbow.	Step forward L.
3(–4)	sl	fd		Step forward R.
5	q	side	Right palm and body lean.	Step side L.
6	q	close		Close R to L.

POINTS TO EMPHASIZE:

1. This is one of the most popular of the steps done to fox trot music.
2. The step does not fit the phrasing of the beats in the measure so that there is an interesting syncopation established between the

music and the dance step. Three measures of music are required for the performance of two magic steps.

3. The step does not alternate sides, but is performed always on the same side, beginning with the L foot.

4. The quality, although generally smooth, is determined, to a large extent, by the quality of the music.

SUGGESTIONS:

1. Practice the magic step forward.

2. Practice the magic step backward.

3. Do two magic steps forward, one magic step backward, and one magic step forward.

4. Do the magic step to the side. This is sometimes called a *swing* step.

side-touch open		side-touch open		side open	together close
L		R		L	R

During the first two steps, immediately after the step is taken to the side, the free foot swings in to touch the instep of the supporting foot.

5. Combine two forward magic steps with two swing steps.

6. Do the magic step, changing the directional pattern to "forward, back, side–together," so that the first two steps become a rock step.

7. Do the magic step variation in Procedure 6, turning to the L, using two magic steps to make one turn:

¼ turn L forward open		¼ turn L backward open	side open	tog. close	¼ turn L forward open		¼ turn L backward open	side open	tog. close
L		R	L	R	L		R	L	R

When making a L turn with the magic step, take the first step forward, with the foot turned out, so that a quarter turn can be made; take the second step backward with the foot turned in, making another quarter turn, followed by a step-close taken to the side. Repeat the step exactly as before in order to complete the turn.

8. Do the magic step turning to the R. Since the magic step is always begun with the L foot, it is necessary, when turning to the R, to make the first step in a backward direction. Step back on the L foot, turning it in to make a quarter turn to the R; then step forward with the R foot, turning it out to make another quarter turn, and finish with the step-close. Repeat the step, exactly as before in order to complete the turn.

9. Combine the magic step with the L and R turns, taking two magic steps forward and one turn to the L, two magic steps forward and one turn to the R (12 measures).

10. Do one magic step, moving forward in closed position; one magic step, still moving into the LOD, using open position for the two slow steps, and closed position for the "side–together"; one magic step to the R, using reverse-open position for the two slow steps, and closed position for the "side–together"; and finish with one swing step, taken in place as the man returns to face the LOD. When the magic step is done to the R in reverse-open position, the first step will be a cross-over step performed with the man's L foot.

Pivot Turn

A pivot turn is performed by alternately transferring the weight from one foot to the other, while turning. It can be done in place or progressing forward, but the turn itself is usually made to the R. In order to master the technique of pivoting, certain preliminary practice activities are helpful.

1. Step forward on the heel of the R foot and transfer the weight to the R toes; step backward L, keeping the weight on the ball of the foot. Practice this action individually until the kinesthetic feeling of rolling the weight forward from the heel to the toes is established. Then begin to turn, pivoting to the R, as you transfer the weight. The R toe is turned outward; the L inward. The weight is maintained over the R foot.

2. Make a series of turns, progressing to the R, stepping onto a turned-out R foot, and onto a turned-in L foot. Keep the turn as smooth as possible.

3. Now try the pivot turn to the R with a partner. Begin by placing the R foot next to the lady's R foot so that R insteps are adjacent. On the second step, swing the L leg around on the far side of the lady, as if wrapping it around her, before stepping onto it. This action will help to augment the turning motion and will increase the ease of its performance. Continue turning by stepping alternately on a turned-out and turned-in foot. The lady does the counterpart.

Points to Emphasize:

1. Keep the R insteps and R knees adjacent throughout the turn.
2. Exaggerate the turn-out and turn-in when stepping, and keep the weight largely over the ball of the R foot.

3. The lady should lean back against the man's hand so that the oppositional pull of the two dancers' bodies will help to increase the momentum of the turn. At the same time, the man must hold the lady very tightly to prevent her from flying off into space. Keep the upper bodies very close together.

SUGGESTIONS:

1. In semi-open position, take four steps forward; on the second and fourth steps the man's R foot and the lady's L foot must cross in front of the body. Then take four steps making a pivot turn; on the first step the man wraps his L leg around the lady as she steps toward him with R foot and moves into closed position.

2. Do the above pattern, performing the pivot steps in double time, taking eight steps to pivot twice or three times around.

Waltz Steps and Grapevine

Waltz

The waltz is the oldest of our currently popular dance steps; it had its roots in the "Volté," a 16th century court dance, the first one ever to be performed in closed position. The waltz, as we know it now, appeared in Austria in the 18th century, but in its early form it was the fast turning dance identified today as the "Viennese waltz"; later, it became smoother and slower and also more interesting, as the hesitation and other waltz variations were added to break the monotony of its continuous whirling. The waltz is a perennial favorite and provides the foundation for many of our other dance steps.

```
            forward   side    together
            open      open    close
        3 |————————  ————————  ————————| (also done backward)
        4 | L         R         L      |
```

Count	Call *	Lead Indication	Step Pattern
1	fd.	Diaphragm and R elbow (no diaphragm contact).	Step forward L, with knees slightly bent.
2	side	Slight pressure R palm.	Step side R (bringing R foot to the L before placing it to the side). Knees begin to straighten.
3	close		Close L to R, rising smoothly onto the balls of the feet.

* In the waltz it is rather pointless to use the terms "slow" or "quick," since all steps require the same amount of time for their performance. The speed of the step depends upon the music. Most American waltzes are slow, and Viennese waltzes are fast; but regardless of the tempo, all steps are even.

Points to Emphasize:

1. Make all steps even. Do not hurry the close.

2. Make the first step a large one, moving the body with the foot so that, upon the completion of the forward step, the weight is directly over it.

3. Make the sideward steps relatively small. The appearance of the second step of the waltz is improved if the dancer remembers to bring the free foot close to the supporting foot before stepping to the side.

4. Be sure to begin the first step of the waltz on count "one," which is the accented beat of the music.

5. Make the movement smooth and gliding, with a lilting quality that is the result of a slight "under-curve" created by bending the knees on the first step, commencing to straighten the knees on the second step, and rising onto the balls of the feet when the feet are brought together.

6. Remember that in the waltz, the dancers' upper bodies may be held farther apart than in other steps, to enable the dancers to make the movements as large and as free as possible.

Suggestions:

1. Do the pattern individually, both forward and backward. In the backward waltz, the movement is the same except that the first step is taken backward instead of forward.

2. Do the pattern with a partner, taking four waltzes forward and four waltzes backward.

3. Do six waltzes forward and two waltzes backward.

4. Do three waltzes forward and one waltz backward; the last two waltzes thus become a box waltz.

Box Waltz and Waltz Turn

The box waltz consists of one waltz forward and one waltz backward; it is exactly like the fox trot box step except that the rhythm is different. In the box waltz, all steps are of equal duration. Many teachers like to introduce the waltz by means of the box waltz which teaches the forward and backward waltz at the same time and provides the basis for the waltz turn. When the plain box waltz has been mastered, students are ready to learn the waltz turn. Again, the principles underlying this step are those of the fox trot box step turn. The only difference is the rhythm. Begin the waltz turn by using four waltz steps to make one turn, alternating a forward waltz with a backward waltz.

¼ turn L (toe out)			¼ turn L (toe in)			¼ turn L (toe out)			¼ turn L (toe in)		
fd	side	tog.	bk	side	tog.	fd	side	tog.	bk	side	tog.
open	open	close	open	open	close	open	open	close	open	open	close

3/4 | L | R | L | R | L | R | L | R | L | R | L | R |

Count	Call	Lead Indication	Step Pattern
1	turn	Diaphragm and R elbow; twist shoulders L, dropping L one slightly; R fingers.	Step forward L, turning the foot out to make a quarter turn (lady steps back R, turning the foot in).
2	side	Slight pressure R palm, pulling to R.	Step side R.
3	close		Close L to R.
1	turn	Twist shoulders L, dropping L one slightly; R fingers.	Step back R, turning the foot in to make a quarter turn (lady steps forward L, turning the foot out).
2	side	Slight pressure R fingers.	Step side L.
3	close		Close R to L.

The dancers have now made a half turn. To complete the turn, repeat the action described above.

POINTS TO EMPHASIZE:

1. Keep all of the steps small so that the turn is done almost in place.
2. Turn the shoulders into the direction of the turn before taking the first step.
3. Practice the turn both to the L and to the R, remembering that in order to turn to the R, it will be necessary to be stepping forward on count one with the R foot instead of the L.

Once this turn has been mastered, make a complete turn, using only two waltzes by turning halfway around on each waltz step. This latter turn is used in many folk dances, and in these dances the turn is nearly always done to the R.

POINTS TO EMPHASIZE:

1. Make the first step of each waltz either directly forward or directly backward into the LOD.
2. Be sure to make a *full* half turn on each waltz step so that only *two* waltz steps are required to turn once around; this can be achieved by exaggerating the rotation of the shoulders and the turn-out or turn-in of the stepping foot on count one, and by pivoting on every step rather than on just the forward and backward steps.
3. The lady should lean back against the man's R hand so that the oppositional pull of the two dancers' bodies will help to increase the momentum of the turn.

SUGGESTIONS:

1. Practice the left turn first, turning continuously and progressing into the LOD.

2. Practice the R turn. In order to begin the turn with the R foot, precede the turn with one forward waltz step. Later, precede the R turn by a backward dip instead of a forward waltz step. The dip is performed by the man stepping back on his L foot on count one, bending the supporting L knee and pulling the lady toward him; and holding during counts two and three, while gradually extending the supporting knee. The lady steps in between the man's legs with her R foot. The movement should be done very smoothly.

3. Combine one backward dip with two waltzes, turning once around to the R; and continue with one waltz forward and four waltzes, turning twice around to the L; repeat all.

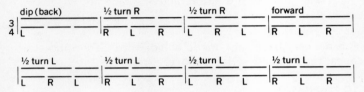

Waltz Hesitation

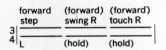

Count	Call	Lead Indication	Step Pattern
1	fd	Diaphragm and R elbow, then R palm, lifting both arms slightly to prevent the lady from taking another step.	Step forward L.
2	swing		Swing R leg forward.
3	touch		Touch R toe lightly to the floor in front of L foot.

The waltz hesitation may also be taken in a backward direction, and the forward and backward hesitation steps are often combined.

POINTS TO EMPHASIZE:

1. Be sure to use the entire three counts for the hesitation.
2. Exaggerate its lilting quality.

SUGGESTIONS:

1. Combine two forward waltzes with one waltz hesitation forward and one waltz hesitation backward.

2. Add to the above combination two waltzes, turning once around to the L, one waltz forward, and a backward dip onto the R foot.

Grapevine

The grapevine is a step that twists alternately from right side position to left side position while the dancers continue to move forward in a zigzag path.

forward closed position			⅛ turn L right side position			¼ turn R left side position			forward closed position		
fd	side	tog.	fd	fd	tog.	fd	fd	tog.	fd	fd	fd
open	open	close	open	open	close	open	open	close	open	(swing L	touch)
L	R	L	R	L	R	L	R	L	R	(hold)	(hold)

(time signature: 3/4)

Count	Call	Lead Indication	Step Pattern
1	fd	Diaphragm and R elbow.	Step forward L.
2	side	R palm.	Step side R.
3	tog.		Close L to R.
1	turn	Make an eighth turn L; lift R elbow slightly; press R fingers.	Make an eighth turn L (lady makes an eighth turn L) into R side position, and step forward R.
2	left		Step forward L instead of stepping to the side.
3	tog.		Close R to L.
1	turn	Make a quarter turn; lift R elbow slightly, press heel of R hand.	Make a quarter turn R (lady makes a quarter turn R) into L side position, and step forward L.
2	right		Step forward R.
3	tog.		Close L to R.
1	fd	Make an eighth turn L; press R fingers; lift both arms slightly.	Make an eighth turn L, returning to closed position; step forward R.
2	swing		Swing L leg forward.
3	touch		Touch L toe to floor in front of R.

POINTS TO EMPHASIZE:

1. After the first waltz step, which is taken in a forward direction, make the second and third waltzes zigzag into the L and R diagonals, respectively, progressing toward the LOD; thus the floor pattern will be as follows: forward, L diagonal, R diagonal, and forward.

Suggestions:

1. After practicing the above pattern, precede it with a balance backward L; one R turn, using two waltz steps; and one forward waltz.

2. Using eight measures of waltz rhythm, combine any of the waltz steps thus far presented into a pattern of your own making. The dancers' repertory of steps from which he may choose can be still further expanded by suggesting that he may also do three dance walks forward or backward in any of the standard dance positions, in place of a waltz step.

Lindy and Variations

Just after Charles Lindbergh made his famous flight to Paris in 1927 a new dance fad sprang up which was named the Lindbergh Hop in his honor. Later the name was shortened to the Lindy Hop and finally to the lindy; it is strictly an American dance, and like the Charleston, was probably much influenced by the American Negro. The early forms of the lindy were also known as "jitterbug," receiving this name from the wild, convulsive movement that characterized its early period. In its present form, the lindy, often referred to as "swing," has been tamed and smoothed, though it is still a lively, fast moving dance. The steps of the lindy are usually quite small, taken directly under the body; and while the movement itself is relaxed and easy, the bodies and arms of the dancers are held quite firm to provide the resistance needed to perform the somewhat intricate figures. The lindy can be danced to any fox trot music, but fast, syncopated rhythms provide the best accompaniment. Most jitterbug, swing, or lindy steps are based on the single, double, and triple lindy in various combinations. With knowledge of these basic steps it is possible to analyze any existing fad dance of a given area.

Single Lindy

The single lindy is the basic step pattern upon which all of the more complex forms are built. In rhythmic structure and step pattern it is exactly like the magic step, differing from it only in the direction in which the steps are taken. Instead of dancing in closed position, partners generally use hand contact only or "shine" position. Facing each other, the man holds the lady's R hand in his L. Arms are held waist high with elbows fairly close to the body.

Count	Call		Lead Indication	Step Pattern
1(–2)	sl or side		Press downward with the L hand to indicate the beginning of the step.	Step sideward L.
3(–4)	sl	side	Release pressure of L hand.	Step sideward R.
1	q	rock	Push partner away from you by pushing on her R arm.	Step backward L, a little behind R heel; both the lady and the man step back.
2	q	step	Pull partner toward you by pulling on her R arm.	Step in place R.

POINTS TO EMPHASIZE:

1. The step stays in place; it does not travel.
2. Since this step, like the magic step, requires a measure and a half for its completion, the first slow step should be slightly emphasized to enable partners to feel the rhythm and to stay together.
3. The secret of good following is to keep resistance in the arm that the man is holding, locking the bent elbow, and keeping the arm firmly attached to the body at the shoulder so that the arm and body move as one piece.
4. During the "rock–step" of the lindy, resistance and equal pull by both partners are necessary to maintain balance. The proper amount of arm tension needed to perform the rock–step successfully can be demonstrated by having partners hold both hands and lean away from each other, balancing on their heels.
5. During the rock–step, when the backward step is taken, the body does not lean backward, but remains forward over the forward foot.

SUGGESTIONS:

1. When first practicing the lindy, dancers may find it helpful to hold both hands, the lady's L in the man's R and her R in the man's L, rather than use the single hand hold.
2. Since a lindy step is related to six instead of the usual four beats of 4/4 meter, it is sometimes easier for students to count the rhythm as a "six" instead of a phrasing of "four" and "two," but one must first be assured that the students are fully aware of the correct rhythmic relationship of the step pattern and the meter.

Double Lindy

Usually dancers find the double lindy more interesting and challenging than the single lindy and it is desirable to progress to this step as soon as possible. There are several versions of the double lindy, but in all of them each of the first two slow steps are divided into two equal parts (1–2) (3–4) by changing the simple basic step to a ball–heel, or a tap–step or step–tap, or a step–hop or step–kick, depending upon local preferences. Analysis for the ball–heel version of the double lindy is given below:

	ball side open	heel	ball side open	heel	step back open	step forward open
$\frac{4}{4}$	L	L	R	R	L	R

Count	Call		Lead Indication	Step Pattern
1	sl or ball		Press downward with L hand to indicate the beginning of the step.	Place ball of L foot to the side, shifting the weight onto it.
2	heel			Lower L heel to the floor.
3	sl or ball		Release pressure of L hand.	Place ball of the R foot to the side.
4	heel			Lower R heel to the floor.
1	q	rock	Push partner away from you.	Step backward L, a little behind R heel.
2	q	step	Pull partner toward you.	Step in place R.

Points to Emphasize: All of the points mentioned for the single lindy apply to the double lindy.

Suggestions: Depending upon what is popular in the local area, the following variations may be practiced:

1. Substitute a step–bend for the ball–heel pattern. Step side L (count 1); bend the L knee (count 2); step side R (count 3); bend the R knee (count 4); rock back (count 1); and step in place (count 2).

2. Substitute a step–touch for the ball–heel pattern. Step side L (count 1); touch the R toe to the floor beside the toe of the L foot, bending the knees slightly and turning the body slightly to the R (count 2); step side R (count 3); touch the L toe to the floor beside the toe at the R foot (count 4); then add the "rock–step," which remains unchanged throughout the variations.

3. Reverse the procedure. Touch the L toe to the floor beside the R foot, bending both knees slightly; step side L, straightening the knees; touch the R toe beside the L foot, bending the knees; step side R, straightening the knees. This bending and straightening of the knees adds to the sense of syncopation by emphasizing the second and fourth counts of the music.

4. Take two even step–hops on the first measure, lifting the free foot to the rear on the hops.

5. Take two step–kicks on the first measure, kicking from the knee and turning the body slightly to face the kicking leg. This pattern

may also be reversed and done as a kick–step. Different double lindys may also be combined; e.g., step–touch, step–kick, rock–step.

Triple Lindy

In the triple lindy, a *step–ball–change* is substituted for the first two basic steps in the single lindy. The step–ball–change is taken with the feet in close contact with the floor, in a very flat-footed manner that might be described as a sort of shuffling step.

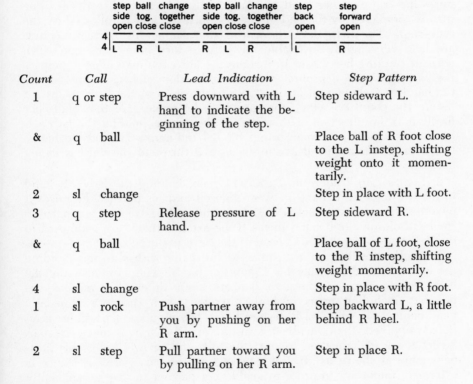

	step ball change	step ball change	step	step
	side tog. together	side tog. together	back	forward
	open close close	open close close	open	open
4/4	L R L	R L R	L	R

Count	Call	Lead Indication	Step Pattern
1	q or step	Press downward with L hand to indicate the beginning of the step.	Step sideward L.
&	q ball		Place ball of R foot close to the L instep, shifting weight onto it momentarily.
2	sl change		Step in place with L foot.
3	q step	Release pressure of L hand.	Step sideward R.
&	q ball		Place ball of L foot, close to the R instep, shifting weight momentarily.
4	sl change		Step in place with R foot.
1	sl rock	Push partner away from you by pushing on her R arm.	Step backward L, a little behind R heel.
2	sl step	Pull partner toward you by pulling on her R arm.	Step in place R.

POINTS TO EMPHASIZE:

1. On the step–ball–change, remember to keep the feet close to the floor. During the count 1–&–2, keep the weight mostly on the L foot, shifting to the R only momentarily at "–&." Permit very little up and down movement in this weight change.

SUGGESTIONS: The triple lindy is often used in combination with the double lindy, i.e:

	tap	step	step ball change	rock	step
4/4	R	L	R L R	L	R

Turns and Variations

The lindy in all of its forms is never done as a simple step with partners facing throughout the dance. Interest is derived from the variety of turning patterns that are made by both the lady and the man. Most turns commence on the first step of the pattern, and the direction in which the steps in the first measure are taken may change according to need. The rock–step, however, remains consistent.

1. *Lady's Right Underarm Turn:* The man extends his L hand, in which he is holding his partner's R, sideward to the L, and as he then raises his arm over her head, the lady turns once around to the R. The turn is completed by the end of the first measure and is followed by the rock–step. The man does the entire step facing his partner. Hands are held very lightly to enable the lady to turn under the man's arm without twisting her wrist. In turning the lady, the man must anticipate the turn and give a preliminary lead indication such as a pressure of the hand or a slight pull in the opposite direction of the turn an instant before the count on which the turn is to be made. He then pulls her firmly into the direction of the turn. If the man is holding the lady's R hand and in his R, the man brings his R hand across his body to his L; he raises it over her head as she makes a R turn and she finishes facing her partner.

2. *Lady's Left Underarm Turn:* The man, holding the lady's R hand in his L brings his L hand between himself and his partner; he raises it over her head as she makes a L turn and finishes facing her partner. If he is holding her R hand in his R, he extends the R arm sideward to the R, lifting it over the lady's head as she turns to the L.

It is also possible for the turns to be made with the man holding the lady's L hand in either his L hand or his R. Thus, by changing the hand relationships of the two dancers eight different variations are possible, including turns in both directions with the four man–lady hand contacts: L–R, L–L, R–R, and R–L. The number of possible variations is doubled when the above turns are made with no contact, the man giving the lead indication to start the turn and then releasing his partner's hand as she turns. In this type of turn the lady's arm resistance is extremely important in order to enable her partner to give a sufficiently strong lead indication to turn her completely around.

It is also possible for both dancers to turn at the same time; or for the man to turn while the lady faces her partner.

3. *The Freshman Break*, for example, in which only the man turns, is performed as follows: The man, holding his lady's R hand in his L, makes a turn to the L into his own L arm. He places the lady's R hand on his R hip, releasing it as he continues to turn. When he has completed the turn he can switch hands if he wishes to do so, by taking her R hand in his R hand instead of his left.

4. *Egg-Beater Turn, or Cuddle:* Partners hold both hands, and the man leads his partner into a L turn without releasing either of her hands; this wraps the lady in toward his R side. The man's arm is around the

lady's waist, holding her L hand. The lady's arms are crossed in front, thus the name "egg-beater." This position is also called "cuddle" for obvious reasons. The rock–step is then done in this position. On the next pattern the man unwraps the lady, releasing her R hand as he pushes her forward with his R elbow into a R turn, causing her to spin away from him so that they end face to face.

5. *Wheel:* Partners can also move around each other. They begin in a "handshake" position, the lady's R in the man's R. Partners lean away from each other and move clockwise around in a circle, doing a double or triple lindy or any of its combinations.

6. *Right and Left Hip Change:* Partners hold both hands, and each makes a quarter turn L so the R hips are together for the first step–ball–change; the man's R arm and the girl's L are extended sideward at shoulder height. For the second step–ball–change, partners each make a half-turn R so that L hips are together and the opposite arms are extended sideward. Partners face each other directly during the rock–step and keep a strong arm resistance. All the while, the two dancers are progressing clockwise around a center point as described above for the wheel.

7. *Shoulder Pass:* The man holds the lady's R hand in his L.

a. On the first step–ball–change, partners move forward toward each other, the lady a little to the L of the man. They each step forward again pivoting halfway to the L as they pass by each other, and take the ball–change in place. Partners have now changed places and finish with the rock–step in their new positions.

b. Changing places with a shoulder pass may also be done with the lady turning to the R under the man's L arm.

SUGGESTIONS: Various combinations of these turns and other figures can be made:

1. Combine two double or triple basics (a "basic" being a lindy done in place, partners facing), a lady's L underarm turn, and a lady's R underarm turn, and repeat.

2. Combine one basic, with partners holding both hands; one egg-beater (2 lindys) finishing with the man holding the lady's L hand in his R; and one man's R turn, ending with partners holding both hands ready to repeat the sequence.

3. Begin with the man holding the lady's R hand in his L. Combine one lady's L underarm turn; one lady's R underarm turn, changing to handshake position (R in R) on the rock–step; continue with a clockwise wheel (4 triple lindys); do one no contact turn, the lady turning L, the man turning R, changing hands to the lady's R in the man's L; and finish with one shoulder pass, the lady turning under the man's R arm.

4. To eight measures of music, create a combination of your own choosing.

Rhumba and Variations

The rhumba is a Cuban dance of African origin. According to legend it evolved from the restricted movement of the slaves in the chain gangs who, with heavy loads balanced on their heads, were unable to look down at the ground—hence the cautious walking step. Whether this account is true or not, it makes an interesting story.

The body carriage for the rhumba is extremely proud, with firmly held abdominal muscles and a strongly lifted rib-cage held quiet so that there is no movement in the upper body. In closed position the man's hand is placed slightly more to the L side of the follower's back than for other ballroom dance steps. The characteristic motion of the rhumba is attained by a delayed action in, the weight transfer, causing the knees to bend and straighten alternately. The knee action produces a subtle side-to-side motion in the hips; this motion should be minimized.

The weight shift is very important. Because it is unlike the natural way of stepping, the movement is difficult to learn and difficult to teach. A North American version of the rhumba permits the weight to be shifted simultaneously with the step, but this version does not possess the Latin flavor. When the step is performed in its proper styling, the foot is placed flat on the floor with the knee bent, and the weight transfer is delayed until time for the next step to be taken. The movement might be compared with the way one might step if he were walking on eggs, hesitant to shift the weight for fear the eggs might break. The knee of the foot that is placed on the floor, without the weight, is always bent; the supporting knee is always straight. The basic step of the rhumba is the Cuban walk.

Cuban Walk

	fd		fd	fd		fd	fd	fd	
	open		open	open	or	open	open	open	
4	────────	─	────────	────────		────────	────────	────────	─
4	L		R	L		L	R	L	

Either rhythm is permissible, but the first rhythm is preferable. The rhumba will be analyzed according to the first rhythm.

Count	Call	Lead Indication	Step Pattern
1(–2)	sl	R elbow; release R palm.	Move the whole L foot forward, placing it on the floor without transferring the weight.

Count	Call	*Lead Indication*	*Step Pattern*
3	q		Transfer the weight quickly onto the L foot and move the R foot forward.
4	q		Transfer the weight quickly into the R foot and move the L foot forward.

POINTS TO EMPHASIZE:

1. Keep the size of the steps very small, and step in a gingerly manner.
2. Avoid any staccato movement in the knees and hips, and try to maintain a continuous flowing movement with a gradual transfer of weight from one foot to the other.
3. Constantly check the body carriage and the weight transfer to ensure correct styling.

SUGGESTIONS:

1. To introduce the Cuban walk, stand with the feet together and shift the weight from one foot to the other, straightening the knee of the supporting leg, while bending the other one (as if waiting for a bus). The bent knee rolls in, slightly overlapping the straightened one.
2. Now start with the feet together with the L knee bent and the weight on the R foot, the R knee straight. Move the L foot forward in close contact with the floor, keeping the knee bent; then transfer the weight onto it, straightening the L knee while simultaneously moving the R foot forward, with the knee bent, and no weight transfer. Continue in this manner, moving forward with alternate feet.
3. Do the step in the slow–quick–quick rhythm, indicated above, and the pattern becomes the Cuban walk.
4. Now try the pattern, moving backward. When stepping backward, place the ball of the foot in back, and roll back onto the whole foot as the weight is shifted.
5. Practice the Cuban walk both forward and backward, changing smoothly from one direction to the other.

Box Step

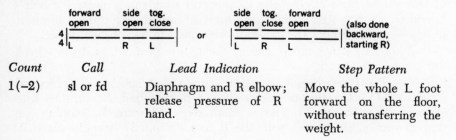

Count	Call	*Lead Indication*	*Step Pattern*
1(–2)	sl or fd	Diaphragm and R elbow; release pressure of R hand.	Move the whole L foot forward on the floor, without transferring the weight.

Count	Call	Lead Indication	Step Pattern
3	q or side		Transfer weight quickly onto L foot and move the whole R foot sideward on the floor, without transferring the weight.
4	q close		Transfer the weight quickly onto R foot, and close L foot to R without transferring the weight.

To complete the box step, the same step is taken backward, commencing with the R foot, as in the fox trot box step. The lead indication in moving backward is a slight pressure with the palm of the R hand.

POINTS TO EMPHASIZE:

1. Be sure to make the steps directly forward, or backward, and sideward.
2. Keep the entire box step confined to a very limited area.

Variations

When these two rhumba steps have been learned, they may be used as the basis for many variations created largely through changes in partner relationship. The following variations are suggested.

1. *Ladies' Underarm Circle:* Starting from a closed position, the lady, performing a Cuban walk, circles to her own R under the upraised L arm of the man, while he executes two box steps in place. As a lead indication, the man releases his hold on the lady with his R hand and raises his L hand, which is holding her R, making a small clockwise circle with his hand while she turns.

2. *Arch Turn:* This turn, a variation of the ladies' underarm circle, may be done with the lady turning around quickly on the first count of the man's forward box step, returning in time to join her partner on the backward part of the box step. Instead of making a small circle with his L hand, the man places his hand over the lady's head, as a lead indication, and helps to twirl her around in place.

3. *Lady-Around-the-Man:* This pattern is actually another variation of ladies' underarm circle. The lady begins by turning under the man's L arm on the first step of the man's forward box, then continues to circle to the R, going around the man, and returning to her original place.

4. *Wheel:* In either the R side or the L side position, partners wheel, using the Cuban walk.

5. *Yale Break:* Starting in closed position, take a half box step forward (measure 1). On the next rhumba, step sideward R, turning into open position (count 1); take a small step backward L, keeping the step in very close contact with the R foot (count 2); step in place R,

returning to closed position (count —&) (measure 2). Reverse the action of measure 2, beginning L, turning into reverse open position and back to closed position (measure 3). Repeat the action of measure 2, turning into open position and back to closed position (measure 4). The lady does the counterpart. The man changes his hands on the lady's waist as she turns from side to side.

SUGGESTIONS:

1. Using eight measures of music, combine one box step (measures 1–2) with an arch turn (measure 3), a half box step backward (measure 4), and finish with the Yale Break (measures 5–8).

2. Using eight measures of music, combine one box step (measures 1–2) with one wheel in R side position (measures 3–5), a half box step backward as the lady begins an underarm circle (measure 6) which she then completes (measures 7–8).

3. Combine one box step in closed position (measures 1–2) and one ladies' underarm circle (measure 3), at the end of which the man places his L hand, in which he is holding the lady's R, on his R hip (measure 4); as she continues moving clockwise around behind him, he releases his L hand and with it takes the lady's L hand as she arrives at his L side; with his R hand he grasps the lady's R hand which is still on his R hip (measures 5–6); together the man and lady wheel once around clockwise, and during the turn he guides the lady over to his R side where they take varsouvienne position (measures 7–8); they continue wheeling clockwise for a second time moving backward (measures 9–10), at the end of which the man raises his L hand and the lady turns clockwise under his raised L arm (measures 11–12); as she completes her turn, he releases her hands and they return to closed position. This combination is sometimes called "around-the-world."

4. To sixteen measures of music, create a combination of your own choosing.

Samba and Variations

The samba is a native dance of Brazil, probably of African origin. Originally, it was a wild and barbaric dance performed at Carnival time, but later became more refined when it was introduced into the ballroom. In its early form as a ballroom step, it was extremely bouncy, but gradually the dance has been modified until now the movements are relaxed and somewhat pendular, with a joyous, lilting quality.

Basic Samba

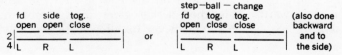

Count	Call	Lead Indication	Step Pattern
1	q or fd	Raise R elbow; press with R thumb and forefinger.	Step forward L. As the forward step is taken, the upper body leans backward in opposition to the foot.
&	q ʻball	Tilt R elbow up and lean body slightly to the L.	Take a very small sideward step to the R with the inside part of the ball of the R foot.
2	sl change		Close L to R.

The forward step alternates with a backward step which is similar in form to the forward step, with the following exceptions:

Count	Call	Lead Indication	Step Pattern
1	q or bk	Lower R elbow; press with R little finger.	Step backward R. As the backward step is taken, the upper body leans forward in opposition to the foot.
&	q ball	Tilt R elbow down and lean body slightly to the R.	Take a very small sideward step to the L with the inside part of the ball of the L foot.
2	sl change		Close R to L.

The pattern as described above creates a slight rolling motion in the body because the upper body is always made to lean in opposition to the direction of the stepping foot. For some people this coordination may seem a little too complex; it can be simplified by eliminating the sideward movement altogether, and taking alternately a forward step–ball–change and a backward step–ball–change, with the body rocking in opposition to the feet; i.e., the upper body rocks back on the forward step–ball–change, and forward on the backward step–ball–change.

POINTS TO EMPHASIZE:

1. In closed position, the man's R hand is placed in the center of his partner's back to control the body tilt.
2. The forward step is always begun with the L and the backward step with the R by both the man and the lady.
3. There is a slight down–up–down–up in the knees. On the forward step the movement of the body is accented downward, with a bending of the knee; on the sideward step, it is upward, with a straightening of the knee; and on the closing step the accent is again downward. This knee action gives to the movement a relaxed bounce, which should never be allowed to become jerky.

4. Although the knees are relaxed, the body itself, should be kept lifted; otherwise, the samba movement becomes very tiring to perform.

5. The tilting of the upper body forward and backward in opposition to the feet gives the impression of a swinging pendulum; or, if the sideward movement is also stressed, creates an undulating circular motion.

Variations

There are numerous variations of the basic samba. Among the most popular of these variations are the following:

1. *Pendulum:* Do the step–ball–change, moving from side to side; take the first step to the side; cross slightly behind on the second step or "ball"; and step in place on the change. Both the lady and the man cross in back. As the body moves from side to side, the oppositional tilt of the body is exaggerated; the extended arms are lifted as the dancers cross to the man's L and are lowered as they cross to the R. This step is called the *pendulum* because of the body and arm action.

2. *Maxixe:* Another variation of the basic samba step is the *maxixe,* pronounced "mä-chē-chä." This step is done individually or in open position, always in a forward direction. Take a short step forward on the L (q); step backward a few inches on the ball of the R foot (q); shift the weight onto the L foot, pulling it backward a few inches toward the R (sl); then repeat the movement, beginning with the other foot, and continue alternately. On the first quick step, the hips are pressed slightly forward, causing the upper body to lean back; as the forward foot is pulled back on count two, the hips are pressed slightly backward, causing the upper body to lean forward. When the step pattern is done individually, there is also an arm pattern that accompanies it. As the forward step is made with the L foot, the L arm is brought forward, with the elbow bent, and the fingers toward the ceiling. The fingertips of the R hand are touching the L elbow. When the forward step is made with the R foot, the arm position is reversed.

3. *Paddle Turn:* This step is really nothing more than a folk dance "buzz step"; it is usually done individually by the dancers, following the maxixe, with partners turning in opposite directions, but it can also be done at other times and in closed position. The paddle turn requires at least two measures for its completion.

Count	*Call*	*Lead Indication*	*Step Pattern*
1	q or step	Press with heel of R hand and give a slight push with the L hand to start the girl spinning.	Step onto L foot.

Count	Call	Lead Indication	Step Pattern
&	q or push		Place ball of R foot to the side and push, turning the body counterclockwise.
2	q	step	Step onto L, continuing to turn L.
&	q	push	Place ball of R foot to R side, continuing to turn L.
1	q	step	Step onto L, continuing to turn L.
&	q	push	Place ball of R foot to R side, continuing to turn L.
2	sl	step	Step onto L foot. The L foot is placed in the same spot on the floor each time while the R foot moves around it.

Change, and go in the opposite direction, starting with the R foot and turning R. As a lead indication, the man takes the lady's R hand in his L, and pulls to start her spinning in the opposite direction.

SUGGESTIONS:

1. Combine four basic samba steps, forward and backward twice; four pendulum steps; four maxixe steps in open position; and one paddle turn with partners turning away from each other, and another paddle turn reversing the direction (16 measures).
2. To sixteen measures of samba music, create your own combination of steps.

Mambo

Musically, the mambo is a sort of "off-beat" rhumba, a fusion of the rhumba and American jazz that necessitated the creation of a new dance step appropriate to its syncopated rhythm. There is less hip movement in the mambo than in the rhumba, but considerably more movement in the arms and upper body; it may be danced in conventional positions or may also include a series of breakaway and solo steps in shine position. Although the correct styling for the mambo is with a delayed weight shift, as in the rhumba, mastery of this technique is seldom within the capabilities of beginning dancers. For this reason the mambo has been presented here with the normal weight shift characterstic of the dance walk.

Basic Mambo

		fd open	fd open	tog. close	(also done
4/4					backward,
		L	R	L	starting R)

Count	Call	Lead Indication	Step Pattern
(1)	(hold)	In its authentic form, the mambo is a no contact dance and the lady follows the man by watching his movement; however, it may also be done in closed rhumba-hold position.	Hold, with feet together, weight on the R foot.
2	q or fd	R elbow; press fingers of R hand.	Step forward L, simultaneously twisting shoulders to the L.
3	q bk	Press heel of R hand.	Step back onto R foot, commencing to return shoulders to their normal position.
4	sl close		Bring L foot to R.

The above pattern is then taken in a backward direction. Alternate the forward and backward mambo steps, as in the basic samba.

POINTS TO EMPHASIZE:

1. The R shoulder is always twisted forward on the first step of the basic mambo, in this instance on count 2, regardless of whether the step is taken forward or backward.

2. The "hold" value is often placed on beats other than the first beat; e.g., the step could be begun on count 1 so that the rhythmic pattern would become 1–2–3 hold; but the pattern given here is especially interesting because it emphasizes the syncopated quality of the music. Wherever the hold is placed, there should be no obvious body movement during that count.

3. When the dance is done without partner contact, the arms are held with the elbows bent and are moved with the shoulders.

The mambo is a difficult step to do correctly, and perhaps because of this its popularity has been superseded by the cha cha cha; it has been included in this chapter principally to explain the derivation of the cha cha cha and to point out similarities and differences between the two steps. Mambo variations are similar to those given for the cha cha cha.

Cha Cha Cha and Variations

In the cha cha cha, which has been evolved from the mambo, three steps (quick–quick–slow) have been substituted for the single closing step of the mambo. The name of the step has been derived from the "cha cha cha" sound made by the feet of the dancers in the performance of these three steps. Because the number of steps has been increased, the cha cha cha rhythm is normally slower than that of the mambo. As with the mambo, the correct styling for the cha cha cha is with a delayed action weight shift, but few people pay attention to this styling detail. Both the mambo and the cha cha cha are begun on the second beat of the measure which gives an intriguing syncopation to the movement pattern; however, many dancers prefer to begin the step on the first beat, following the natural accents of the music. With beginning students, it is probably wise to follow the latter procedure until the dancers have gained sufficient rhythmic security to enjoy the challenge of the syncopated rhythm. The step is analyzed both ways in the diagrams that follow.

Basic Cha Cha Cha

Beginning on count 2—

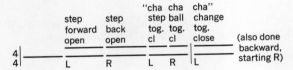

A combination of one forward pattern and one backward pattern constitutes the basic cha cha cha.

Count	Call	Lead Indication	Step Pattern
(1)	(hold)		Hold, with feet together, weight on R foot.
2	sl or fd	In closed position, raise R elbow and release pressure of R hand.	Step forward L, as described for the mambo— but with only a suggestion of the twisting of the shoulders.
3	sl bk	Press with palm of R hand.	Step back onto R foot, returning the shoulders to their normal position.
4	q step		Step onto L foot, placing it beside the R.
&	q ball		Step in place on ball of R foot.
1	sl change		Step in place on L foot.

Beginning on count one—

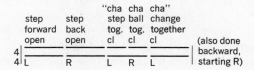

	step forward open	step back open	"cha cha cha" step ball change tog. tog. together cl cl cl	
4				(also done
4	L	R	L R L	backward, starting R)

Count	Call		Lead Indication	Step Pattern
1	sl or fd		In closed position, raise R elbow and release pressure of R hand.	Step forward L as described for the mambo— but with only a suggestion of the twisting of the shoulders.
2	sl	bk	Press with palm of R hand.	Step back onto R foot, returning the shoulders to their normal position.
3	q	step		Step onto L foot, placing it beside the R.
&	q	ball		Step in place on ball of R foot.
4	sl	change		Step in place on L foot.

POINTS TO EMPHASIZE:

1. Do not slide the feet on the floor in stepping; pick them up and place them down.
2. Always begin the forward step with the L foot and the backward step with the R foot.

SUGGESTIONS:

1. Practice the step first in two lines facing each other, with no contact between partners; then practice it with partners holding both hands or holding one hand (the man's L, the lady's R) before taking the steps in closed position. All of these positions are used on the dance floor.
2. Do the basic cha cha cha pattern and travel on the three "cha cha cha" steps instead of taking them in place; the pattern becomes fd–bk–bk-bk-bk; bk–fd–fd-fd-fd. Be sure that the feet pass each other on each of the three steps.
3. When the dancers become fairly expert in the performance of the simple cha cha cha, practice incorporating a subtle delayed action shift of weight as in the rhumba. This technique, though difficult, adds authenticity to the movement.

Variations

1. *Cross Break:* Cross the L over the R (count 2), turning to face R; step back into place (count 3); and do the last three steps, or the "cha

cha cha" (counts 4–&–1) in place, facing forward as in the beginning. Both the man and the lady step across in front on the first step, but the lady starts with her R, crossing to the L first. Cross the R over the L, turning to face L (count 2); step back in place (count 3); and do the "cha cha cha" (counts 4–&–1) in place. The step is begun with partners holding both hands. As they start the step the man releases his R hand, and partners change hands when the direction of the step is reversed. The lead is begun after the man has completed one forward cha cha cha pattern. He then takes the first two steps of his backward cha cha cha (back–forward), and on the three quick steps he turns to his R so that the next cha cha cha is the cross break. The lead indication is a push–pull action of the hand.

2. *Cha Cha Cha Turn:* A turn can be made by stepping across, as described above for the cross break (count 2); continuing to turn around to the R on the second step (count 3) (the lady turns L); and finally facing forward again on the "cha cha cha" (counts 4–&–1). This step can be done in both directions. The lead consists of a strong push and a quick release of the hand.

3. *Pursuit Turn:* This turn is done by stepping forward L on the first step (count 2); while making a half pivot to face backward, then shifting the weight to the R foot, which has remained in place (count 3); and taking the "cha cha cha" in place. On the second pattern, the first step is taken forward R, while pivoting L to face front again (count 2); the weight is then transferred to the L (count 3); and the "cha cha cha" is taken in place (counts 4–&–1). This is a no-contact step. The man starts the turn first, taking a half turn away from the lady, while she does a backward pattern without turning. On the second pattern the man turns to face the lady as she makes a half turn away from him. In this way partners appear to be in pursuit of each other. They continue turning (back-to-face) in this fashion until the man decides to stop. To return to a face-to-face relationship the man simply does the pattern without turning while the lady makes one more half turn to face her partner.

4. *Shine Step:* The forward pattern is performed as described for the basic step, with the body turning to the R on the forward step. On the "cha cha cha," the body has turned to the L, and the first step (count 4) is taken by the L foot in a backward direction; the R foot crosses in front of the L foot (count –&) and the L foot steps backward again (count 1). Similarly, on the second pattern, the body turns to the R on the backward step; on the "cha cha cha," the body has turned to the L, and the R foot steps forward (count 4); the L foot crosses in back of the R (count –&); and the R foot steps forward again (count 1). The man and the lady dovetail into each other and the step has a grapevine effect.

5. *Heel–Toe Step:* In this variation a heel–toe pattern is substituted for the first two slow steps as follows: on count 2, the L heel is placed on the floor slightly to the side, and the body makes an eighth turn L;

on count 3 the body turns to the R and the toe of the L foot is placed on the floor, knees touching and bending; the "cha cha cha" steps are then done as side–close–side (counts 4-&-1), beginning with the L foot. The whole pattern may then be repeated to the opposite side. Partners use a two-hand hold for this step variation.

SUGGESTIONS:

1. Combine a basic step, one forward pattern and one backward pattern; two heel–toe steps; one cross break to each side; and two cha cha cha turns (8 measures).

2. Combine one basic step, four pursuit turns, ending face to face, one heel–toe step, and one cha cha cha turn (8 measures).

3. To eight measures of cha cha cha music create your own combination of steps.

Tango and Variations

The tango in its traditional styling is one of the most sensuous, dramatic, and highly sophisticated of all social dance forms. Having its roots in the Andalusian gypsy dancing of Spain, the tango flowered in South America where it became the national dance of Argentina. It was later popularized in the United States by Irene and Vernon Castle in the early twentieth century. In Argentina, the gauchos with spurs on their heels performed the dance with señoritas in full, ruffled skirts. The typical "drawing in" of the foot in the tango can be attributed to effort on the part of the gaucho to get his spurs safely out of the way of other dancers. Furthermore, it was often necessary for the man to step obliquely in order to avoid stepping on his partner's dress, and sudden reversals of direction that characterize the tango often required the lady to perform a decorative flick of her skirt with the foot in order to facilitate the turn.

In the tango the dancers' bodies are held in very close contact, with diaphragms together; but upper bodies are drawn apart, with the lady looking over her left shoulder away from the man, creating an air of haughty indifference. An amusing, though perhaps fanciful reason is given for this body relationship. In the early days the gauchos liked to ride from the pampas directly into town where they would commandeer a girl and commence to dance. The ladies who found the manly odor of their partners somewhat less than delicate, retreated in the only way possible to them. Although this exaggerated styling is greatly modified for ballroom use, the fact remains that when a tango is well executed, bodies are lifted, the man's hand is placed low on his partner's back (at the small of the back), holding her firmly so that her diaphragm is pressed against his own. In the traditional tango dancers stand exactly face to face, but beginning dancers may find it more comfortable to move if the lady stands slightly to the R of the man. Partners' shoulders are kept parallel so that even on the cross-over steps in semi-open position only the hips are permitted to turn. Knees remain slightly bent throughout the dance, with the hips neither forward nor backward, and all of the movement is made very horizontal so that there is no "down-up" movement whatsoever, even when the feet are drawn together. Tango movement has been called "cat-like" because of the way that smooth, slow movements, reluctantly executed, are contrasted with quick, decisive direction changes and sudden holds.

The dance walk of the tango involves a greater use of the knee and lifting of the foot when stepping than any other ballroom step. The lady always brings her free foot up to her supporting foot on all walking or promenading steps so that she is ready for any sudden change of direction. There is also a very subtle countermotion in the body so that as the L foot steps forward the R shoulder twists slightly forward, and vice versa. Although the steps of the tango are quite simple, it is their subtlety of styling that is so difficult for beginning ballroom dancers to master.

The meter of the Argentine tango is a slow 2/4 which sounds deceivingly like 4/4 because of the strongly accented eighth notes in the bass. A rhythmic pattern characteristic of many tango figures is a slow–slow–quick–quick–slow, requiring two measures for its completion.

Tango Promenade

The basic tango promenade is a pattern that can be varied in several ways and can be combined with other tango steps. The *closed forward promenade* is performed in closed position as follows:

	forward open	forward open	fd open	side open	draw* close	
2 4 L		R	L	R	(R)	(also done backward)

Count	Call	Lead Indication	Step Pattern
1	sl or fd	Diaphragm and R elbow.	Step forward L.
2	sl fd		Step forward R.
1	q fd		Step forward L.
&	q side	Sideward pressure R palm.	Step sideward R.

* These last three steps (forward–side–draw) performed in a quick–quick–slow rhythm are known as a "tango-close" which can be added to any tango figure to complete the phrase.

Count	Call	Lead Indication	Step Pattern
2	sl draw	Continued sideward pressure of R palm.	Draw L foot slowly to R foot without transferring the weight.

POINTS TO EMPHASIZE:

1. Maintain diaphragm contact with partner and a quiet, regal, completely controlled upper body. (The lady is equally responsible for maintaining this diaphragm contact while at the same time offering resistance in her upper body by leaning back slightly.)
2. Keep the knees slightly bent at all times, and make each step large and very decisive, deliberately lifting the stepping foot from the floor and placing it down again. Avoid all up-and-down movement in the body.
3. Make the direction change from forward to sideward quick and definite.
4. Draw the free foot to the supporting one slowly, with resistance.
5. Do not transfer the weight after drawing the free foot to the supporting one. To prevent the lady from shifting her weight to the closing foot the man maintains a slight sideward pressure with his R palm.

Variations

The closed forward or backward promenade can provide the basis for a number of simple variations.

1. *Parallel Forward Promenade:* In closed position, begin the pattern by making an eighth turn R. Take the first two steps forward into the LOD so that the steps are actually on a slight diagonal in relation to the body (counts 1–2). (On the second step the man steps with his R foot to the R side of the lady's feet rather than in between them.) On the third forward step (the first quick step) (count 1) make an eighth turn L to face the LOD again. Complete the pattern with a "side-draw," stepping sideward R, and drawing the L foot to the R as in the closed forward promenade (counts –&–2).
2. *Forward Promenade with a Quarter Turn Left:* In closed position, take the first two steps forward into the LOD (counts 1–2). Make a quarter turn L on the third forward step (the first quick step) (count 1); and complete the pattern with a side-draw, moving sideward toward the LOD (counts –&–2).
3. *Left Turn Promenade:* In closed position, step sideward L with the L foot (count 1); cross the R foot in front of L (lady crossing L foot in front of R) (count 2); step forward into LOD, pivoting a half turn L (count 1); and complete the pattern with a side-draw (counts –&–2). The man is now facing counter to the LOD.

4. *Right Turn Promenade:* In closed position, step sideward L with the L foot (count 1); cross the R foot in front of L (count 2); step sideward L with the L foot, pivoting a half turn R (count 1); and complete the pattern with a side-draw (counts –&–2).

5. *Open Promenade:* Standing sideward to the LOD with hips turned into semi-open position but shoulders parallel, take the first two steps forward into the LOD (counts 1–2). On the third step the man makes a half turn L while pulling the lady into closed position (count 1), and completes the pattern with a side-draw into the LOD (counts –&–2).

6. *Forward Promenade with Cross-over:* In closed position, step sideward with the L foot (count 1); cross the R foot in front of L with the heel of the foot leading (lady crossing the L foot in *back* of R) (count 2); step forward L (count 1); and complete the pattern with a side-draw (counts –&–2).

7. *Reverse Cross Promenade:* In semi-open position, as described for open promenade, step forward with the L foot (count 1), step forward with the R foot (count 2); turn into reverse open position and step through with the L foot, counter to the LOD (count 1); complete the pattern by turning into closed position and taking the side-draw counter to the LOD (counts –&–2).

SUGGESTIONS:

1. Using eight measures of music, combine one closed forward promenade (measures 1–2); one right turn promenade (measures 3–4); and one left turn promenade (measures 5–6); and one closed forward promenade (measures 7–8).

2. Using eight measures of music, combine one parallel forward promenade (measures 1–2); one forward promenade with a quarter turn left (measures 3–4); one open promenade (measures 5–6); and a reverse cross promenade (measures 7–8).

3. Using eight measures of music, create a combination of your own.

Habanera

The habanera is a forward and backward rocking step performed very smoothly in a quick-quick-slow rhythm.

Count	Call	Lead Indication	Step Pattern
1	q or fd	Diaphragm and R elbow.	Step forward L.
&	q bk	Press palm of R hand.	Step backward R.
2	sl fd	Diaphragm and R elbow.	Step forward L.

The habanera is sometimes repeated, beginning R, to complete the two measure phrase.

POINTS TO EMPHASIZE:

1. Keep the upper body quiet by controlling the movement in the ankle, knee, and hip joints.
2. Rock onto the whole of the forward foot and the ball of the back foot.
3. Keep the feet in position; don't allow the rear foot to creep forward.

Variations

1. *Rock-Change Step:* Rock forward and backward (counts 1–&–), and step backward (count 2).

SUGGESTIONS:

1. Using eight measures of music, combine one habanera forward L with one habanera forward R (measures 1–2); one closed forward promenade (measures 3–4); one habanera forward L with one rock-change step R (measures 5–6); and one forward promenade with cross-over (measures 7–8).

Corté or Dip

The corté is not a dance figure but an embellishment; it is a moderately deep step or dip, usually followed by a change of direction. In exhibition dancing the dip is often exaggerated, but it is performed more conservatively on the ballroom dance floor. The man takes a moderately long step backward with his L foot and then bends the L knee, turning it outward to avoid his partner's R knee. The lead for the backward corté is a diagonally donward pressure with the R arm and hand as the supporting knee is bent. The corté may also be taken in a forward direction. The lead for the forward corté is a forward pressure of the diaphragm and release of the R hand followed by a knee bend.

POINTS TO EMPHASIZE:

1. Turn the foot and knee out when stepping into the corté to provide space for the lady's foot and knee. (The lady takes a large step, placing her foot as close as possible to her partner's).
2. Keep the weight balanced over the dipping foot.
3. Don't allow the hips to protrude; keep the hips under when stepping backward, and keep the hips pressed forward when stepping forward.
4. Don't lunge or fall into the corté. Step first and then bend the knee smoothly.
5. Keep the free foot in contact with the floor during the corté.

The corté is combined with other steps in many ways. Below are a few combinations.

1. *Fundamental Corté:* Step forward L (count 1); close the R foot to the L (count &); corté backward L (count 2).

2. *Single Corté With A Tango-Close:* Corté backward L (count 1); step forward R (count 2); step forward L (count 1); and complete the pattern with a side-draw (counts –&–2).

3. *Medio Corté With A Tango-Close:* This pattern is interesting because of its irregular phrasing with the music:

medio corté				medio corté				tango-close		
fd open	bk open	bk corté	fd open	fd open	bk open	bk corté	fd open	fd open	side open	draw close
L	R	L	R	L	R	L	R	L	R	(R)

$\frac{2}{4}$

Count	Call		Lead Indication	Step Pattern
1	q or fd		Diaphragm and R elbow.	Step forward L.
&	q	bk	Slight pressure R palm.	Step backward R.
2	sl	corté	Continued pressure R palm, followed by knee bend.	Take a slightly longer step backward L and then bend L knee.
1	sl	fd.	Diaphragm and R elbow.	Step forward R.
2	q	fd		Step forward L.
&	q	bk	Slight pressure R palm.	Step backward R.
1	sl	corté	Continued pressure R palm, followed by knee bend.	Take a slightly longer step backward L and then bend L knee.
2	sl	fd	Diaphragm and R elbow.	Step forward R.
1	q	fd		Step forward L.
&	q	side	Slight pressure R palm.	Step sideward R.
2	sl	close	Continued sideward pressure R palm.	Draw L foot slowly to R foot without transferring the weight.

4. *Doble Corté:*

fd corté	bk open	bk open	bk corté	fd open	fd open	fd corté	bk open	bk open	bk open	side open	close close
L	R	L	R	L	R	L	R	L	R	L	R

$\frac{2}{4}$

Count	Call		Lead Indication	Step Pattern
1	q or corté		Diaphragm and R elbow, followed by knee bend.	Take a moderately long step forward and then bend L knee.
&	q	bk	Slight pressure R palm.	Step backward R.
2	sl	bk		Step backward L.

Count	Call		Lead Indication	Step Pattern
1	q or corté		Continued pressure R palm, followed by knee bend.	Take a slightly longer step backward R and then bend R knee.
&	q	fd	Diaphragm and R elbow.	Step forward L.
2	sl	fd		Step forward R.
1	q	corté	Diaphragm and R elbow, followed by knee bend.	Take a slightly longer step forward L and then bend the L knee.
&	q	bk	Slight pressure R palm.	Step backward R.
2	sl	bk		Step backward L.
1	q	bk		Step backward R.
&	q	side	Sideward pressure R palm.	Step sideward L.
2	sl	close		Close R foot to L foot and *transfer* the weight.

Tango Walk Around

Man's part:

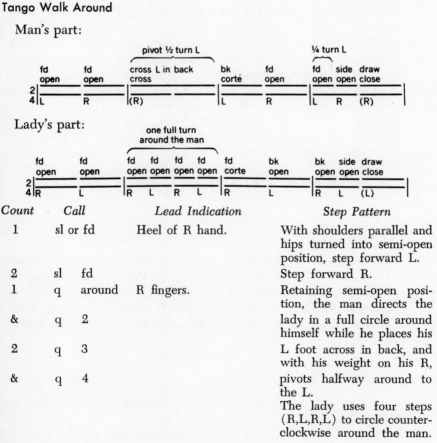

Lady's part:

Count	Call		Lead Indication	Step Pattern
1	sl or fd		Heel of R hand.	With shoulders parallel and hips turned into semi-open position, step forward L.
2	sl	fd		Step forward R.
1	q	around	R fingers.	Retaining semi-open position, the man directs the
&	q	2		lady in a full circle around himself while he places his
2	q	3		L foot across in back, and with his weight on his R,
&	q	4		pivots halfway around to the L.
				The lady uses four steps (R,L,R,L) to circle counterclockwise around the man.

Count	Call		Lead Indication	Step Pattern
1	sl	or corté	R palm, followed by knee bend.	Pulling the lady into closed position, take a moderately long step backward L and then bend the L knee.
2	sl	fd	Diaphragm and R elbow.	Step forward R.
1	q	turn	R fingers; twist R shoulder forward.	Step forward L, making a quarter turn L.
&	q	side	Sideward pressure R palm.	Step sideward R.
2	sl	draw	Continue sideward pressure R palm.	Draw the L foot slowly to the R foot without transferring the weight.

SUGGESTIONS:

1. Using eight measures of music, combine one single corté with a tango-close (measures 1–2); one open promenade (measures 3–4); and one doble corté (measures 5–8).

2. Using eight measures of music, combine one forward promenade (measures 1–2); one forward promenade with cross-over (measures 3–4); and one medio corté (measures 5–8).

3. Using eight measures of music, combine one parallel promenade (measures 1–2); one reverse cross promenade (measures 3–4); and a tango walk around (measures 5–8).

4. Using eight measures of music, create a pattern of your own, remembering that a tango-close can be placed anywhere in a phrase and that a series of walking steps can be used at any time to bridge one phrase with another.

MIXERS

The teacher who has a large repertory of mixers at his fingertips can not only aid the shy student in finding a partner, and implement frequent partner changes by all, but also add novelty and variety to the class experience, thereby increasing everyone's enjoyment. The following mixers are a few of the many that have been found effective.

Finding Partners

1. Each man asks a lady to dance whose eyes are the same color as his own.

2. Men who are wearing red find partners who are wearing blue or

green, and vice versa. The remaining people pair off. (Other colors might be substituted.)

3. Each man is given a slip of paper with a number on it, and duplicate numbers are given to the ladies. Those having the same numbers will be partners.

4. The men are given black playing cards, the ladies red ones. The men holding spades will dance with the ladies holding corresponding cards in hearts; the men holding clubs will dance with ladies holding similar cards in diamonds. If there are a large number of participants, two packs of cards may be used and those having duplicate cards will be partners.

5. All of the ladies put their left shoes in a pile in the center of the room; the men go to the center, choose a shoe and dance with the lady who is wearing the mate.

6. Ladies form a line on one side of the room; men form a line on the other side, all with their backs to the center. On signal, both lines move backward, and each man dances with the lady he bumps into.

7. Ladies form a line on one side of the room; men on the other. The two lines move toward the end of the room where they meet and perform a grand march. The lines should move toward the end of the room that will place the lady on the right of her partner. The leader may continue a few figures of the grand march, if he so desires, before calling "Everyone dance."

8. Ladies join hands in a circle, and men join hands to form a circle around them. Men move to the L; ladies to the R. When the music stops the two circles face, and each man dances with the lady he is facing.

9. The formation is a double circle, with partners facing counterclockwise, the ladies on the outside. Extra men stand in the middle of the circle. Couples move around the circle, and on signal, the men turn and move in the opposite direction, with the extra men joining in. When the music stops, the circles face and each man dances with the lady in front of him.

10. Five or six men join hands to form a merry-go-round in the center of the room. The rest of the group form a circle around them. The men circle to the L with walking steps, while the outside circle moves to the R. On signal, the ladies rush forward to try to get on the merry-go-round by placing their hands on the shoulders of a man in the center circle. The circling is then resumed. On the next signal, the men try to get on the merry-go-round by placing their hands on the ladies' shoulders. The procedure is continued until all are on the merry-go-round (men and ladies alternating). Each man then dances with the lady in back of him.

Changing Partners

1. Couples stop dancing and change partners with the couple nearest to them.

2. Partners stop dancing and stand back to back, then each one moves forward in the direction he is facing until he meets a new partner; those facing a wall, go to the center and find a partner.

3. Couples make a single circle, with the lady on the right of her partner. Partners face, and giving right hands to each other, continue around the circle with a grand right and left until the music stops. The man dances with the lady he is facing.

4. In closed position, couples dance counterclockwise around the room in a single circle, doing six waltzes into the LOD. During the seventh measure, the man twirls the lady clockwise under his L arm. On the eighth measure, the men stand still while the ladies, facing clockwise, take three walking steps around the outside of the mens' circle to meet a new partner; or the twirl can be omitted, and instead, the ladies take six walking steps to meet a new partner.

5. Partners are in a double circle, facing counterclockwise, with the ladies on the outside. Partners' inside hands are joined. To the accompaniment of a marching tune, all take four steps forward into the LOD, facing each other on the fourth step. Partners then take four steps backward away from each other, the men moving toward the center, the ladies away from it. On the next four steps, partners move diagonally forward to their own right to meet a new partner. With four more steps, partners circle once around, with both hands joined. The pattern is repeated continuously until the music ends. The man continues to dance with the last lady he has met.

6. Tant' Hessie, described on page 285.

SELECTED BIBLIOGRAPHY

Harris, Jane; Pittman, Anne; and Waller, Marilyn S. *Dance A While*, rev. ed. Minneapolis: Burgess Publishing Company, 1955. Chapter IX and X.

Heaton, Alma and Israel C. *Ballroom Dance Rhythms*. Dubuque, Iowa: W. C. Brown Company, 1961.

Heaton, Alma, Marie and Israel C. *Fun Dances*, rev. ed. Dubuque, Iowa: W. C. Brown Company, 1958.

Hostetler, L. A. *Walk Your Way to Better Dancing*, rev. ed. New York: The Ronald Press, Co., 1952.

Murray, Arthur. *How to Become a Good Dancer*, rev. ed. New York: Simon and Schuster, Inc., 1954.

Turner, Margery. *Dance Handbook*. Englewood Cliffs, N.J.: Prentice-Hall, Inc., 1959. Chapters IV and IX.

Yerrington, Beverly, and Outland, Tressie A. *Social Dance*. Palo Alto, California: National Press, 1961.

7

Teaching Folk Dances

Folk dancing has a fascinating history. Many of the dances done today originally stemmed from various rites that celebrated important events in men's lives—the planting of crops, the harvest, weddings, and even religious sacrifices. Most of the ritualistic significance of these dances has long been forgotten except by a few anthropologists and dance historians, but the social satisfaction that comes to people when they move together in rhythmic harmony remains. Because folk dances have been gathered from innumerable cultural sources, our folk dance heritage is rich in its variety of movement qualities, styles, and patterns. Yet with all these differences, there is a universality to be found in folk dancing that makes it—even more than a reflection of a given culture—an expression of the human race.

EDUCATIONAL OBJECTIVES

Folk dancing, like ballroom dancing, is above all, a social activity. The educational benefits of both forms of dance are very much the same. Generally speaking, however, folk dance is concerned more with the execution of traditional forms than it is with the invention of new ones. The creative energies of the folk dancer are centered upon the development of an expressive movement style rather than upon the creation of new patterns of movement. Students can, of course, make up their own dance patterns that are designed to be performed in the *manner* of traditional dances; and they can also theatricalize characteristic folk dance steps and move-

241

ment styles in creating dances that are intended for the theater. By and large, however, the chief function of folk dancing in our present day culture, in addition to its being good exercise, is to provide people with a common movement experience in which they can participate together, as in community singing, sharing with each other their mutual enjoyment of the communal expression. Furthermore, because folk dancing includes the performance of dances of other nations as well as those of one's own culture, appreciation for the dance expression of other peoples can be intensified, and through this appreciation an understanding of the people themselves can be increased.

It goes without saying that for the attainment of fullest enjoyment, both folk and ballroom dance forms should be experienced as coeducational activities. With adolescents and pre-adolescents who are reluctant to dance in closed position, folk dancing is often used successfully as a lead-up activity for ballroom dance. Unquestionably there is considerable carry-over from the one dance form to the other, especially with regard to such steps as the two-step and the waltz that are used in both types of dance. However, to create the impression that folk dance is merely a lead-up activity to "adult" forms of dancing would be both unfortunate and erroneous. As a social experience, folk dancing has as much adult appeal as ballroom dance, and it is important to teach it in a way that will engender enthusiasm and create in the students a desire to participate which will be carried over into adult life. In many localities, as a result of good teaching, folk dancing has once again become a popular community pastime that provides opportunity for young and old to participate together in a wonderfully exhilarating group experience.

The potential educational benefits to be gained from folk dancing might be summarized then, as follows:

1. Muscular coordination and physical endurance can be improved and general physical and mental alertness intensified.

2. Kinesthetic awareness of how the body is moving, and of how such movement feels, can be heightened.

3. Rhythmic awareness can be increased, as well as the ability to give to movement a particular rhythmic structure, related to an established beat.

4. Intellectual knowledge of specific folk dance steps in terms of their step patterns, rhythmic structure, movement qualities and styles can be gained, and based upon this knowledge, physical skill in the performance of these steps developed.

5. Physical release and intellectual and emotional satisfaction can be gained from participating in challenging, often exuberant, rhythmic activity.

6. Social satisfaction can be experienced in participating as a cooperative member of a group and in sharing the sense of unity and pleasure that attends such communal expression.

7. Opportunity is provided for expressive interpretation through an endeavor to re-create the specific mood and style of movement characteristic of each national dance form.

8. Appreciation for peoples of other nations and their cultures can be deepened through acquaintance with their folk customs, costumes, and music, and through experiencing some of their dance forms.

9. Social skills can be developed through increased knowledge of social etiquette and heterosexual experiences that help students to become at ease with the opposite sex.

ACHIEVEMENT OF OBJECTIVES

Again, merely talking about the benefits of folk dancing will not cause them to exist for the students. The instructor will need consciously to orient his teaching toward their attainment. Verbal analyses of steps as well as descriptions of movement quality will have to supplement teaching demonstrations in order to heighten students' intellectual and kinesthetic awareness of what they are doing. Rhythmic awareness can be developed only if attention is called to this aspect of the movement. Each new step will need to be analyzed rhythmically for the students so that they will have a knowledge of its rhythmic structure and can perform it without depending upon the teacher or the dance music to establish the pattern for them. Such students are then self-reliant and can easily relate a step, once learned, to a new folk dance situation. Student appreciation of the dances and of the peoples who danced them is brought about by sharing with them such background knowledge as the teacher may possess; by assigning research projects about the people and their customs; by cooperatively studying and re-creating their costumes; and by encouraging students to take pride in their endeavor to capture the authentic flavor of each dance that they perform. Finally, social ease and enjoyment are achieved by taking time to teach rules of social conduct that will enable students to feel secure in their own behavior; by creating opportunities for students to intermingle and to utilize their social knowledges; and by establishing a climate of congenial informality conducive to social enjoyment.

SELECTION OF DANCES

With the vast array of folk dances that are now available, the task of selection becomes a difficult one. A first consideration is that of choosing dances that are appropriate to the abilities and interests of the class. It is well to stay with simple dances until the technical skill level of the group has been established; but such dances should be sufficiently interesting not to seem infantile. There are many delightful dances to challenge the learner that consist of nothing more than fundamental steps in which the interest is in the movement style and the changing group formations.

In planning a lesson or an evening of folk dancing, one should endeavor to choose dances that will provide a contrast of steps, formations, numbers of people, and movement qualities. For long folk dance sessions, it is usually wise to begin with a moderately slow dance and to alternate fast dances with others of slow or moderate tempo. In an ordinary class period of short duration, however, change of pace may not be quite so important. A group dance, without partners, in which everyone can participate, makes a good opener. For groups in which only one sex is involved, or where the sexes are very unequal in numbers, there are many good dances like the horas and kolos that do not require dancing with a partner. The teacher or dance leader should be aware of the social needs of the group and should include a sufficient number of mixers and dances that accomodate extra people so that everyone can participate and have a good time. Some of the social dance mixers described in Chapter 6 can also be used with folk dance classes, but there are numerous folk dances that are themselves excellent mixers. Dances can also be so arranged that persons of either sex can cut-in at appropriate times, thereby taking care of the problem of extra people. Where square dancing is the featured activity, the inclusion of occasional round dances, periodically spaced, will not only add variety but allow opportunity for square dance sets to be rearranged and new sets to be formed.

Students enjoy being challenged by difficult dances, providing these dances are within the realm of their capabilities; but it is wise to intersperse these complex forms with simple dances that all can enjoy. Dances that require concentrated effort on the part of the performers are usually best placed in the middle of a folk dance session. While it is important to expand the group repertory, it is also good to remember that people need to be given an opportunity to review and perfect familiar dances and to enjoy re-experiencing old favorites. Whenever possible, it is good to end the session with a familiar dance chosen by the class.

TEACHING TECHNIQUE

Before teaching a folk dance, it is essential that the instructor be thoroughly grounded in its traditional form, tempo, and style. Even when a dance has been clearly described in textbooks, it is sometimes difficult to interpret correctly its movement style if it has not been observed or personally experienced by the teacher. When the correct tempo of the music is not specified, an incorrect choice of it can seriously alter the quality of the dance. Fortunately, the abundance of good recordings of folk dance accompaniment in which the normal tempo is indicated has done much to eliminate this problem. In certain situations the instructor may wish to modify a dance, simplifying it or making it more challenging to meet the needs of the performers. While such practice might occasionally be justified, provided the changes are minor ones and are still consistent with the original quality and styling of the dance, a preferable solution is to find another dance more suitable to the particular group. When the movement quality and styling of a dance is altered, the whole flavor of the dance as a reflection of national culture is lost. Regional variations of the same dance are bound to occur, but unless the basic form and character of the common root is retained, one of the chief values of folk dancing—that of providing a common movement experience in which diverse peoples may share— will be nullified.

Teaching the Steps

Teaching techniques for any subject are largely governed by the teaching objectives and the order of importance in which those objectives are held. Time limitations imposed by most school situations sometimes necessitate the partial sacrificing of certain objectives in order to accomplish others. In the case of folk dancing, the time required to teach each new step creatively and not at all imitatively would delay and limit the achievement of other values that are to be gained only through performing the dances themselves. If the social and recreational values of folk dancing are considered to be of prime importance, then the teaching of steps will need to be accomplished as quickly as possible.

Although certain folk dance steps are closely identified with specific cultures, there are other steps that seem to be part of an almost universal folk language. Among these widely used "traditional" steps are the two-step, polka, schottische, and waltz. Because these steps are to be found in so many popular folk dances, some authorities like to teach all the traditional steps they intend to, use first, as a preliminary to the dances, and thus give the dancers a basic vocabulary of steps with which to proceed; others, however, prefer to commence with the teaching of dances as soon as possible, introducing the traditional steps only as the need arises. Regardless of when a step is taught, it should be presented in a way that makes the experience pleasurable, rather than laborious; this can be accomplished by relating the new coordinations to familiar locomotor experiences wherever such relationships exist, and by directing the practice period so that the step is experienced in different directions, different couple relationships, and with a variety of partners.

Since all folk dance steps are immediately related to the eight fundamental steps, it is often advisable to begin with a quick review of these basic fundamentals in order to establish a common terminology and a point of departure. (Careless use of terminology, such as calling a leap a jump, is often a major source of confusion. It is therefore essential for the instructor to be consistent in his use of terms if he expects to communicate effectively to his students.) Traditional folk dance steps can all be derived from the fundamental steps, and many of the traditional steps can be developed from each other. The schottische, for example, can be evolved from three walks and a hop; and the 2/4 polka can be derived from the schottische (see Chapter 4, Unit One, Lesson V). It is possible to develop a step from many different beginnings. The starting point that the teacher selects will often be determined by the students' previous experience—the steps with which he is already familiar. Below are some suggested ways for introducing some of the traditional folk dance steps.

Two-Step

The folk dance two-step is like the ballroom step except that the folk form is usually in 2/4 time, which doubles the speed of the step pattern. When the ballroom form is already familiar, it becomes an easy matter to increase the tempo:

The step can also be taught from a walk. The first two steps are quick; the third is slow. Because the second step is a closing step, the first step should be taken to the side, which makes the close seem natural and necessary. The third step can be taken in any direction. Perhaps the easiest way to practice the two-step is to take it from side to side, alternating one two-step to the R and one to the L. Then, after the coordination of closing on the second step has become established, the first step can be taken in a forward, or diagonally forward direction. The quality of the step is lively, but fairly smooth.

2/4 Polka

In addition to being similar to the schottische, as previously mentioned, the 2/4 polka is also closely related to the two-step, and it is a simple matter to go from one of these steps to the other. To change the two-step into a 2/4 polka, one needs only to add a hop as a kind of "afterthought" at the very end of the pattern. The third step is held as long as possible so that the time value of the hop is very short. The hop might also be thought of as a "pick-up" or up-beat that precedes the two-step:

However the 2/4 polka is taught, two points should be emphasized: The tempo is quick, and the rhythm of the step–hop is uneven. The step has a vivacious, bouncy quality.

Schottische

Just as it is possible to develop the 2/4 polka from the schottische, it is also possible to reverse the procedure and develop the schottische from the 2/4 polka by decreasing the tempo, relating the steps to four beats instead of only two, and by making the rhythmic pattern even and the movement quality smooth:

Not all schottisches require the feet to be closed on the second step. When not, the schottische pattern is a simple step–step–step–hop and the most direct teaching approach is that of developing the step from a walk, substituting a hop for a walk on the fourth count.

Waltz

The waltz, which is in a triple rather than a duple meter, is probably best developed from a walk in the manner described in Chapter 6, either in the form of the box waltz or as a pattern that progresses consistently forward or backward. Though there are many variations of the waltz, the step is usually smooth and lilting. Once the basic step has been mastered, its variations are rather easily learned and can be introduced later as the need arises.

Mazurka

Another traditional folk dance step, the mazurka, is also in triple meter; it is a step native to Poland that is found in various forms in many dances. Musically, the rhythm is characterized by an accent that occurs on the second, rather than on the first beat of the measure. Although there are actually many different steps that are done to mazurka music in Poland, at least one mazurka step is rather universally performed; it consists of a step, a close, and a hop, executed in an even rhythm; if repeated, it continues on the same side:

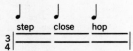

This step, like the waltz, is probably evolved most effectively from the fundamental steps. The movement should be taken first in a sideward direction so that the close on the second beat will occur naturally. After the basic coordination has been mastered, attention can be given to performance details. When taken to the R, the R foot makes a long, smooth gliding step sideward; then the L foot closes to the R, displacing the R foot so that it may be extended quickly into the line of direction. On the hop, the extended R leg is bent at the knee and the R foot brought in to the ankle or across in front of the supporting foot. The step can then be adapted to a forward or diagonal direction. The movement is gay and sprightly.

It is from this lively mazurka step that a variation has been derived which is performed in the American varsouvienne. In this dance step, the hop has been modified so that the supporting foot does not actually leave the floor. Instead, the supporting knee is bent on count three; this bend causes the body to dip slightly, almost as though making a bow. The step is also begun on an up-beat so that the now modified hop, or "dip," is used to commence the pattern. Thus the once spirited mazurka step has become grounded and robbed of its former vitality, taking on the grace and delicacy reminiscent of the 18th century minuet.

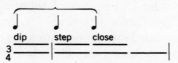

By observing their forms, one often discovers that new steps are simply permutations of old ones that the students already know. As the teacher learns to recognize these relationships of steps to each other, he will undoubtedly find his own preferred routes by which to arrive at his objectives.

Teaching the Dances

In preparing to teach a folk dance, the pattern of movement should be worked out in detail ahead of time; and with difficult dances, not just mentally, but with a practice group, if possible. It is also extremely essential to know the music as it is related to the dance structure; to know how many measures are required for each part of the dance, and how each step is related to the music. Along with teaching the dance steps, there is the matter of style and quality that the teacher must not only recognize and understand but must also translate into dance movement. The use of appropriate word imagery descriptive of the movement quality, accurate analysis of body control, and a good demonstration by the instructor or by class members can help to clarify this aspect of folk dancing.

Procedures

When introducing a new dance, one should begin by stating its name and nationality, writing the name, correctly spelled, on the blackboard, commenting, when necessary, upon its pronunciation, perhaps asking the class to pronounce it with him. Whenever such information is available, a very brief history of the dance, its origin and significance, and a commentary concerning where, how, and by whom it is performed today can intensify the student's interest in the dance he is about to learn. Hearing a bit of the music before commencing to learn the steps gives the dancer an idea of the quality and correct tempo of the movement. The more nearly the dancer is able to capture the authentic style of the dancing of other peoples the greater will be his appreciation of the peoples and the national cultures from which these dances have sprung.

Unless the dance is very simple, it is usually advisable to teach it one section at a time, breaking the dance down, however, only as much as is necessary for the students to learn and retain each section easily. Attention to the fine points of technique can be minimized until the dancers have learned to feel at home with the dance as a whole, though the general movement quality should be stressed from the very start. Instructions should be brief and explicit, with an effort made to get the group moving as soon as possible; over-teaching can quickly dampen class enthusiasm. A good teaching progression might be as follows: explain, and demonstrate if necessary, a section of the dance; have the students practice the movement sequence, without the music, to count or verbal cue; demonstrate the dance pattern with the music to establish their rhythmic relationship; have the students practice the movement with the music. Then approach the next section in the same way. Add the first and second sections together, giving special attention to the transition between the two parts. Continue in this manner, adding each new section to the previously learned material until the dance has been completed. When a new step or particularly difficult coordination is contained in a dance, the step or movement pattern should be taught first before teaching the dance as a whole. After all of the parts have been presented, a demonstration of the dance in its entirety can be helpful as a means of reinforcing the dance sequence and movement quality in the minds of the dancers.

Verbal cues are especially helpful as teaching aids; at first, they need to be given in advance of each change in the step pattern to remind the dancers of the movement sequence in plenty of time for them to perform it. Later, when the dancers have become familiar with the step progression, the cues may be given simultaneously with the dance action to prompt the dancers who have a tendency to get lost and to emphasize the correct rhythm of the movement. Even after the music has been added, verbal cueing may be advisable, depending upon the complexity of the dance. Eventually, all such prompting should be omitted so that the dancers may become completely self-reliant. Whenever verbal cueing is used, the words should be spoken in the exact rhythm in which the action is to be performed so that the cue can help to clarify the *rhythm* of the dance action as well as the action itself. After a dance has been learned, performance of it should be continued until a point of real enjoyment is reached, but stopped while interest is high so that the group will look forward to repeating it again at some later occasion.

Teaching Tips

General Suggestions

1. When using records, select and organize them and check to see that the record player is in working order before time for the class to begin.
2. Train the group to listen to verbal instructions and to the music when they are dancing.
3. When using an accompanist rather than records, remember to give an adequate signal for the music to begin and to cease. A double signal, such as "ready (pause) and" or "with the music (pause) begin," given so that all may hear, enables the accompanist and the performing group to begin together.
4. Allow time for the group to laugh and talk at the end of a dance, but arrange some signal for silence, such as the sound of the teacher's voice, if the acoustics are good, or a raised hand to which the group will quickly respond.
5. Be consistent in your use of terminology.
6. Remind students of which foot should bear the weight at the beginning of a dance.
7. Train the group to start and stop each section of the dance promptly on the musical cue so that their movement does not spill over into the next phrase.
8. Help the group to become conscious of and to learn to maintain their proper spatial relationships in group formations. For example, when the dancers are moving around the room in a double circle formation, if each couple becomes responsible for maintaining the designated spacing between themselves and the couple ahead of them, all spacing difficulties will be eliminated.
9. Accustom the group to the idea that in most dances, when partners are standing side by side, the lady's place is on the right of her partner. Much unnecessary confusion can be eliminated when this point is remembered.
10. Praise generously and criticize sparingly. Direct corrections to the group as a whole, first, and when individual corrections become necessary, give them as inconspicuously as possible.
11. After a dance has been taught, if there are a few students who still are unable to perform the steps correctly, arrange to help them before or after class or ask an advanced student to assist them.
12. If a large number of students are having trouble, stop the dance and re-teach the section that is causing the difficulty.
13. Be conscious of the social atmosphere of the group. Make sure that everyone is dancing and that partner changes are frequent.

14. Be enthusiastic. Establish an environment of pleasant, but disciplined informality. Try to eliminate tension by a friendly, positive attitude that will be encouraging to students who are having movement difficulties and are feeling awkward and insecure. Have a good time yourself and your own enjoyment will be reflected by the members of the class.

Suggestions for Square Dancing:

When teaching square dancing, a few additional points need to be remembered:

1. Practice your calling with the record or whatever accompaniment you plan to use. Call in the same rhythm as the music. Tapping one's foot in time with the music or using some other movement device, can sometimes help one to become aware of the musical beat.

2. Memorize the call so that you can keep your eyes on the dancers.

3. When teaching a new dance formation involving a "patter" call, illustrate the formation with a demonstration set when possible, then walk the dancers through it, giving first the call and then the explanation.

4. When calling, keep the voice fairly low, but alive, and give your instructions with clarity and command. Accent the key words whenever possible.

5. Keep the call slightly ahead of the performing group so that the instructions are timed to precede the action. A singing call must, of necessity, be kept with the music, but since the call is not varied spontaneously by the caller, the dancers can move along with the call once they have learned the pattern.

6. Group your call into movement phrases rather than pausing after each instruction and thereby breaking the rhythmic flow of the calling.

7. Vary the call as soon as the participants have sufficient experience to follow the instructions; in this way, the dancers will be unable to anticipate the call and thus tend to get ahead of the caller. Keep the call very simple at first without the confusion of too much "patter." When both the caller and the dancers have become thoroughly familiar with the basic call, patter can then be added for verbal and rhythmic interest.

9. Keep up with the current material; square dancing is a changing field.

10. Try to develop a calling style as a result of your particular timing and voice inflection.

11. Discourage students from clapping with the music in square dancing since they must be able to hear the caller. In other dances in

which no call is involved, clapping the rhythm is, of course, permissible.

12. As in ballroom dancing, if using a P.A. system, check ahead of time to see that all the mechanical devices are in working order, and be sure that you have practiced calling with the microphone.

RATING STUDENT ACCOMPLISHMENT

Procedures used for rating accomplishment in ballroom dance can be applied to folk dance up to a point. Knowledge of folk dance terms and informational material concerning the dances, analysis of steps, and so forth, can be tested by means of a written examination. Appraisal of each student's ability to perform certain folk dance steps or step combinations correctly in proper style and relation to the music can be ascertained by the same procedures used for evaluating similar skills in ballroom dance (see page 198).

The area of evaluation that is likely to provide difficulty for the teacher is that of grading students on their knowledge and ability to do the dances themselves—particularly those that require a group of people for their performance. Such appraisal is probably best made day by day. For this reason, it is particularly essential for the instructor to become personally acquainted with the class members as soon as possible. When classes are very large, as they often are, the initial use of name tags can help a teacher to identify his students until such help is no longer needed. An alert teacher, by careful observation each day, will at least know by the end of a folk dance unit those students who are well acquainted with the folk dance patterns and are highly skilled in their performance and those who are at the opposite end of the scale.

SELECTED BIBLIOGRAPHY

Bol, Lawrence (ed.). *Chicago Park District Square Dance Manual.* Chicago: Best Advertising Service, 1950. Pp. 7–54.

Czarnowski, Lucile K. *Folk Dance Teaching Cues.* Stockton, California: University of the Pacific Folk Dance Camp, 1961.

Duggan, Anne; Schlottman, Jeanette; and Rutledge, Abbie. *The Teaching of Folk Dance.* New York: The Ronald Press Co., 1948. Chapters 1–5.

Harris, Jane; Pittman, Anne; and Waller, Marilyn S. *Dance A While,* rev. ed. Minneapolis: Burgess Publishing Company, 1955. Chapters I–VI.

Kraus, Richard. *Folk Dancing.* New York: The Macmillan Co., 1962. Chapters 1–5, 14.

Kraus, Richard. *Square Dances Today and How to Call Them.* New York: The Ronald Press Co., 1950. Chapters 1–3, 8.

Shaw, Lloyd. *The Round Dance Book,* Caldwell, Idaho: Caxton Printers Ltd., 1948.

Turner, Margery. *Dance Handbook,* Englewood Cliffs, N.J.: Prentice-Hall, Inc., 1959. Chapters V–VII, IX.

8

Selected Folk Dances

To make a selection of a few folk dances appropriate for high school and college age students is difficult because there are so many delightful ones from which to choose. Every culture has produced its share of beautiful dances. The following dances of beginning and intermediate levels of difficulty have been special favorites with students; they have been chosen for this text because they contain a variety of steps, formations, tempos, and movement qualities, and because the recorded music for them is readily available. Dances for advanced level students can be found in sources listed in the bibliography. Whenever possible, however, such dances should be learned directly from authorities who can clarify complicated patterns and technical details, and can demonstrate the cultural flavor of the dance movement. Examples of square dances have been omitted from the chapter since much good material is already available and the selection of square dances is usually not a serious problem for the instructor. The collection contains a number of kolos and Israeli circle dances that can be enjoyed equally by both mixed groups and groups of the separate sexes.

Among these folk dances there are several excellent ones with which to begin. "Tant' Hessie" and "Ve' David" are both simple, mixer type dances that require no advance knowledge of traditional folk dance steps. Of the traditional steps, the schottische, the two-step, and the polka are usually somewhat easier than the waltz for beginning folk dancers to master. If commencing with the polka, "Doudlebska Polka" is a highly enjoyable dance in which this newly learned dance step can be experienced. For the schottische, "Road to the Isles" and "Milanovo Kolo" are both good introductory dances. Although "Jaegermarsch" is an easy dance containing a "dreher" or turning waltz, "Little Man in a Fix" is perhaps a better dance with which to introduce a waltz turn because the style of the waltz is similar to that used in American ballroom dancing and the turn is not a continuous one. When choosing dances for beginners, the important thing is to select relatively short dances containing simple or familiar coordinations and no extremely complex changes of formation.

The number of dances that can be covered in a class period depends largely upon the dancers. Some groups learn very rapidly; others require more explanation and practice. The observant teacher is soon able to gauge the learning rate of his class and to plan his lessons accordingly. It is often possible to teach three moderately short dances in a forty-five minute class period. Difficult dances or those with many different figures may necessitate the use of an entire class period or two periods if class time is short. When a dance contains a difficult step, it is sometimes helpful to teach the step during the previous class period so that the students can practice it outside of class and can come prepared to enjoy the dance itself. Dances being reviewed will require a much smaller time allotment than those being taught for the first time if no re-teaching or special attention to styling is necessary. Normally, a folk dance class of average length will consist of the presentation of one or two new dances and a review of several familiar ones.

CLASSIFICATION OF DANCES

Schottisches

Fado Blanquita
Korobushka
Milanovo Kolo
Road to the Isles
Salty Dog Rag

Two-Steps

Boston Two-Step
Ziogelis

Easy Dances

Doudlebska Polka
Hakke–Tone
Heel–Toe Polka
Hineh Ma Tov
Jaegermarsch

Polkas

Doudlebska Polka
Hakke–Tone
Heel–Toe Polka
Sonderburg Double Quadrille

Waltzes

Cielito Lindo
Jaegermarsch
Little Man in a Fix
Oslo Waltz
Ranchera

Milanovo Kolo
Road to the Isles
Sonderburg Double Quadrille
Tant' Hessie
Ve' David

Moderately Easy Dances

Boston Two-Step
Cielito Lindo
Fado Blanquita
Korobushka
Little Man in a Fix
Harmonica
Mayim

Misirlou
Oslo Waltz
Ranchera
Salty Dog Rag
Sarajevka
Sauerlaender Quadrille
Ziogelis

Partner Dances

Boston Two-Step
Cielito Lindo
Doudlebska Polka
Fado Blanquita
Hakke–Tone
Heel–Toe Polka
Jaegermarsch
Korobushka
Little Man in a Fix
Oslo Waltz
Ranchera
Road to the Isles
Salty Dog Rag
Sauerlander Quadrille
Sonderburg Double Quadrille
Tant' Hessie
Ve' David
Ziogelis

Partner Change Dances

Cielito Lindo
Doudlebska Polka
Korobushka
Jaegermarsch
Little Man in a Fix
Oslo Waltz
Tant' Hessie
Ve' David

Non-Partner Dances

Harmonica
Hineh Ma Tov
Mayim
Milanovo Kolo
Misirlou
Sarajevka

DANCE DESCRIPTIONS

BOSTON TWO-STEP
(English-American)

Records: Western Jubilee 707
Decca 9–46292

This is a modernized adaptation of an old English dance brought to the United States about 1850. Originally, it was a slow, smooth dance performed to the "Boston Two-Step." To enliven the dance and heighten its appeal to young people, the dance has since been set to "Tennessee Saturday Night." The steps have been slightly modified to make them easier to perform in quick time.

STEPS: Two-step, three-step turn, walk, step-swing.

STYLING: Although the English version was smooth and restrained; the American version, described here, is fast and swingy.

FORMATION: Couples in a double circle or spaced informally about the room. Partners stand a little bit apart, side by side, with inside hands joined.

METER: 4/4.

Measures   *Movement Pattern*

1   Commencing with inside feet, partners take one two-step sideward toward each other, and another two-step away from each other.*

2   Commencing with inside feet, partners take 3 steps exchanging places, the man pulling the lady across in front of him to his L side while she makes a three-step turn counterclockwise. Hold (count 4).

3   Partners, having re-taken inside hands, do one two-step sideward toward each other and another two-step away from each other.

4   Commencing with inside feet, partners take 4 walking steps backward away from the LOD.

5   Partners face, and with inside hands still joined, the man steps L, swinging the R leg across in front, then steps R swinging the L across in front. The lady does the same, starting with the R foot.

6   With inside hands still joined, the lady makes a clockwise turn under the man's L arm, using 3 steps to cross to his R side, while the man takes 3 steps in place. On the 4th step they take closed position.

7   Partners use 2 two-steps to make one full turn around to the R, progressing into the LOD.

8   With another two-step, the lady turns under the man's L arm (while he two-steps in place) so that she finishes standing beside her partner in open position as in the beginning of the dance; they both step in place with outside feet (count 3), and hold (count 4).

Repeat the entire dance as often as desired.

* In the original English version, partners began with outside feet, two-stepping away from each other and then together. When the tempo is fast, however, the three-step cross-over following the two-steps can be made more easily if partners begin with inside feet, two-stepping together and away, and then begin the cross-over with inside feet.

CIELITO LINDO
(American)

Record: MacGregor 633

The background of the dance (pronounced Sēálē'tō Lē'ndō), is somewhat uncertain; it was learned by the late Lloyd Shaw from a Miss Clara Luther in Sioux City, Iowa, and was popularized by him and his Cheyenne Mountain Dancers.

STEPS: Balance-waltz, preparation dip and waltz turn, walk.

STYLING: The movement is gay and lilting.

FORMATION: Couples in a double circle, facing counterclockwise, with inside hands joined. The man places his L hand on his hip, palm up; the lady holds her skirt with her R.

METER: 3/4.

Measures   *Movement Pattern*

Part I (Music A) *Diamond Waltz*

1   Beginning with outside feet, partners take one balance-waltz diagonally away from each other, swinging joined hands forward as they turn partially back-to-back.

Balance-waltz: Step (count 1), draw the free foot to the supporting foot, transferring the weight to the ball of that foot (count 2), returning the weight to the other foot (whole foot) (count 3); it is a "step–ball–change" performed in an *even* rhythm.

2   Partners do a balance-waltz diagonally toward each other, swinging the joined hands backward. (Since the dancers progress into the LOD on both balance-waltzes their floor pattern of "away and together" creates a diamond shape on the floor.)

3–8   Repeat measures 1–2 three more times.

Part II (Music A cont'd) *Preparation Dip and Waltz*

9   On count one, the man, who is facing the LOD, pulls the lady around into closed position with his R arm, stepping backward L as she steps toward him with her R foot. The supporting leg is bent and the free leg extended, the man's leg forward, the lady's backward; they rise slightly onto the ball of the supporting foot (count 2) and lower the weight to the whole foot immediately (count 3). The pattern, which is performed very smoothly, is called a *preparation dip.*

10–15   In closed position, partners do 6 waltzes, turning clockwise and traveling into the LOD. The man commences R, the lady L. It is important during this waltz turn for the couples to maintain their position in relation to the other couples in the circle.

16   The man turns the lady under their joined hands, his L, her R; and they finish in a single circle facing each other, the lady with her back to the LOD.

Part III (Music B) *Balance Forward and Back, and Pass One–Two, Take Three*

1–2   With R hands joined, partners do a balance-waltz forward toward each other, on the R foot, and another one backward on the L.

3–4   Starting R, both the man and the lady take 6 smooth walking steps forward, the man traveling counterclockwise and the lady clockwise, and join R hands with the third person they meet.

5–12   Repeat measures 1–4 two more times.

Part IV (Music B cont'd) *Dip and Waltz*

13–15   With the new partner take a dip, as described in Part II (the man must change feet quickly in order to step back L), and 2 waltzes, turning once around clockwise while progressing in the LOD.

16   The man turns the lady under their joined hands and places her on his R ready to repeat the dance.

Repeat all from the beginning.

In some recordings of Cielito Lindo the tempo is too fast to be used as accompaniment for this dance. In other recordings the chorus (Music B) is repeated before returning to the beginning, in which case it is suggested that the pattern in Part III be performed 4 times instead of 3, and the waltz turn pattern in Part IV be extended to 14 waltzes instead of 2 waltzes. The dance will then fit the music.

DOUDLEBSKA POLKA
(Czechoslovakian)

Record: Folk Dancer MH 3016

The dance (pronounced Dōōd-lĕb'skà Polka), is a simple, but lively Czechoslovakian mixer, introduced at Michael Herman's Folk Dance Camp by Jeanette Novak.

STEPS: Polka, walk.

STYLING: The dance is gay and lively. The men's clapping is done in a spirit of mock hostility while the ladies polka daintily around them.

FORMATION: Couples are spaced informally about the room. Partners are in closed position; or a shoulder-waist grasp, the lady placing her hands on her partner's shoulders and the man placing his hands on the lady's waist, may be substituted.

METER: 2/4.

Measures   *Movement Pattern*

Part I (Music A) *Polka*

1–16   Partners polka freely about the room, men beginning L foot, the ladies R.

Part II (Music B) *Circle March*

1–16   The man puts his R arm around his lady's waist and the lady places her L arm on the man's R shoulder, so that partners are side by side. Couples who are in close proximity move together to form a double circle, facing counterclockwise. The man places his L hand on the shoulder of the man in front of him and all walk briskly around the circle, singing tra-la-la in rhythm with the music. There may be several circles.

Part III (Music C) *Ladies Polka, Men Clap*

1–16   The men face the center of the circle and clap their own hands twice (counts 1–&); then turn their palms outward to clap the hands of the two men on either side of them once (count 2). They continue this clapping pattern for the entire 16 measures. The ladies, meanwhile, turn away from their partners, and in single file, polka clockwise around their own circle; or they may change places with the ladies of another circle. Extra men and extra women may join in the dance during this section. At the end of the music, each gentleman turns around and takes the nearest lady as his new partner with whom to repeat the dance. Repeat the dance as often as desired.

FADO BLANQUITA
(Portuguese)

Records: RCA Victor 4129
Folkraft 1173

The source of this dance (pronounced Fädō Bloun-kē'tä) is variously attributed to Portugal, Portuguese Brazil, and Spain. There are several versions of which one of the most popular is described below.

STEPS: Run, schottische (s–cl–s–h), jump, hop.

STYLING: The movement is proud and smooth, with a slightly Spanish flavor.

FORMATION: Couples (with the lady on the R) are in a single circle with hands joined.

METER: 4/4.

Measures   *Movement Pattern*

Part I (Music A) *Circle Left and Right*

1–4   All take 16 small, light, running steps to the L, starting with the R foot.

5–8   All take 16 running steps to the R.

Part II (Music B) *Schottische Turns*

1–2   All face the center, with joined hands and arms raised (elbows bent), and sway in place (R–L–R–L).

3–5   Face partner, and with R hands joined (elbows bent and fingers pointing up), turn once around with 3 smooth schottische steps (R–L–R–R, L–R–L–L, R–L–R–R). The free hand is on the hip.

6–8   Join L hands with the corner person, (the lady who is on the L of the man) and beginning L, turn once around with 3 schottische steps, returning to place.

9–14   Repeat the action of measures 3–8.

15–16   All face the center and sway (R–L) and take 3 quick, light stamps in place (R–L–R).

Part III (Music C) *Jump–Kicks, and to Center and Back*

1   With hands joined in a single circle, all jump in place on both feet (count 1); hop R, swinging L foot across in front (count 2). Jump in place (count 3); and hop L, swinging R foot across in front (count 4).

2   Jump in place on both feet (count 1); and dropping hands, jump again making a half-turn to the R (count 2); hold (counts 3–4). (The call for measures 1–2 can be: "jump–kick–jump–kick, jump–jump.")

3–4   The dancers now have their backs to the center of the circle. All rejoin hands and repeat the action of measures 1–2, so that all are facing the center again.

5–8   Beginning R, all take 3 slow walking steps toward the center (using two counts for each step) and swing the L foot forward, slowly raising joined hands while doing so. Beginning L, all take 4 slow steps backward, lowering the arms.

9–16   Repeat the action of measures 1–8.

Repeat the entire dance three more times.

HAKKE–TONE
(Dutch)

Record: Folkraft 337–001

Hakke–Tone (pronounced Häkĕ–Tŏ′nĕ) means "heel–toe" and is a popular heel–toe polka from the Netherlands.

STEPS: Heel–toe polka performed as follows: hop, placing the heel of the free foot forward on the floor (count 1); hop again, touching the toe of the free foot to the floor beside the supporting foot (count 2); polka (h–s–cl–s) (counts –a–3–&–4).

STYLING: The dance is performed in the characteristically gay, bouncy movement quality of the polka.

FORMATION: A double circle with couples in open ballroom dance position, facing counterclockwise.

METER: 4/4.

Measures *Movement Pattern*

Part I (Music A) *Polka Forward*

1 Beginning with weight on inside feet, partners take one heel–toe polka forward.

2 Repeat the action of measure 1, beginning with weight on outside feet.

3 Repeat the action of measure 1.

4 Repeat the action of measure 2, ending with 3 stamps, in place, instead of the polka.

Part II (Music A) *Polka Away and Toward Partner*

1–2 Facing each other, the man with his arms folded, the lady with her hands on her hips, partners take 2 heel–toe polkas backward away from each other. The man moves toward the center of the circle, the lady toward the outside.

3–4 Partners move forward toward each other with 2 heel–toe polkas, but ending with 3 stamps as in Part I, measure 4.

Part III (Music B) *Polka Sideward and Return*

1 Facing partner, take one heel–toe polka sideward, both moving counterclockwise around the circle.

2 With another heel–toe polka, move in the opposite direction.

3–4 Repeat the 2 heel–toe polkas from side to side, ending with 3 stamps on the last polka.

Part IV (Music B) *Polka Turning*

1–4 Partners take shoulder-waist position and polka, turning clockwise, progressing counterclockwise around the circle.

Repeat the dance twice more in its entirety and end with the men lifting the ladies.

HARMONICA
(Israeli)

Records: Folk Dancer MH1091
Folkraft 1109
Argi R 312–1

This dance, which has many of the chacteristics typical of the Jewish horas, is intended to symbolize the movement of an accordian; it was first introduced to American folk dancers by Dvora Lapson.

STEPS: Grapevine (Tscherkessia), step–hop, run.

STYLING: The movement style is relaxed, light and easy.

FORMATION: A single circle of dancers of either sex or of both sexes. The dancers' hands are joined and held low.

METER: 3/4.

Measures   *Movement Pattern*

Part I (Music A) *Grapevine (Tscherkessia)*

1   Facing center and moving counterclockwise, step L across in front of R (count 1); step R to side (count 2); step L across behind R (count 3); and leap to the side R, swinging the L leg diagonally forward to the R (count 4), (This pattern is called a *Tscherkessia step.*)

2   Facing R, take 2 even step–hops, moving counterclockwise (counts 1–2–3–4).

3–8   Repeat the action of measures 1–2 three more times.

Part II (Music B) *Cross Step and Step–Hop*

1   Facing center, step L across in front of R, turning the body to face diagonally R and pushing the hips forward (count 1); step R in place (count 2); step L in place (count 3); hop L, turning the body to face diagonally L (count 4).

2   Repeat all to the opposite side.

3   Repeat the action of measure one.

4   Facing clockwise, take two even step–hops (R–L) in LOD (counts 1–2–3–4).

5–8   Repeat measures 1–4 to the opposite side, beginning with the R foot.

Part III (Music C) *Friendship Circle Sway*

1   Place the hands on the upper arms of the adjacent dancers. Keeping the feet in place, sway to the L (counts 1–2); sway to the R (counts 3–4).

2   Facing L, and moving clockwise, take 4 running steps, beginning with the L foot.

3–8   Repeat the action of measures 1–2 three times.

Repeat the entire dance as often as desired.

HEEL–TOE POLKA
(American)
Record: Windsor 4624 or any good steady polka

There are many variations of the heel–toe polka that are characteristic of American round dancing. Several patterns similar to those described below were popularized by Lloyd Shaw of Colorado. Any or all of the figures can be taught, and students can make up their own variations.

STEPS: Heel–toe polka, toe–toe polka, polka.

STYLING: The movement is bouncy, or smooth, depending upon the variation.

FORMATION: Couples are spaced informally over the floor.

METER: 2/4.

Measures   *Movement Pattern*

Figure I—*Heel–Toe in Closed Position*

1–2   Partners are in closed position. The man touches his L heel to the floor sideward L (count 1), then touches his L toe to the floor close beside his supporting foot (count 2) and beginning L, he takes a step–close–step sideward L (counts 1–&–2). The lady does the counterpart.

3–4   The pattern is repeated to the opposite side.

5–8   Partners take 4 polkas, turning clockwise while progressing counterclockwise around the room (hop–step–close–step) (counts a–1–&–2). (Some dancers prefer not to leave the floor on the "hop," rising to the ball of the foot instead of hopping, so the pattern becomes lift–step–close–step. The rhythmic pattern is still uneven so that the lift or hop appears as a pick-up.)

9–32   The entire pattern is repeated three more times.

Figure II—*Toe–Toe in Open Position*

Partners are in open position. The man places his left hand on his hip; the lady holds her skirt in her R hand or places her hand on her hip.

1   Both the lady and the man touch R toes to the floor diagonally forward (count 1), then touch R toes to the floor at the instep of the supporting foot (count 2).

2–4	Partners take 3 smooth step–close–steps straight forward beginning R (R–L–R, L–R–L, R–L–R) (counts 1–&–2, 1–&–2, 1–&–2).
5–8	The pattern of measures 1–4 is repeated, beginning L.
9–16	The man quickly shifts his weight to the R foot as partners take closed position, and they do 8 polkas, turning clockwise while progressing counterclockwise around the room.
17–32	The entire pattern is then repeated. If it is difficult for the man to change weight on measure 9 in order to begin the polka turn, partners can begin the first part of the figure with outside feet and then no change will be necessary.

Figure III—*Toe–Toe in Varsouvienne Position*

1	Partners take varsouvienne position and beginning with R feet, they perform the toe–toe pattern described in Figure II, measure one.
2	Releasing the lady's R hand, the man leads her across in front of him to his L side where she turns L to face him; she moves across with three open steps, beginning R, while the man takes a step–close–step moving slightly to the R.
3–4	The toe–toe pattern is then repeated with the L foot and the lady returns to her place on the R of her partner by taking three steps forward under the man's L arm, while the man takes a step–close–step moving slightly to the L.
5–8	The pattern of measures 1–4 is repeated.
9–16	The man quickly shifts his weight to his R foot as partners take closed position, and they do 8 polkas, turning clockwise while progressing counterclockwise around the room.
17–32	The entire pattern is then repeated.

As in Figure II, partners may begin this pattern on outside feet and thus avoid the change of weight for the man on measure 9. If this procedure is followed, however, the man will take the step–close–step (measures 2 and 4) in place rather than moving R and L.

HINEH MA TOV
(Israeli)

Record: Folk Dancer MH 1091

Hineh Ma Tov (pronounced Hēně Mà Tōv) is a popular line dance of Israel in which the Yemenite influence is evident, both in the music and in the dance steps. The words of the song refer to a biblical passage describing the joys of dwelling together as brethren.

STEPS: Step–bend, run, twinkle (variation), Yemenite three-step.

STYLING: The dance movement is light and resilient, with the knees, easy, the upper torso lifted and the head held proudly.

FORMATION: A broken circle of dancers of either sex or of both sexes. The dancers' hands are lightly joined and held down at the sides.

METER: 4/4.

Measures   *Movement Pattern*
  1–2   Introduction.

Part I (Music A) *Step-bends and Runs*

  1–2   Face counterclockwise and move into the LOD with 4 *step–bends* (step forward R (count 1); bend both knees slightly (count 2); step forward L (count 3); bend both knees slightly (count 4) and repeat all). Keep the movement very smooth and easy.

  3–4   Continue moving counterclockwise with 8 running steps (1 count each).

  5–8   Repeat the action of measures 1–4.

Part II (Music B) *Twinkle (variation) and Yemenite Three-step*

  1   All face the center and stamp R, transferring the weight, while raising joined hands to shoulder level (count 1); hold (count 2); step backward on L, bringing joined hands down (count 3); close R to L (count 4).

  2   Step forward L, bringing joined hands up again (count 1); hold (count 2); tap R foot beside L (count 3); hold (count 4).

  3   Do a *Yemenite three-step* as follows: Step sideward R with the R foot (count 1); step L in place (count 2); step R, crossing in front of L (count 3); hold (count 4). The step is done smoothly, with light knee bends on each step; the body does not turn, but remains facing the center of the circle.

  4   Repeat the Yemenite three-step beginning with the L foot.
  5–8   Repeat the action of Part II measures 1–4.

The dance is repeated five times and is finished with a simple bow.

JAEGERMARSCH
(German)

Record: Folk Dancer MH2013

Jaegermarsch (pronounced Yāgermärch), a popular German mixer, has many versions, some of which are described below. One may use all of the versions or as many as needed.

STEPS: March, dreher (or turning) waltz.

STYLING: The march section is vigorous and proud. The waltz turn is done very smoothly, with each step taken on the flat foot. There is no up and down action or swaying of the body. The movement is continuous and flowing.

FORMATION: Couples in a double circle, facing counterclockwise. The man's R arm is held forward from the elbow and the lady rests her L hand on her partner's R. The lady's R hand is on her hip. The man has his L thumb thrust in his real or imaginary suspenders.

METER: 4/4, 3/4.

Measures   *Movement Pattern*

Figure I—Part I (Music A) *March*

1–8   Couples march counterclockwise around the circle for 32 steps.

9–16   The men continue going the same way, the ladies turn and march clockwise for 32 steps. All clap hands, the ladies clapping on the "oom" and the men on the "pah."

Part II (Music B) *Waltz Turn*

1–32   The man takes the lady he meets at the end of the march as his new partner; in closed position, with the extended arms held downward, all do a dreher waltz, moving around the circle in a counterclockwise direction, turning continuously to the R.* To begin the turn to the R, do one waltz straight forward before commencing the turn.

Figure II

Repeat the entire pattern; but in Part I, measures 9–16, the *men* reverse directions while the ladies continue marching counterclockwise.

Figure III

Repeat the entire pattern; but in Part I, measures 9–16, the men make a single circle, facing the center, raising joined hands to form arches. The ladies, passing to the R of their partners, weave in and out under the arches, progressing counterclockwise.

Figure IV

Repeat the entire pattern; but in Part I, measures 9–16, the ladies make the arches and the men weave in and out, progressing counterclockwise.

---

* People who find themselves without partners with whom to waltz should be directed to go to the center of the ring. Extra ladies or men can enter the dance during the parts where the dancers are moving in opposite directions or are not waltzing.

KOROBUSHKA
(Russian)

Records: RCA Victor 26–5017
Folk Dancer MH1059
Kismet A 106

This dance (pronounced Kô-rō′-bōotch-kȧ) actually originated in the United States, created by a group of Russian immigrants after World War I to the Russian folk music "Korobushka" which means "little basket" or "peddler's pack."

STEPS: Schottische, Hungarian break step, three-step turn, balance.

STYLING: The movement is strong and precise, performed in a proud, haughty manner that characterizes Cossack dancing.

FORMATION: Double circle, ladies on the outside, partners facing. Dancers join both hands in Indian grip (ladies' palms turned up, men's palms turned down, with fingers curled over partner's fingers).

METER: 4/4.

Measures   *Movement Pattern*

Part I (Music A) *Schottische and Hungarian Break Step*

1   Men commence L, ladies R, taking one schottische step (s–cl–s–h) away from the center of the circle, ladies moving backward.

2   All take one schottische toward the center of the circle.

3   All take one schottische away from the center of the circle. During the schottisches the dancers' joined hands are moved in opposition back and forth in a kind of easy circular motion.

4   Men hop 3 times on L foot, ladies hop on R (counts 1–2–3). On the first hop, the free foot is touched across in front of the supporting foot; on the second hop, the free foot is touched to the side; and on the third hop the feet are brought together, clicking the heels; this is called a *Hungarian break step*.

Part II (Music B) *Three-Step Turn*

1   Partners drop hands, and both the man and the lady make a three-step turn, turning once around while moving to their own R (R–L–R) and clapping on the fourth count.

2   Partners make a three-step turn moving to the L (L–R–L) and clap.

3   Partners join R hands and balance toward each other (step forward R, touch L beside R) (counts 1–2); and balance away from each other (step back L, touch R beside L) (counts 3–4).

4   With R hands still joined, partners change places with 4 walking steps (R–L–R–L), the lady turning L under the man's R arm.

5   All drop hands and make another three-step turn (R–L–R), moving to their own R, and clap on the fourth count.

6   All make a three-step turn *in place*, turning L (L–R–L), and clap.

7   The dancers, having moved one person to the L are now facing a new partner; they give that partner their R hand and balance forward and back, as in measure 3.

8   Partners change places as in measure 4, so the lady is once again on the outside of the circle.

Repeat the entire dance as often as desired.

LITTLE MAN IN A FIX
(Danish)

Records: Victor 20449
Folk Dancer MH1054

The dance title stems from the fact that the dance is performed by an odd number of couples. The couple left out, when sets of two couples are formed at the beginning of the dance, represents the "man in a fix" who is scolded by his partner for being unable to find another couple with whom to dance.

STEPS: Runs, balance waltz, and waltz.

STYLING: The first part of the dance is vigorous, but not boisterous; the waltz section is gay and lilting.

FORMATION: Two couples stand side by side, facing in opposite directions.

The men hook L elbows and place their R arms around their ladies' waists. Each lady places her R hand on her R hip and rests her L hand on her partner's R shoulder.

With groups of young people who like to turn vigorously, a different kind of hold can be used by the ladies that will give them increased security while turning: with her R hand the lady grasps her partner's R hand that is around her waist, and with her L hand she reaches behind her partner so that the opposite man can grasp it with his L hand.

METER: 3/4.

Measures   *Movement Pattern*

Part I (Music A) *Wheel and Four-Leaf Clover*

1–8   With running steps, the two couples wheel around counterclockwise, lightly accenting the first beat of each measure.

9–12   Continuing the running steps in place, the men join L hands, forming an arch; with their R arms they swing the ladies in front of them and take the ladies' L hands in their own R. The ladies run under the arch and immediately make a half turn L in order to face each other. The men lower their joined L hands, and the ladies grasp R hands over the men's L hand grasp. They now have formed a "four-leaf clover."

13–16   Pulling slightly backward, all wheel around counterclockwise with running steps.

Part II (Music B) *Balance waltz and Waltz Turn*

1–4   All drop hands and each lady turns to face the opposite man who takes her L hand in his R. Couples do 4 balance waltz steps as follows: stepping diagonally away from each other with outside feet, turning partially back to back (count 1), they draw the free foot to the supporting one and transfer the weight to the ball of that foot (count 2) and return the weight to the outside foot (count 3). The second balance step is taken with inside feet, partners turning toward each other. The entire pattern is then repeated.

5–8   Partners do 4 waltzes, turning in closed position. The first waltz is taken straight forward; the second and third waltzes are used to make one complete turn clockwise; and the fourth waltz is again taken in a forward direction. (For some dancers it may be easier to start the turn to the R by substituting a preparation dip (see description page 258) on the L foot for the first forward waltz. The preparation dip also adds rhythmic variation to the pattern.

9–16   The action described for measures 1–8 is then repeated. At the end of the dance, partners scramble to find another couple with whom to repeat the dance, and the odd couple joins in, leaving a new "man in a fix." The couple left out must do the running steps alone with both hands joined during the first part of the dance but may join with the others on Part II.

Repeat the entire dance as often as desired.

MILANOVO KOLO
(Serbian)

Records: RCA Victor 4129
Stanchel 1011

Kolo means "wheel" or "circle" and this kind of dance with its repetitious step pattern is a typical Slavic dance. The kolo was originally a ritualistic pagan dance in honor of Light which eventually lost its symbolic meaning and was done on all occasions. There are many different kolo tunes and step combinations of which the Milanovo Kolo (pronounced Mǐ-lăn-ō'-và Kō-lō) is a representative example.

STEPS: Step–hop, schottische (s–s–s–h) and (s–cl–s–h).

STYLING: The movement is light and easy, danced in a flat-footed manner with ankles flexed rather than extended.

FORMATION: A broken circle, or a closed circle if preferred, of dancers of either sex or of both sexes. The dancers' hands are joined lightly and held straight down at the sides. The leader on the right end of the broken circle, and the person at the other end have their free hands behind their backs.

METER: 4/4.

Measures   *Movement Pattern*

Part I (Music A) *To the Right, Backward, Forward, and to the Left*

1   Beginning with the R foot, take 2 even step–hops (R–R–L–L), moving to the R around the circle.

2   Take one schottische (s–s–s–h) (R–L–R–R), moving backward away from the center of the circle.

3   Take 2 even step–hops (L–L–R–R), moving toward the center of the circle.

4   Take one schottische (s–s–s–h) (L–R–L–L), facing R and moving backward to the L (clockwise) around the circle.

Part II (Music B) *To Center and Back*

1–2   Take one schottische (s–cl–s–h) (R–L–R–R), moving toward the center of the circle, crossing R over in front of the L foot on the first step. Repeat the pattern, starting with the other foot (L–R–L–L). Bring the arms forward toward the center of the circle while doing the 2 schottisches.

3–4   Repeat the action described for measures 1–2, only cross in back on the first step and move away from the center of the circle (R–L–R–R) (L–R–L–L). Bring the arms down to the sides.

Repeat the entire pattern continuously until the end of the music.

MAYIM

(Israeli)

Records: Folkraft 1108
Israel 114

The word *Mayim* (pronounced Mǐ'-yǐm) means "water." The movement of the dance suggests the motion of waves and of going to the well, and is an expression of thanks and rejoicing at the discovery of water in the desert. The dance was created in a Kibbutz on the shores of Galilee.

STEPS: Grapevine (Tscherkessia), run, tap and clap.

STYLING: The movement is alive and buoyant, with springy steps performed in a light, easy manner.

FORMATION: A single circle of dancers of either sex or both sexes. The dancers' hands are joined and held low. The dance may also be done in a double circle with both circles facing the center or with the inside circle facing the outside circle.

METER: 4/4.

Measures   *Movement Pattern*

Part I (Music A) *Grapevine* (*Tscherkessia*)

1   Facing the center and moving clockwise, step R across in front of L (count 1) step L to side (count 2); step R across behind L (count 3) and leap to side L (count 4).

2–4   Repeat the Tscherkessia step, described above, three more times.

Part II (Music A cont'd) *To Center and Back*

5   Move to the center with 4 running steps, beginning R (making the first step a small leap), simultaneously scooping the joined hands forward and upward as high as possible.

6   Repeat the action of measure 5, moving backward away from the center and lowering joined hands to the sides.

7–8   Repeat the action of measures 5–6.

Part III (Music B) *Run to the Left, Tap and Clap*

1   Facing slightly L, take 3 running steps beginning R, moving clockwise around the circle (counts 1–2–3). With the weight on the R foot, turn to face the center of the circle (count 4).

2   Hop R, tapping L toe across in front of R, (turning the foot in slightly) (count 1); hop R, tapping L toe to the side (count 2). Repeat the action (counts 3–4).

3   Continue the action of measure 2.

4   Change weight to the L, tapping R toe across in front of L, simultaneously clapping hands directly forward at arms length (count 1); hop L, tapping R toe to the side, while swinging the arms out to the side at shoulder height (count 2). Hop twice more on the L, repeating the same arm and foot pattern (counts 3–4).

5   Continue the action of measure 4.

Repeat all from the beginning.

The following words are often sung with the dance, beginning with Part II, or measure 5 and continuing until the end of the dance:

> Part II
>
> Ma-yim, ma-yim, ma-yim, ma-yim, U($\overline{oo}$), ma-yim, Bi-sa-son (Bē-sä-sŏn) (Repeat)

> Part III
>
> Hey! Hey! Hey! Hey!
> Ma-yim, ma-yim, ma-yim, ma-yim
> Ma-yim, ma-yim, Bi-sa-son
> Ma-yim, ma-yim, ma-yim, ma-yim
> Ma-yim, ma-yim, Bi-sa-son.

MISIRLOU
(Greek-American)

Records *: RCA Victor 4129
and LPM 1620
Kolo Festival 804

This dance (pronounced Mĭz'-ĕr-lōō) is a modified version of the Greek dance "Kritikos." The name has been derived from the title of a Greek tango to which the dance was performed by a group of dancers at a Greek Festival in Pittsburgh, Pennsylvania, when the original Kritikos music was unavailable. This version of the Greek dance has become popular with American folk dancers and is now a world favorite.

STEPS: Grapevine, walk.

STYLING: The dance movement is very smooth and gliding, emphasizing the quick changes of direction characteristic of the tango.

FORMATION: A broken circle of dancers of either sex or of both sexes with the lead dancer at the R end of the line. The dancers' arms are raised so that their hands are about head height; their little fingers are lightly joined with those of the people on either side. All face the center of the broken circle.

METER: 4/4.

Measures   *Movement Pattern*

1   Step in place with the R (count 1); pause (count 2); tap the L toe on the floor directly in front of the R foot (count

---

* The Misirlou music has recently become popularized and several jazz versions of it have been released. Whenever possible the authentic music should be used in order to reinforce the established movement quality of the dance.

3); and swing the L leg around to the back, describing an
arc (count 4).

2   Step L deep in back of R, bending the knees slightly (count
1); facing R (counterclockwise) step forward R (count 2);
step forward L (still facing R) (count 3); pivot quickly
on the L foot to face clockwise, bringing the R leg around
to the front with the R knee leading (count 4).

3   Beginning with the R foot, take 3 very smooth steps forward
in a clockwise direction (R–L–R) (counts 1–2–3). Lift the
L foot in back (count 4).

4   Continuing to face clockwise, take 3 smooth steps backward,
in a counterclockwise direction (L–R–L) (counts 1–2–3).
Lift the R foot in front (count 4).

Repeat all until the end of the music.

During the dancing, the leader guides the line over the floor
in a circle or a serpentine.

OSLO WALTZ
(English-Scottish)

Record: Folk Dancer 3016

Although the dance itself is English, it is performed to a Nor-
wegian waltz from Oslo from which it takes its name.

STEPS: Balance-waltz, step–swing, three-step turn, slide, waltz turn.
STYLING: The movement is smooth and lilting.
FORMATION: Couples in a single circle, facing the center. All hands are
              joined and held low.
METER: 3/4.

Measures   *Movement Pattern*

Part I (Music A) *Balance-Waltz and Ladies Cross Over*

1   All do a balance-waltz (step–ball–change, counts 1–2–3)
forward toward the center of the circle, men beginning L,
ladies R, keeping the movement very smooth and the
rhythm even.

2   All do a balance-waltz backward away from the center of
the circle, beginning with the other foot.

3–4   The man, standing in place, drops the hand of the lady on
his R, and with his L hand he pulls the lady on his L across
to his R side. She moves across with 6 smooth gliding steps,
beginning with the R foot. All immediately re-join hands
in a single circle.

5–16   The action described above is repeated three more times.

Part II (Music A) *Step–swings and Three-Step Turn*

1   Partners, the man and the new lady on his R, face each other and join both hands. Stepping on feet nearest the center of the circle (the man's L and lady's R) (count 1), they swing their outside feet across toward the center of the circle.

2   Partners repeat the step–swing away from the center of the circle, starting with the other feet.

3–4   The man and lady individually make a three-step turn toward the center of the circle (counts 1 (–2)–3–1); draw the free foot up beside the supporting one (count 2) and pause (count 3).

5–8   The action described for measures 1–4 is repeated, performed to the opposite side.

Part III (Music B) *Slides to Center and Out; and Waltz Turns*

1–2   With both hands joined, partners take a slide and a half, or step–close–step, (counts 1(–2)–3–1) toward the center of the circle, and draw the free foot up to the weight bearing foot (count 2), and hold (count 3).

3–4   The action described for measures 1–2 is repeated, moving away from the center of the circle.

5   In closed position, with the men facing counterclockwise around the circle, partners take one waltz forward.

6–7   Using 2 waltz steps, couples make one complete turn to the R.

8   As the man faces the center, the lady turns under the man's L arm and all join hands in a single circle ready to repeat the dance.

RANCHERA
(Argentine)

Record: Imperial 1085

This Argentine waltz, (pronounced Răn-chēr'-à) was brought to California by Dr. Juan Rael, a Stanford professor, and his daughter, Maria.

STEPS: Argentine waltz, performed as follows: the first step is made by stepping flatly on the whole foot, the next two steps are taken on the balls of the feet. All steps are even and are open, taken in the line of direction, and are extremely small and controlled. The Argentine waltz is performed continuously throughout the dance.

STYLING: The dance is very smooth, dignified and restrained. The
                upper body and head are held proudly. There is no sway
                from side to side.

FORMATION: Couples are in a double circle, facing counterclockwise,
                with hands in "back skating" position in the following man-
                ner: with his R hand, the man holds the lady's R hand on
                her R hip; their L hands are joined and extended forward
                to the L. The couples in the circle are numbered off with
                no more than 12 couples in each unit. There may be several
                units in the circle. The first couple in each unit is designated
                as the head couple.

METER: 3/4.

Measures   *Movement Pattern*

                Part I (Music A) *Forward Promenade*

1–12   The man commences L, the lady R; they continue on op-
                posite feet throughout the entire dance. Partners take 12
                Argentine waltz steps forward in LOD.

                Part II (Music B) *Woman Turns*

1–4   Continuing forward, the man releases the lady's R hand and
                with his L hand he leads her across in front of him on the
                first waltz, both continuing to face the LOD; they both
                waltz forward in that relationship on the second waltz; the
                lady turns R under their joined hands on the third waltz;
                and they return to their original back skating position, side
                by side, on the fourth waltz.

5–16   The action of measures 1–4 is repeated three more times.

                Part III (Music C) *Couples Turn in Place*

1–8   Continuing in back skating position, partners turn once
                around to the L in place, making the 8 waltz steps very
                small in order not to complete the turn too quickly. The
                man turns backward, the lady forward, and they end
                facing the LOD.

9–16   The pivot turn is repeated to the R with the lady turning
                backward and the man moving forward; they end facing
                the LOD.

                Part IV (Music D) *Grapevine Twist Step*

1–12   Couples assume semi-open ballroom position, and continu-
                ing in LOD, the man takes 12 waltzes forward, starting L.
                On the first waltz the lady, starting R, takes the first two
                steps into the LOD and on the third step the man turns the
                lady toward him to face backward; on the next waltz,

the lady takes the first two steps backward and on the third step the man returns her to semi-open position. This grapevine pattern is continued for a total of 12 measures. The lady always turns on count 3.

13–16   In back skating position, partners take 4 waltzes forward into the LOD.

Part V (Music A, B) *Tunnel Figure*

1–28   Couple number one in each unit turns to face clockwise, (the man remaining on the inside of the circle) joining inside hands to form an arch and placing outside hands on hips; they travel clockwise while the other couples travel forward under the arch. Each couple upon reaching the head of the line turns, makes an arch, and follows couple number one in forming the "tunnel." When couple one and each succeeding couple reaches the end of the line, they each turn and move forward through the tunnel assuming back skating position as they start through, until all have returned to their original positions. The man remains on the inside of the circle during the entire figure. The Argentine waltz is maintained throughout.

Part VI (Music C, D) *To Center and Back*

1–4   All couples swing around to face the center. The ladies, with hands on hips, do 4 waltzes toward the center, beginning R; while the men, with hands clasped in back, do 4 waltzes moving backward away from the center, beginning L.

5–8   With 4 more waltzes, the ladies starting backward R and the men starting forward L, all return to their original positions.

9–16   Assuming back skating position, partners pivot once around in place to the L as in Part III, measures 1–8, and end facing the center.

17–24   Repeat Part VI, measures 1–8.

25–32   Assuming semi-open position, partners repeat eight measures of the grapevine twist (Part IV) into the LOD.

Part VII (Music A) *Woman Circles Man*

1–12   Partners join L hands. The man has his R hand low on his back; the lady holds her skirt in her R hand. As the man travels in the LOD, the lady circles the man 3 times using 4 waltz steps for each circle; they finish with the man's back to the center of the circle, the lady facing her partner. On the last count of the final step, without releasing her part-

ner's hand, the lady swishes her skirt to the L across between them and holds her final pose.

ROAD TO THE ISLES
(Scottish)

Records: Folk Dancer MH3003
Educational Dance
Recordings EKL–206

This simple schottische, probably of fairly recent origin, is performed to an old Scottish pipe tune.

STEPS: Grapevine, schottische (s–s–s–h).

STYLING: The body carriage is proud and the footwork is performed
with Scottish precision.

FORMATION: Couples in a double circle, facing counterclockwise, in varsouvienne position.

METER: 2/4.

Measures   *Movement Pattern*
(The footwork is the same for both the lady and man.)

Part I (Music A) *Point and Grapevine*

1   Point L toe forward, slightly to the L and hold.

2–3   Take 3 steps, crossing L behind R (count 1), stepping sideward R (count 2) and crossing L in front of R (count 1);
hold (count 2).

4   Point R toe forward, slightly to the L and hold.

5–6   Take 3 steps, crossing R behind L (count 1), stepping sideward L (count 2) and crossing R in front of L (count 1);
hold (count 2).

7   Point the L toe forward and hold.

8   Point the L toe backward and hold.

Part II (Music B) *Schottische*

1–2   Schottische forward (s–s–s–h) (L–R–L–L) slightly to the L.

3–4   Schottische forward (s–s–s–h) (R–L–R–R) slightly to the
R, making a half-turn to the R on the hop to face the opposite direction. Hands remain joined at shoulder height.
Couples are now facing clockwise with the lady on the left
of her partner.

5–6   Schottische forward in a clockwise direction (s–s–s–h)
(L–R–L–L), making a half-turn L on the hop to face the
original direction.

7–8   Take 3 little steps in place (R–L–R) and hold.

The entire dance is repeated until the end of the music.

SALTY DOG RAG
(American)

Record: Decca 9–27981

This American round dance became a favorite with folk dancers in the San Diego, California area in the early 1950's; it was originally danced to the music of "Josephine" and later set to "Salty Dog Rag." The dance has many variations.

STEPS: Schottische, step–hop, and three-step turn.

STYLING: With young dancers, the dance is done in a jivy, swing style.

FORMATION: Couples in a double circle, facing counterclockwise, or spaced informally about the room. Partners are in varsouvienne position.

METER: 4/4.

Measures | Movement Pattern

Part I (Music A) *Schottisches and Step–Hops Forward*

1   Beginning with R feet, partners take one schottische diagonally forward R. (Step diagonally forward R; step L, crossing L foot behind R; step diagonally forward R; and hop R swinging L leg across into the R diagonal) (counts 1–2–3–4).

2   Beginning with L feet, partners take one schottische diagonally forward L.

3–4   Partners take 4 even step–hops forward, beginning with the R foot.

5–8   The entire pattern is then repeated.

Part II (Music B) *Partners Change Places and Wheel*

1   Dropping R hands, partners take one schottische, beginning R. The man schottisches in place while leading his lady across to his L side with his L hand so that they finish at arms length, facing opposite directions, the lady facing against LOD.

2   With another schottische, beginning L, partners change places, each moving to his own L with a three-step spin turn during the schottische. The lady passes in front of the man. The man, after pulling on the lady's L hand to start the spin, releases her hand during the turn, and takes her R hand in his R on completion of the turn. Partners are now standing at arms length, facing opposite directions.

3–4   With R hands joined, partners wheel once around clockwise, with 4 even step–hops.

5   Beginning R, partners each do a sideward schottische to their own R, changing from a R to a L hand hold.

6　　　　With another schottische, beginning L, partners repeat the three-step spin turn to the L, described for measure 2.

7–8　　　The action of measures 3–4 is then repeated. Upon completing the R hand wheel, the lady pivots halfway around to the L to face LOD, ready to repeat the dance from the beginning.

Repeat the entire dance as often as desired.

SARAJEVKA
(Yugoslavian)

Record: Balkan 538

The dance (pronounced Sä-rä-yĕv′-kȧ) is a characteristič Balkan kolo from Sarajevo, interesting because of its contrasting fast and slow sections.

STEPS:　　　Step–hop, kolo pas-de-basque, step–bend, step–touch.

STYLING:　　The body is held very erect, and the steps are taken directly under the body. The free foot is flexed when it is released from the floor.

FORMATION:　A broken circle of dancers of either or both sexes. The dancers hands are lightly joined and held down at the sides. The leader is at the right end.

METER:　　　2/4.

Measures　*Movement Pattern*

Part I (Music A) *Fast Pattern*

1　　　　Facing R, dancers step forward R (count 1); hop on R foot (count 2).

2　　　　Continuing in LOD, dancers step L (count 1); then hop L (count 2).

3　　　　Facing center, step sideward R (count 1); then cross L behind R (count 2).

4　　　　Pas-de-basque R: step sideward R (count 1); shift weight onto ball of L in front of R, but without crossing over, (count –&); return weight to R (count 2). This is known as a *kolo pas-de-basque*.

5　　　　Pas-de-basque L (L–R–L) (counts 1–&–2).

6　　　　Pas-de-basque R (R–L–R) (counts 1–&–2).

7–8　　　Facing L, take 3 walking steps, moving clockwise, (L–R–L) (counts 1–2–1), and hop L (count 2), turning to face R on the hop.

9–16　　　Repeat all.

Part II (Music B) *Slow Variation*

1   Facing R, dancers step forward R (count 1); and bend both knees (count 2).

2   Continuing in LOD dancers step forward L (count 1); and bend both knees (count 2).

3   Facing center, step side R (count 1); then close L to R (count 2).

4   Step side R (count 1); and touch L foot beside R (count 2).

5   Repeat the step–touch to the L (counts 1–2).

6   Repeat the step–touch to the R (counts 1–2).

7–8   Facing L, take 3 walking steps, moving clockwise (L–R–L) (counts 1–2–1), and turn to face R, as in Part I but without actually leaving the floor on the hop (count 2).

9–16   Repeat all.

Part III (Music C) *Fast Pattern*

1–16   Repeat the movement pattern described for Part I.
Repeat the entire dance.

SAUERLAENDER QUADRILLE NO. 5
(German)

Record: Folk Dancer MH1129

The dance (pronounced Zowr'-länder Quadrille) is a very old dance from Neheim-Husten, Westphalia, brought to the United States by Gretel and Paul Dunsing.

STEPS: Neheimer Step, (a step from Neheimer Village) is used throughout the dance. The step takes 2 measures; it is performed as follows:

Measure 1 (done in place)

Hop lightly R, touching L toe to floor beside R foot, with heel turned out and knee turned in (count 1); hop R, touching L toe to floor beside R foot, with heel turned in and knee turned out (count –&); hop R, touching L heel to floor beside R toe, with feet parallel (count 2); hop R, touching L toe to floor beside R toe, with feet parallel (count –&). The call can be: "toe–toe–heel–toe."

Measure 2 (moving)

When moving sideward: step L sideward L (count 1); step R behind L (count –&); close L to R with weight evenly divided on both feet (count 2). Call: "side–back–jump."

When moving forward: step forward L (count 1); step forward R (count –&); close L to R with weight evenly divided on both feet (count 2). Call: "step–step–jump."

The step may also be done to the opposite side, beginning with the other foot.

STYLING: Bodies are held tall with hands down at sides. Dancers stand quietly, with feet together, facing the center of the set except when actually dancing. Don't reveal in advance who is going to be the next to dance. The actual movement is bouncy, but controlled; the foot work is precise.

FORMATION: Four couples in a square formation, couple 1 facing the music, couple 2 opposite them, couple 3 to R of couple 1, and couple 4 to L of couple 1.

METER: 2/4.

Measures   *Movement Pattern*

Introduction

1–2   (hold)

3   Bow to partner.

4   Bow to corner.

Part I (Music A) *Peek-a-Boo*

1–4   Man 1 and lady 2 do one Neheimer step (NS) sideward, the man to L, lady to R, playing "peek-a-boo" around couple 4. They return to places with another NS step, beginning with the opposite foot.

5–8   Man 2 and lady 1 do the same action around couple 3.

9–12   Man 3 and lady 4 do the same action around couple 1.

13–16   Man 4 and lady 3 do the same action around couple 2.

Part II (Music B) *Couples to Right and Back*

1–4   Man and lady of couple 1 face each other and do one NS to R and one NS to L, ending in original position, facing center.

5–8   Couple 2 does the same action.

9–12   Couple 3 does the same action.

13–16   Couple 4 does the same action.

Part III (Music A) *Couple Cross Over*

1–2   Couples 1 and 2 dance toward each other with one NS, starting R foot, momentarily forming a single line standing shoulder to shoulder in the center, the men on the outside and ladies with L shoulders adjacent.

3–4   Couples 1 and 2 continue forward with one NS, starting L foot, and turn in toward partner to face the center on the last movement as the feet are brought together (measure 4, count 2). Couples 1 and 2 have now exchanged places.

5–8   Couples 3 and 4 do the same action.

9–16   The action of measures 1–8 is repeated with couples ending in their original positions. When couples meet in the center the ladies are on the outside and the men have L shoulders adjacent.

Part IV (Music B) *Right-Hand Turn*

1–2   Man and lady of couple 1 face each other, joining R hands, and starting L, do one NS step into partner's place.

3–4   With another NS step, starting R, continue turning clockwise to return to original position.

5–8   Couple 2 does the same action.

9–12   Couple 3 does the same action.

13–16 Couple 4 does the same action.

Part V (Music A) *Grand Slam*

1–4   Couples 1 and 2 cross over as described in Part III, while couples 3 and 4 dance sideward to corners and back, as described in Part I.

5–8   The action is then repeated with couples 3 and 4 crossing over, and couples 1 and 2 dancing sideward to corners and back.

9–16   The action is then repeated, with all couples returning to their places.

(Music B)

1–4   All 4 couples simultaneously repeat the action of Part II to R and back.

5–8   All 4 couples simultaneously repeat the right-hand turn of Part IV.

9–16   All 4 couples once again repeat Part II and Part IV, to R and back, and right-hand turn.

SONDERBURG DOUBLE QUADRILLE
(Danish)

Record: The World of Fun
Methodist Publishing House
EI–KC–5606

The dance is of Danish origin, coming from Sonderburg on Alsen Island; it is actually not a quadrille but a contra or longways dance. The name "Double Quadrille" refers to the 8 couples used in the set.

The dance pattern, one of several versions, was introduced to American folk dancers by Gretel and Paul Dunsing.

STEPS: Walk, polka.

STYLING: The dance is begun in a smooth, very erect, Germanic style, and finishes in a gay and lively mood.

FORMATION: Four couples facing four couples in a double line or contra formation. The four couples at one end of the set are the head couples; the four remaining couples are the foot couples.

METER: 2/4.

Measures   *Movement Pattern*

Part I (Music A) *Two Circles*

1–8   The four head couples join hands in a circle; the four foot couples do the same. Both groups circle L with 16 walking steps.

9–16   Both groups circle R with 16 walking steps, finishing in home position.

Part II (Music B) *Promenade Through the Aisle*

1–8   The four head couples face the foot of the set, joining inside hands with the opposite person, and walk 7 steps down the aisle formed by the foot couples; they turn on the 8th count, and joining inside hands, return to their places with 8 walking steps.

9–16   The four foot couples face the head of the set and promenade up and back in the same fashion described for the head couples.

Part III (Music B) *Four Circles*

1–8   Partners join hands with the opposite couple so that 4 circles are formed. All circle L with 16 walking steps.

9–16   All circle R with 16 walking steps, finishing in home position.

Part IV (Music C) *Chain*

1–8   The chain is performed by opposite couples (as in Part III) in the following manner. Join R hands with the opposite person. Take 3 steps forward, passing that person and releasing hands; and on the fourth step make a sharp quarter turn to face your partner. Join L hands with partner; pass him, and turn sharply on the fourth step to face your corner. Repeat the action with corner and partner, moving around in a small square to return to home position. When partners pass the second time, they retain hands, and turning to face each other, the lady curtsies and the gentleman bows (count 16).

The call for this chain pattern might be as follows:

Chain–two–three–turn
Left–two–three–turn
Right–two–three–turn
Left–two–three–bow.

9–16   Repeat the entire chain pattern.

Part V (Music C) *Polka Turn*

1–16   Partners take the shoulder-waist position, the man placing his hands on the lady's waist, while she places her hands on his shoulders; then polka, turning clockwise and progressing counterclockwise around the space formed by the whole set until they have returned to their original positions. A polka or two-step in open position or varsouvienne position may be substituted.

TANT' HESSIE
(South African)

Record: Folkraft 337–006B (*second* band)

"Tant' Hessie Se Witperd," meaning Aunt Esther's white horse, is an easy mixer of South African origin introduced by Huig Hofman at the University of Pacific Folk Dance Camp.

STEPS: Walk, buzz step.

STYLING: The walk could almost be described as a strut; it consists of a step–bend on each walking step, with the arms, slightly bent at the elbows, swinging in opposition. Partners look at each other flirtatiously throughout the dance.

FORMATION: Double circle, ladies on the outside, partners facing and slightly apart.

METER: 2/4.

Measures *Movement Pattern*

Part I (Music A) *Forward and Back*

1–2   With 4 walking steps, partners move forward until R shoulders are adjacent, so that all dancers are forming a single circle; they nod to each other on the fourth step.

3–4   All take 4 walking steps back to place.

5–8   The pattern is repeated with L shoulders adjacent.

Part II (Music B) *Do-si-do*

1–4   Partners do a do-si-do, passing R shoulders and moving around each other, back-to-back.

5–8   The do-si-do is repeated, partners passing L shoulders.

Part III (Music A) *Buzz Step Turn*

1–8   In shoulder-waist position, partners turn clockwise with 16 buzz steps; stepping onto the R foot, which is placed next to partner's R, they pivot in place by taking a series of small pushes with the L foot; there is a slight down-up action in the legs on each buzz step. Partners end facing each other in a double circle as at the beginning of the dance.

The pattern is then repeated with the person to the R, and the dance is continued, moving one person to the R on each repetition.

On Part II, dancers sing "Tra-la-la" with the music; on Part III, they sing "Oompah, oompah, oompah-pah."

VE' DAVID
(Israeli)

Records: Folkraft 1432
Symphonia Records LP HS201

This dance (pronounced Vē Dä-vē'd) is performed to music and lyrics entitled "Ve' David Yefei-Einayim," which translated means "David of the beautiful eyes," composed by M. Shelem. The dance, a simple but gay mixer dance, was taught in Israel to Miriam and Charles Lidster by Rivka Sturman, choreographer and authority on Israeli folk dancing.

STEPS: Walk, buzz step.

STYLING: The dance quality is smooth, but lively.

FORMATION: Couples in a double circle, facing counterclockwise, the lady on the R of the man. Partners have inside hands joined and the R foot free.

METER: 4/4.

Measures   *Movement Pattern*

1   With 4 walking steps forward, beginning R, partners move counterclockwise around the circle.

2   With 4 walking steps, beginning R, partners wheel backward to form a single circle. All face the center with hands joined.

3–4   Beginning R, all take 4 steps toward the center, bringing the arms forward and upward; then all take 4 steps backward, bringing the arms down.

5–6   The men stand in place, clapping the accented beats, while the ladies take 4 steps forward to the center again, beginning R, and 4 steps backward to place.

7   The ladies stand in place, while the men, still clapping, walk 4 steps forward to the center, beginning R. On the "–&" of count 4 each man pivots to his R to face the lady standing to the R of his partner.

8   Still clapping, the man takes 4 steps forward, beginning R, to meet this new lady.

9–12   The man and his new partner, with R hips adjacent, place R arms around each others' waists, extend L arms diagonally upward, and swing around clockwise with 8 buzz steps— stepping on the R foot, which is placed next to partner's R, they pivot in place by taking 7 small pushes with the L foot. The entire dance is then repeated until the end of the music.

ZIOGELIS
(Lithuanian)

Record: Folkraft F 1052B

Ziogelis, (pronounced Zjō-gā'-lĭs) means "the grasshoppers," whose movements the dance is presumed to describe. The dance was introduced to the California Folk Dancers by Vyts Beliajus in 1949.

STEPS: Grasshopper step, Lithuanian "polka" (a polka performed in an even rhythm), walk, skip and slide.

STYLING: The steps are danced on the balls of the feet in a light and springy manner, and the forward and backward movement of the body in the grasshopper step is emphasized.

FORMATION: Sets of 6 people in two lines of three people each (one man with a lady on either side of him) facing about six or eight feet apart. The trios are numbered one and two. The man's hands are around the ladies' waists. The ladies' inside hands are resting on the man's shoulder; their outside hands are holding their skirts.

METER: 2/4.

Measures   *Movement Pattern*

Figure I—Part I (Music A) *Grasshopper Refrain*

1–2   Starting with R foot, all do one Lithuanian polka forward (s–s–s–h), keeping steps very small and close to floor (counts 1–&–2–&); then step forward L (count 1); step forward R (count –&); drop forward onto L foot with an accent, bending the body forward and extending R foot back (count 2); pause (count –&).

3–4   Starting with the R foot, do one polka step backward (measure 1); do 2 more steps backward (L–R) (counts 1–&),

drop backward onto L foot, leaning the body backward while extending L foot forward (count 2); pause (count –&). The pattern described here is called the *grasshopper step*.

5–8   Repeat Measures 1–4.

Part II (Music B) *Elbow Swing and Change*

1–4   The ladies on each man's R clap hands, and with 8 skipping steps, move toward each other diagonally across the set; hook R elbows; turn once and a half around; and retire to opposite positions, changing places. The man and remaining lady balance forward and backward, while partially facing each other.

5–8   The action is then repeated with the ladies on the L exchanging places.

Figure II—Part I (Music A) *Grasshopper Refrain*

1–8   Repeat Figure I, Part I.

Part II (Music B) *Slide and Elbow Hook*

1–4   The ladies on the R return to their original positions by passing back to back with 4 sliding steps, R shoulders leading; upon arriving home they turn in place with 4 walking steps. Meanwhile, the man and the left-hand lady hook R elbows and skip around in place.

5–8   The action is then repeated with the ladies on the L returning home.

Figure III—Part I (Music A) *Grasshopper Refrain*

1–8   Repeat Figure I, Part I.

Part II (Music B) *Slide and Arch*

1–4   The men, with hands on hips, take 4 slides diagonally to their own R, passing in front of the right-hand lady, and stop at the outside center of the set, facing each other; there they do 4 leg extensions in place, as follows: hop on L foot, extending R heel forward (count 1); hop on R foot, extending L heel forward (count 2); repeat all (counts 1–2). The ladies, meanwhile, with inside hands joined and outside hands on their hips, take 4 polka steps moving across the set (No. 1 ladies passing under the arch made by No. 2 ladies); they drop hands and face the center of the set.

5–8   Rejoining inside hands, the ladies polka back to place (No. 2 ladies passing under the arch made by No. 1 ladies), and once again turn to face the center of the set. The men continue doing 4 more leg extensions (counts 1–2–1–2) and return to their original positions with 4 sliding steps.

Figure IV—Part I (Music A) *Grasshopper Refrain*

1–8   Repeat Figure I, Part I.

Part II (Music B) *Trio Arch*

1–4   Each man holds his ladies' inside hands. The two ladies exchange places with 4 polka steps, the right-hand lady passing under the arch formed by the man and the left-hand lady. The man follows through the same arch, turning under his own arm. The trios are now facing away from the center of the set.

5–8   Repeat the action, but with the left-hand lady going under the arch. The trios are now facing the center of the set again.

Figure V—Part I (Music A) *Grasshopper Refrain*

1–8   Repeat Figure I, Part I

Part II (Music B) *Two Small Circles*

1–4   Each trio joins hands, forming two circles; all do 4 polkas to the R.

5–8   Repeat the action of measures 1–4, reversing the direction to the L. Drop hands and end with the trios facing each other again.

Figure VI—Part I (Music A) *Grasshopper Refrain*

1–8   Repeat Figure I, Part I.

Part II (Music B) *Large Circle*

1–4   All join hands to form one large circle and do 4 polka steps to the R.

5–8   Repeat the action of measures 1–4, reversing the direction to the L. Finish with a slight bow.

SELECTED BIBLIOGRAPHY

Beliajus, V. F. *Dance and Be Merry.* 2 vols. Evanston, Ill.: Summy-Birchard Company, 1940.

Bol, Lawrence (ed.). *Chicago Park District Square Dance Manual.* Chicago: Best Advertising Service, 1950. Pp. 55–280.

Chochem, Corinne, and Roth, Muriel. *Palestine Dances.* New York: Behrman House, 1941.

Duggan, Anne; Schlottman, Jeanette; and Rutledge, Abbie. *Folk Dances of the British Isles, Folk Dances of European Countries, Folk Dances of Scandinavia, Folk Dances of the United States and Mexico.* New York: The Ronald Press Co., 1948.

Durlacher, Ed. *Honor Your Partner.* New York: Devin-Adair Company, 1949.

Folk Dance Federation of California. *Dances from Near and Far* (vol. I–VIII). Berkeley, California: California Book Co., Ltd.

Gowing, Gene. *The Square Dancers' Guide.* New York: Crown Publishers, 1957.

Greggerson, Herbert F. *Herb's Blue Bonnet Calls.* Ruidoso, New Mexico: Carrizo Lodge, Box A, 1946.

Harris, Jane; Pittman, Anne; Waller, Marilyn S. *Dance A While*, rev. ed. Minneapolis: Burgess Publishing Co., 1955. Chap. VI–VIII.

Herman, Michael. *Folk Dance Syllabus No. 1.* New York: Folk Dance House, 1953.

Herman, Michael. *Folk Dances for All.* New York: Barnes and Noble, Inc., 1947.

Kraus, Richard. *Folk Dancing.* New York: The Macmillan Co., 1962. Chaps. 7–13.

Kraus, Richard. *Square Dances Today and How to Call Them.* New York: The Ronald Press Co., 1950. Chaps. 4–7, 9.

Lapson, Dvora. *Dances of the Jewish People.* New York: The Jewish Education Committee of New York, 1954.

Shaw, Lloyd. *The Round Dance Book.* Caldwell, Idaho: Caxton Printers, Ltd., 1948.

Turner, Margery. *Dance Handbook.* Englewood Cliffs, N.J.: Prentice-Hall, Inc., 1959. Chaps. V, VI and VII.

Periodicals

Let's Dance. Folk Dance Federation of California, 293–299 Broadway, Melbrae, Cailfornia.

Sets in Order. P.O. Box 89, Santa Barbara, California, (Bob Osgood, Editor).

The Folk Dancer. P.O. Box 201, Flushing, Long Island, New York.

Viltis. Box 1226, Denver 1, Colorado (Vyts Beliajus, ed.).

9

Accompaniment for Dance Classes

The time was when the lack of an accompanist was looked upon as an adequate excuse for omitting dance from a school curriculum, but such omission is no longer justifiable on that ground. Excellent folk and ballroom dance records are now available, as are records that can be used for modern dance. However, the number of good recordings appropriate for modern dance techniques is limited, and the constant necessity of starting and stopping the record with each new activity can become a distracting interruption to class procedure. When live piano accompaniment is not available, a teacher can easily provide his own percussion accompaniment, or he can dispense with accompaniment altogether except for that which he creates with his own voice.

VOICE ACCOMPANIMENT

The human voice should not be overlooked as an important source of dance accompaniment; it has many values. First, the voice is always readily available, and second, it is a versatile instrument. By a verbalization of a *movement* pattern as the class performs it, such as "step—r-e-a-c-h—drop," the teacher, through his choice of words, rhythm, and voice inflection, can help the students perform it in its proper structure, timing, and movement quality. The accompaniment might also consist of a verbalization of the *rhythmic* pattern, such as "*1-&-a, 2-&-a, 3-&, 4-&; 1, 2, 3-&, 4,*" spoken in a way that will underline the rhythm, dynamics, and quality of the dance movement. But besides the use of words it is also possible to use descriptive vocal sounds that have no intellectual meaning, but that auditorily establish the rhythm or stimulate a particular quality of movement response, such as "ch-ch-ch-ch-ch" or "da-ta-da-ta"; or "pa-dum-pum-pum" or "shwisssssh." The choice of the vocal sounds will depend to some extent upon what the instructor wishes to emphasize at the moment, but in all vocal accompaniment it is safe to say that the quality, dynamic character, and rhythm established by the voice is more important than the words themselves. In certain situations students can be encouraged to accompany themselves by vocalizing their breathing or by making other sounds appropriate to the dance movement.

Constant use of the voice as accompaniment can eventually become fatiguing to an instructor, so it is usually desirable to supplement this technique with other forms of accompaniment. Hand-clapping, finger-snapping, or striking the body or an article of furniture with the hand can be used to set the tempo and the rhythmic pattern, but these devices can do little to establish movement quality, and if used solely or habitually, can become a source of irritation to the dancers.

PERCUSSION ACCOMPANIMENT

Anyone with a good rhythmic sense can learn to accompany movement with percussion instruments. A great variety of sounds can be produced with an extremely limited number of instruments. Probably the most useful piece of equipment for the teacher of modern dance to possess, if he is to supply his own accompaniment, is a drum that he can carry with him as he moves among his students. A single headed tuneable dance drum, sometimes called a "Wigman drum," played with a lamb's wool beater or with the hand, and a single or double bongo drum played with the hand, are two excellent possibilities. Also recommended is a set of three single headed plastic drums that possess pleasing timbre and are extremely light and convenient to carry. In addition to the possession of a satisfactory hand-drum, the following selected list of percussion instruments might be purchased to provide a variety of accompanying sound in terms of tone, timbre, duration, and intensity:

A drum with a deep tone and good resonance, but not so much resonance that the sound of the beat becomes fuzzy.

A set of temple blocks or wood blocks, placed on a mat so they will vibrate properly or clamped to a bar.

A pair of maracas.

A large cymbal of the hanging type, or a gong of fairly deep tone.

A pair of lamb's wool beaters.

A pair of wire brushes.

Other standard instruments that are useful for dance accompaniment are:

American Indian drums	Finger cymbals
Chinese drums	Castanets
African drums	Tambourines
Timpani	Bells of all types
Recorders and other melodic or-	Gongs
chestral instruments	Sandpaper blocks
Claves	Triangles
Rattles of all types	Ratchets
Hand cymbals	

With a little ingenuity, it is also possible to create from everyday materials other percussion instruments that have surprisingly attractive sound qualities. Different sounds can be created with halves of coconut shells. Striking one of the rounded sides creates a muffled wood-block type of sound, while striking the hollow sides together produces a sharp, resonant sound useful as accompaniment for such activities as skips, gallops, or percussive movement. An automobile brake drum, struck with a metal mallet, or one half of a large metal oil drum, struck with a wooden stick or a beater can produce beautiful tones. Pieces of bamboo may be used in various ways: they may be held in the hands and struck together, or different sized pieces that will produce different tones may be hung on strings, as in a Chinese wind instrument which when struck creates a delicate, tinkling sound. In a similar fashion, long nails may be suspended on strings and shaken together or struck individually like a xylophone. A thundersheet, made by fastening a string to a flexible sheet of tin, so that the tin can be shaken, will provide a very dramatic sound effect. Another useful instrument for dance accompaniment may be acquired by obtaining a piano sounding board (with strings), from an old dismantled piano. One should not overlook the possible use of dime-store percussion instruments which are very inexpensive and can furnish a variety of percussion sounds. Through the process of experimentation one may discover numerous other interesting possibilities. The main thing is to *experiment*, not only with the choice of instruments used for accompaniment but also with how they are played.

Percussion Techniques

A single instrument can often produce many different sounds, depending upon how it is played. Take the drum, for example. The sound produced will be the result of how it is struck, where it is struck, and with what instrument. Normally, in striking any percussion instrument, the attack is directed at right angles to the surface that is being struck, and an effort is made to "hit out of" the instrument; by this is meant that the striking object (beater, stick, hand, et cetera) is rebounded away from the surface of the instrument immediately after the moment of impact to allow for maximum reverberation of the instrument head. Occassionally, however, a movement might warrant the opposite treatment, whereby the attacking instrument is allowed to remain on the drum surface so that the sound has a dull, thud-like quality. The deepest tone and greatest resonance of a drum is achieved by striking it about two-thirds of the way in toward the center of the drumhead; but contrasts in pitch, resonance, and timbre can be obtained by striking the outer edges of the drumhead, or the sides of the drum, or the metal rim, as with timpani. For variation in its sound a double-headed drum can be placed on end or turned on its side; and the two drumheads will probably be found to have slight differences in pitch. When drumsticks are used, sharply contrasting sound effects are created by striking the drum with the beater head in a normal fashion, striking the edge of the drum with the side of the drumstick, and holding the beater head and striking the drumhead with the end of the stick. The hands, when used in place of the drumsticks, will produce still different sounds depending upon what part of the hand is permitted to strike the drum. Possibilities include the fingers, all hitting simultaneously or flipping sequentially onto the drum surface; the thumb; the heel of the hand; the palm; the side; and the back of the hand. Completely different effects again results from the use of wire brushes, striking, circling the surface, beating a tremolo upon the drumhead, or scraping the edge of the drum. Differences of intensity of accompaniment will also affect the sound. It is through combining these many available sound effects, combining not only the different ways of striking the drum but also the striking instruments themselves, that interesting accompaniment is achieved.

With experimentation, one can discover that other instruments are likewise versatile in the uses to which they can be put. Rattles or maracas can be shaken, circled, or struck gently upon the hand or a drumhead. A cymbal can be struck with the hand, or metal mallet, or two cymbals can be struck together to produce different degrees of stridence. The cymbal may be struck repeatedly in rapid succession, this creating a tremolo, or struck only once and allowed to reverberate, or struck and caught with the hand to stop the vibration, or held with the hand and hit, or hit while holding and then released.

Accompanying Movement Qualities

With the availability of such a variety of sounds, percussion accompaniment can not only provide the rhythmic framework for the dance movement but can also suggest the movement quality. There is no specific way of accompanying a given movement quality; nevertheless, the following suggested procedures may be helpful. They are only some of the obvious ways of accompanying movement qualities. As students become increasingly self-assured in their movement and less dependent upon external motivation, and the teacher becomes increasingly free in his experimentation with percussion instruments, ways can be found of making the accompaniment complement rather than merely support the dance movement.

Swinging

1. GONGS or CYMBALS. Allow them to reverberate for only three counts. This may require an additional person to "stop" the gong sound if several gongs are to be played in succession.
2. DRUM—with wire brush, beaters, or with the hands. Use three beats for each swing in moderate 6/8, 3/8 or fast 3/4 meter. Establish the ternary rhythm first and then intersperse variations, such as

Leave out the first beat occasionally.

Pulsating—Ternary

The pulsation is related to three fast counts and the movement is somewhat relaxed, as in easy bounces.

1. DRUMS. Use a very fast *ternary* rhythm, frequently grouping the beats as in the following rhythmic diagrams:

A wire brush used on the drumhead provides a percussion sound that is "sympathetic" to this type of movement.
2. TEMPLE BLOCKS. Use the same as drums.
3. RATTLES. Use the same as drums.

Pulsating—Binary

The pulsation is performed with urgency and tension to a very fast two-count or *binary* rhythm.

1. DRUMS—using either the beater head or the drumstick. Alternate two tones in very rapid succession or accent the first of every two beats. Occasionally the beat can be doubled or two beats can be grouped together as indicated below, but the fast duple rhythm must remain constant.

2. CLAVES. Use in a manner similar to that for drums.
3. RATTLES or CASTINETS. Use in a manner similar to that for drums.
4. WOODBLOCKS or TEMPLE BLOCKS. Use in a manner similar to that for drums.

Vibratory

The movement might be described as a very fast oscillation of a portion of the body.

1. DRUMS—played with the hands, beater or wire brush, on the drumhead or the rim. Tremolo.
2. CYMBAL or GONG. Tremolo.
3. MARACAS. Shaken.

Sustained

1. DRUM. Use a binary division or grouping of beats when possible in preference to ternary, so that there will be no tendency to make the movement into a swing. Strike the drum with a soft even attack and subdivide the beat into small binary beat divisions:

Wire brushes circling the drum surface or used to play a tremolo can build inner excitement comparable to a drum roll. The voice used in a humming quality along with the drum sound can also emphasize the sustained quality.

2. CYMBALS and GONGS. Allow them to reverberate until the end of the movement, or play with a tremolo.
3. RATTLES. Circle or shake continuously, without accent.
4. REED INSTRUMENTS.

Staccato

1. WOOD BLOCKS and TEMPLE BLOCKS.
2. DRUM. Use a hard beater on a tight-headed drum or strike the rim or the side of the drum with the drumstick. Regardless of the instrument used, the attack should be sharp and clipped.

Explosive

1. CYMBAL or GONG. Crash.
2. DRUM. Make the sound sharp and loud, with the resonance allowed to continue. Movement excitement can be intensified by preceding the explosion with a preliminary tremolo or crescendo or by using a voice sound to anticipate the explosion.

Collapsing

1. DRUM—preferably one with a forceful, low-pitched sound. Here, again, a preliminary anticipatory build-up, created by the use of a series of up-beats preceding the actual collapse, may be desirable:

Accompanying Locomotor Activities

When percussion is used to accompany locomotor activities, such as the fundamental steps, the polka, the schottische, and so forth, the rhythmic structure needs to be stressed in particular; the tempo is also important. Correct tempo will vary according to the age and physical size of the performers and according to the manner in which the step is to be performed. Steps requiring high elevation demand a slower than normal tempo, but too slow a tempo will leave the performers completely grounded by retarding their momentum. Since skips, slides, and gallops are ternary in their rhythmic structure, it is wise to give them a ternary accompaniment even though much of the music written for these steps employs dotted eighths and sixteenth notes. When students are *learning* steps such as the polka or the schottische, it is advisable to follow the exact rhythmic structure of the step in order to help establish it in their minds. Once the step has been learned, rhythmic liberties can be taken in the accompaniment, provided the correct tempo and the underlying beat remain constant. Rhythmic accuracy is particularly necessary in reference to the 2/4 polka in order to emphasize its characteristic uneven rhythm:

The following suggestions are given as possibilities for accompanying some of the basic locomotor steps and their combinations.

Walks, Runs, and Leaps

A beat for every step is definite, but earthy.

$$\frac{4}{4}\ \ \text{step}\quad\text{step}\quad\text{step}\quad\text{step}$$

Doubling the beat drives the movement forward.

$$\frac{4}{4}\ \ \text{step}\quad\text{step}\quad\text{step}\quad\text{step}$$

Tripling the beat makes for a swingy, bouncy quality.

$$\frac{4}{4}\ \ \text{step}\quad\text{step}\quad\text{step}\quad\text{step}$$

Syncopation makes the movement exciting and demands concentration.

$$\frac{4}{4}\ \ \text{step}\quad\text{step}\quad\text{step}\quad\text{step}$$

Any meter based upon a quarter note can be used in place of 4/4.

Hops and Jumps

A beat for each movement is good, but a little heavy.

$$\frac{4}{4}\ \ \text{jump}\quad\text{jump}\quad\text{jump}\quad\text{jump}$$

This rhythm helps with the feeling of lift, but still emphasizes the landing.

$$\frac{4}{4}\ \ \text{jump}\quad\text{jump}\quad\text{jump}\quad\text{jump}$$

This rhythm emphasizes the air moment.

$$\frac{4}{4}\ \ \text{jump}\quad\text{jump}\quad\text{jump}\quad\text{jump}$$

A triplet makes a bouncy movement and is good for beginners.

$$\frac{4}{4}\ \ \text{jump}\quad\text{jump}\quad\text{jump}\quad\text{jump}$$

Skips, Slides, and Gallops

Combinations of these patterns are good.

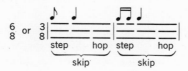

This rhythm emphasizes the air moment, but is hard for beginners to follow.

Hints for the Percussionist

1. Keep the accompaniment simple.
2. Always analyze carefully the quality and the rhythmic structure of the movement that is being performed so that you can accompany it with assurance.
3. Be definite. Uncertain or timid accompaniment is worse than none at all.
4. Make the accompaniment strong, but not nerve shattering.
5. When students are doing a specific movement pattern across the floor, allow the first group of performers to set the tempo for the class if the teacher has not already done so.
6. Keep a steady tempo. Once the tempo is set, be careful not to speed it or slow it unless there is a reason for doing so. There is often a natural tendency to speed accompaniment unless precaution is taken.
7. Always take the natural rhythm of the movement for beginners; assist them as much as possible; then syncopate later.
8. Don't watch a person's feet when accompanying locomotor activities. Movement is initiated in the body, and one can anticipate the movement of the feet by watching the body.
9. Always let the performers know where count "one" is; identify it by changing the intensity, pitch, or timbre or by using an up-beat preceding count one.
10. Decide which part of the movement should be given the emphasis (where the greatest amount of energy is to be spent), and give this part dynamic support in your accompaniment. To emphasize the addition of force in a movement it is often helpful to use an up-beat or tremolo just before the important beat, and then to place additional intensity on or change the timbre of the beat to be emphasized.

11. In accompanying sustained movement that has no definite grouping of beats, keep a steady pulse, doubling the beat occasionally for interest; but in general, keep the rhythm simple.

12. If the class has been asked to *improvise* movement within a given quality, play within the quality but don't establish a definite rhythmic structure that may influence their movement.

13. Strive for variety in rhythm, pitch, and dynamics in your playing to stimulate the class. Also vary the instruments used.

14. Leave occasional empty spaces in the accompaniment which will urge the dancer to intensify his efforts in order to maintain the rhythm and to fill the silences with movement.

15. Remember that movement can be done to odd meters such as fives and sevens as well as to the standard twos, threes, fours and sixes, and percussion accompaniment can be adapted readily to any rhythm or phrasing.

16. Learn to be facile in using both hands in accompanying; experiment with using one hand to supply the underlying beat and the other hand for embellishments. Practice!

17. Any good beginning percussion book will help one in acquiring skill in playing percussion instruments. Learn the correct techniques (particularly in reference to the use of drum beaters) before incorrect habits are formed, and remember that practice makes perfect.

18. Don't be afraid to try!

PIANO ACCOMPANIMENT

In some schools modern dance is taught with the aid of piano accompaniment. When piano accompaniment is good it can lend poetic overtones to movement that might otherwise become gymnastic routine, and it can intensify the individual's emotional responsiveness. On the other hand, when piano accompaniment is poor, it becomes an obstruction to learning. An accompanist who sight-reads music with ease and assurance is a tremendous help to the dance teacher, while one who can improvise and compose appropriate music for modern dance with its irregular rhythms and strange dynamic nuances, is invaluable. Although piano accompaniment can also be used for folk, square, and ballroom dance activities, good recordings are readily available, easy to use, and are often better able to suggest the qualitative flavor of the dance through their particular instrumentation. When piano accompaniment is used for these activities, the chief concern is that of finding an accompanist who can sight-read easily and who has an infallible sense of timing.

It is the purpose of this chapter to discuss the mutual responsibilities of the dance teacher and the piano accompanist in working together to produce a successful class lesson rather than to deal
in any detail with methods of composing or improvising for dance.
Discussion in this chapter will also be limited to the consideration
of accompaniment for dance classes, omitting problems concerning accompaniment for dance choreography. The following points
are offered merely as suggestions to the teacher and the accompanist with the intention of helping them to understand each other's
needs.

Suggestions for the Dance Teacher

A smooth and satisfying dance class can be greatly insured by the
teacher's doing what he can to establish a feeling of confidence and
good will between himself and his accompanist. An attitude of
professional and personal respect should be mutual; it can be pro-
moted to a high degree by the observance of a few simple procedures
that will serve to clarify the teaching objectives and the continuity
of the lesson.

1. Confer with the pianist in advance, especially if either you or he is
inexperienced. Tell him your plan for the lesson. Give him whatever
specific music you wish him to play and indicate what it is for; how
much in advance of the lesson you do this depends upon the musician's
experience and ability to sight-read. If necessary, go through the entire
lesson so that movement and musical tempos, qualities, and general styles
can be made to harmonize.

2. See that the pianist is placed in a position where he can see the
class and can see and hear you when you are instructing.

3. In giving your instructions to the class, speak so that both the
accompanist and the class can hear you.

4. Be sure to set the tempo, the rhythm, and the quality of the activity;
this is your responsibility, not the accompanist's. Frequently it is good
for the class to experience the movement without the music first so that
they can experiment and set their own natural tempo.

5. After giving directions, allow a few seconds to elapse before signal-
ing the class to begin, so that the accompanist and the class can assimilate
your directions, but don't wait too long or the class will tend to drag.

6. If the accompanist is inexperienced, it may be necessary, occasionally, to demonstrate the movement in order to establish the desired
rhythm and quality.

7. When teaching a folk dance, indicate the number of bars you wish
to have played, unless the accompanist is thoroughly familiar with the

dance music and can make this judgment for himself as a result of your instructions to the class.

8. When directing the class to begin an activity, give your signals, such as "ready–(pause)–and" or "ready–(pause)–begin" in a slightly different tone than is used in the explanation; this will alert the class and the accompanist to prepare for action.

9. Set the number of times the class is to perform a dance technique or a folk dance before beginning the activity; or indicate with a raised hand or a nod to the accompanist when you wish him to stop; or say "and rest" to the class. Try, whenever possible, to stop the movement at the end of a musical phrase; anticipate the cadence.

10. In modern dance, when your accompanist is unable to improvise or is inexperienced in following irregular rhythms and phrases, try to plan your movement sequences to fit the traditional musical phrasing of two, four, or eight measures to a phrase.

11. While, in general, it is desirable to have the dancers and the music begin together, it is also possible to have the class commence to move and then signal the accompanist to pick up the rhythm from the class. Do not say to the accompanist, "Would you like to play?" simply say, "With the music," if you have been working without music for a time, and you wish him to begin.

12. Do not, as a rule, make a special issue of instructing your accompanist while teaching, since this practice divides the interest of the students, drawing their attention to a third person. Make no issue of errors that are made in accompaniment. Clarify the misunderstanding and proceed from there.

13. Do not give vague, meaningless instructions to your accompanist, such as "Play something in 4/4," or "Play something slow." Know what you want and be able to state your needs in terms that the musician can understand, such as "Play a slow, sustained accompaniment in 4/4 meter."

Suggestions for the Dance Accompanist *

Improvisation can be a rewarding experience for the pianist, who may find that the special needs of movement accompaniment can lead him into interesting areas of melodic, harmonic, and rhythmic freedom and creativity hitherto unexplored. A pianist who has received years of training in conventional keyboard techniques may find it difficult to set aside these patterns in favor of other approaches that will provide an effective background for dance movement. Undoubtedly, the first attempts at improvisation for dance will be somewhat bewildering. The following suggestions may help the

* Nearly all of the points made in reference to percussion accompaniment apply equally to piano accompaniment.

accompanist in his efforts to create spontaneous accompaniment that will support and stimulate the movement response of the dancers. Although these suggestions are directed to accompanists for modern dance, points 9 and 10 are equally applicable to accompanists for folk, square, or ballroom dance.

1. While the movement activity is being described by the instructor, try to assimilate mentally and feel kinesthetically the movement to be done. Formulate a musical beginning at this time.

2. Begin simply, outlining the movement rhythmically, stressing accents, clarifying the time pattern by what may seem an oversimplification in the accompaniment; this is important in beginning classes. A single melodic line is often good.

3. Avoid "grabbing" a handful of keys or making masses of sound unless the character of the movement demands such weighty accompaniment.

4. Keep in front of you several "references." Many good ideas, as points of departure, can be absorbed at a glance and can prevent monotony and the development of personal clichés.

5. Learn what intervals and chords are inherently appropriate for certain movement qualities; and be alert to devices that can suggest certain styles of movement so that they can be "magically" produced when needed, (e.g., open 5ths in violin tuning style for country dance movement; parallel octaves for proud, dignified or "spacey" movement; lowered 3rds and 7ths for blues; embellishments for pre-classic movement styles; chords built in 4ths for the "modern" sound; or a non-chord tone added to an ordinary major or minor chord for tension and pull).*

6. Repetition and sequential development are not only highly desirable as contributing factors in creating musical form, but when improvising they enable one to keep going.

7. Don't allow the accompaniment to wander in various directions. Try to keep in mind your beginning rhythmic figure so that, in case you roam, you can use it to unify the accompaniment.

8. Be sensitive to a need for occasional semi-cadences to enable the instructor to find a stopping point if he so desires.

9. Keep your eyes on the class most of the time and not on the keyboard or on the music. Follow the dance movement.

10. In general, if the tempo has been established by the instructor, keep it constant. Don't be led astray by faltering students. Part of the discipline of the dancer is to learn to stay with the music; there will be, of course, exceptions to this practice.

11. Consider the possibility of combining piano and percussion accompaniment when such a combination is feasible.

* Other specific suggestions for improvisation may be found in the author's book *Dance Composition and Production* (New York: The Ronald Press Co., 1954) Chapter 9.

12. Through study and experimentation learn to be aware of the influences of pitch, timbre, duration, intensity, and tempo of music in relation to movement. Know when to mirror movement with your accompaniment and when to complement it with an opposition in rhythm, dynamics, or speed. Try the use of silence as a foil to strongly accented movement. Above all, use the experiences that satisfy you as the springboard to further exploration.

13. Don't hesitate to improvise. Play with one finger if necessary at first, but try! Be experimental even at the expense of occasional failures.

RECORDINGS

The vast increase in the supply of first-quality recordings for folk, square, and ballroom dance has placed good accompaniment for these activities within the reach of any teacher who has access to a record player. There is also a small number of excellent recordings of accompaniment for modern dance classes that can be used satisfactorily, provided the class activities are arranged to correspond to the rhythm, phrasing, and quality of the recorded music. The difficulty with the use of such recordings is their lack of flexibility.

Even though the recorded accompaniment cannot be changed, a modern dance teacher may find that a variety of movement activities of similar quality can be adapted to fit a single piece of music. Sometimes it is possible to organize a series of dance exercises to fit the musical sequences on a record which avoids the necessity of finding a different piece of music for each individual exercise. On the whole, however, the exclusive use of recordings for modern dance accompaniment is restricting; it tends to promote the teaching of dance routines rather than encouraging inventiveness in the use of unusual rhythms, unique phrasing, and new movement combinations. When used as a supplement to other forms of accompaniment, however, recordings can sometimes provide highly satisfactory moments in a modern dance class and can supply good musical background for dance studies. A selected list of recordings for modern dance classes is included in the appendix.

The use of folk, square, and ballroom dance recordings poses no special problems. However, certain arrangements of a musical composition may be more suitable as dance accompaniment than others, so it is important for an instructor to check the recordings that he intends to use to see that they are appropriate to the dance activity. Recordings for ballroom dance will need to establish the desired tempo and movement quality, and above all, keep a steady rhythm. Often a number of different folk dance patterns have been set to a single folk melody so that there may be variations in the phrasing and tempo of the different recordings of that melody. It is therefore essential to make sure that the recording selected is structured to fit the pattern of the dance that one intends to teach.

Suggestions on the Use of Recordings

When recordings are to be used, the following suggestions may prove helpful:

1. Choose your records with care. Listen to them, if possible, before you purchase them to make sure the tempo and arrangement are suitable to your needs.
2. Organize the records ahead of time and know exactly what band or bands you want to use.
3. Know your record player and be able to check quickly the record speed, needle, volume, and so forth.
4. Except when you wish the students to hear the music before they start to move, teach the movement first; then put on the record. This practice obviates running back and forth and also permits teaching the movement at a reduced tempo.
5. Handle your records carefully, and establish a filing system that will enable you to find them easily when you need them.

SELECTED BIBLIOGRAPHY

Gilbert, Pia, and Lockhart, Aileene. *Music for the Modern Dance.* Dubuque, Iowa: W. C. Brown Company, 1961.

Hayes, Elizabeth R. *Dance Composition and Production.* New York: The Ronald Press Co., 1954. Chap. 9.

Lockhart, Aileene. *Modern Dance—Building and Teaching Lessons,* rev. ed. Dubuque, Iowa: W. C. Brown Company, 1957. Chaps. XIV, XV, XVI.

Murray, Ruth. *Dance in Elementary Education,* rev. ed. New York: Harper & Row, 1963.

10

Dance Performances and
Other Extracurricular Activities

Because dance, in addition to being a physical education activity, is also one of the performing arts, it is natural that performance should be one of its outcomes. The particular type of performance that is educationally appropriate to a given situation, however, depends upon several considerations: first, the kind of dance involved (i.e. folk, square, ballroom, modern); second, the level of experience and the needs of the participating students; third, the performance opportunities offered; fourth, the expectations of the individual school administrators; and fifth, the physical facilities available.

DANCE PERFORMANCES

Folk, square, and ballroom dance forms are predominantly social in function. Generally speaking, these dances are done for the personal satisfaction that the dancers themselves receive from the physical and social participation, rather than for the sake of entertaining others. Technical skill is important, not as an end in itself, but as an accomplishment that contributes to the social pleasure. When the dancers become expert, however, their grace and virtuosity can also be an aesthetic satisfaction to others. Exhibition dancing, well planned and executed, becomes an enjoyable form of entertainment.

High level performance is seldom achievable in beginning classes. Advanced classes provide opportunities for students to expand and perfect their dance skills and to develop the technical proficiency and detail of movement styling necessary for exhibition dancing.

Advanced ballroom dance classes, also, can provide opportunities for students to create visually appealing step combinations and group patterns for exhibition purposes. If advanced classes in these activities are not offered in the school curriculum, the same results can be obtained extracurricularly through folk, or square, or ballroom dance clubs.

A program of exhibition dancing needs to be so planned that it is enjoyable to the spectators as well as the performers. The level of difficulty of the dances chosen should be challenging, yet within the realm of capability of the participants so that the audience can feel comfortable in watching the performance. As far as possible, dances should be selected that contain engrossing changes of formation and floor pattern, and varied, though not necessarily difficult, step patterns. Contrasts in tempo, rhythm, and musical quality from one dance to another are other important considerations.

Dances must be practiced until the mechanics of the dance patterns become second nature to the participants and their attention can be freed to enjoy the social aspects of the performance. As has been previously mentioned, no folk or ballroom dance pattern can be considered adequately taught without attention to the movement styling. Such styling details as movement quality, arm and hand gestures, and facial expression need to be doubly emphasized with exhibition groups who are attempting to present dances with some degree of authenticity. Transitions from one dance to another also need to be practiced so that the group members will know how to change their formations smoothly and efficiently. When dances have thus been appropriately chosen and adequately practiced, the pleasures of performance will be shared vicariously by the viewer.

Authentic costumes, while increasing the attractiveness of a folk dance spectacle, are expensive and not at all requisite. A simple, basic costume that can be modified to suggest a particular nationality by the addition of colorful, appropriate accessories such as sashes, vests, aprons and hats, is often used to advantage. Costumes for ballroom dance exhibitions can be simple, afternoon attire, or the girls may wish to wear ballet or floor length formals. Choice of costume will depend to some extent upon the types of dances being presented. When footwork is important, street or ballet length skirts for the girls are advisable. When dances such as the waltz predominate, their effectiveness can be greatly enhanced by the use of full skirts that swirl in response to the dance movement. In any case, there should be some attempt made to achieve a uniform style of costume within the performing group. Particular attention should be paid to the choice of color combinations that will add to the total visual effectiveness. Since floor pattern in exhibition dancing is usually an important part of the visual interest, the seats for the spectators should be elevated if possible to enable them to enjoy this aspect of the performance.

Because modern dance is intended to be an expressive art form, its purpose is to communicate, which necessitates an audience. The type of audience, however, will vary according to the situation; it may consist of only one person, or a small group of persons, such as one's classmates or friends, or a large group, constituting the general public. The presentation of movement studies or dances for the members of one's own class to enjoy and evaluate is frequently used as a culmination to a unit on creative dance. For many beginning dancers this type of performance is adequate to satisfy their need to share with others their ideas and feelings expressed through movement. The time may arrive, however, when some of the students will wish to present the best of their efforts for their parents and friends, and then the teacher must decide what type of program is suitable for this occasion. When students are relatively inexperienced dancers, the more informal the presentation the better. Theatrical costuming, staging and lighting leads an audience to anticipate a technically polished, theatrical performance; whereas a simple presentation with a minimum of theatrical effects prepares an audience to enjoy simple dance forms without expecting more of students than they are able to produce. A "dance night" or "guest night" program held in the gymnasium or dance studio, in which a few of the culminating activities from the various dance classes are presented to parents, friends and other dance students can be an extremely worthwhile experience from an educational viewpoint. Not only does this type of presentation give the students a chance to share their creative efforts with each other and with their friends, but it enables parents to see some of the educational aspects of dance under relatively normal conditions. Suitable seating for viewers can be provided by movable bleachers when no balcony or permanent bleachers are available. Regular class leotards can be worn by the dancers, with the addition, when necessary, of simple, improvised accessories. If the room in which the performance is to be given is attractive and uncluttered, no special staging may be necessary; but when it contains such distracting equipment as stall bars, basketball backboards or mirrors that cannot be removed, a curtain of neutral color might be hung at the end of the room or flats covered with muslin, painted in some neutral tone, and fastened together to form folding screens might be used to provide a suitable background. Additional screens, placed on each side of the performing area to mask entrances and exits and to give depth to the dance space, are desirable, though not essential. One may also wish to amplify the diffused gymnasium lighting with a few inexpensive pars that can be placed on the floor or clamped to volleyball standards or overhead girders and focused on the dance area. Side lighting, is especially helpful in emphasizing the sculptural aspects of the human form and heightening the three dimensional quality of the dance movement.

The various participating groups might be seated informally along the sides of the room until it is their turn to perform; or if space is limited, they might wait their turn in an adjoining room provided they have had a previous opportunity to see the work of the other dancers. An informal explanation by the teacher or by one the students or by the dancers themselves in place of a printed program can serve as another means of communicating directly with the audience. Often an imaginatively choreographed presentation of a series of dance techniques can be of interest to the observers and can provide a good introduction to the dance studies or dances that have been evolved from these technical experiences. If a dance club has been organized, one or two numbers presented by this group might be used to climax the performance. Such a program could consist entirely of modern dance material, or it could also include some exhibition social (folk, square, or ballroom) dance forms. Whatever the content, the program should be brief and move along quickly, since bleachers grow increasingly uncomfortable after the first hour. Even though the program is an informal one, students need to be taught that it deserves their best efforts; otherwise they will be imposing upon the time of their invited guests. The performers must be well rehearsed; and since there will be no curtain, and in most cases no "blackouts," entrances to and exits from the performing area need to be carefully planned and practiced.

Eventually students reach the point at which they are ready to perform in a theater. It is an important part of their dance education for students to learn to judge when their dancing has reached that degree of technical skill and expressiveness that is required to transmit form and meaning across the footlights to an audience. Many dances that appear quite charming in the intimacy of the dance studio seem to fade out completely when put to the test of a theater performance. An opportunity to view dances in perspective from the back of an auditorium is sometimes necessary in order to enable students to evaluate their dances objectively.

The question may occur, "Should one expect a really polished performance from high school students?" The answer is that one should expect the best that students are capable of giving to a performance; unfortunately, their best is not always required of them. There are several causes for this apparent lack of high standard. One is a common misconception that quality of performance is unimportant, just so long as students perform. "Participation" has sometimes become a watchword in education to the exclusion of other important considerations—the more people on stage the better! This practice of measuring educational progress in terms of the number of participants encourages teachers to require students who are rhythmically and motorly inept to perform publicly, often subjecting them to ridicule, as well as causing them to spoil the performance for the other dancers. Such a situation is comparable to that of requiring a student who sings off-key to perform in an acapella chorus. Actually, nothing is gained by such practice. The uncoordinated student is seldom so naive that he is unaware of his own deficiencies, and his resulting discomfiture usually prompts him to avoid further dance experience instead of seeking the help that it might offer him as a means of improving his motor ability and as a private outlet for self-expression. Dance has many therapeutic values to be sure, but the place for dance therapy is not on a stage before an unconditioned audience. On the other hand, the practice of limiting performance experience to a very small, highly talented minority can be equally bad. If dance techniques are kept relatively simple and emphasis is placed upon performing these movements with control and meaning, there will be many students both qualified and eager to perform.

Another cause of mediocrity of performance is an inclination to give too many performances. Sometimes this situation is occasioned by a lack of wisdom on the part of over-enthusiastic teachers and students; frequently, it is the result of lack of understanding on the part of well-intentioned administrators. Dance classes are often looked upon as a convenient source of entertainment for assemblies and P.T.A. programs with the consequence that class time is consumed with rehearsing "routines" that must be teacher-imposed since there is not time for students to learn to choreograph for themselves. Students are subsequently deprived of opportunities to grow technically, to dance just for the personal satisfaction they find in learning to move with control, and to experience the pleasure of creating their own dances. If the function of dance is thus limited, few of its educational values can be realized. It is then the dance teacher's responsibility to alert the school administration to the values of dance as an aspect of education and of art expression rather than as mere entertainment. The teacher owes this responsibility not only to his students, to see that they can reap the greatest possible reward from their dance study, but also to dance itself, to see that it commands respect and appreciation from the student body and community members when it is presented as a performing art.

One should not infer from the foregoing discussion that dance teachers have no responsibility to cooperate with others in helping to produce such theater presentations as operettas and plays that require the use of dance, or to contribute to P.T.A. programs; what is implied is that one must use discretion in the number of such assignments that he accepts in order not to jeopardize the program of *dance education* and reduce to mediocrity the quality of public performance. Whenever possible, such commitments should be scheduled early in the school years so that the chosen activities can be integrated into the total dance plan. If necessary, large productions that have overlapping functions (such as operettas and dance programs) can be given on alternate years in order not to make inordinate demands upon the time and talents of interested students.

PREPARING A PROGRAM OF MODERN DANCE

In directing a dance performance involving students who have had little previous contact with modern dance either as observers or performers, the teacher is required to decide what his own role should be. Should he insist that students make their own compositions on the grounds that it is good for their development in spite of the fact that their experience provides them with no examples of good choreography? Or should he choreograph for the students during this initial stage, thus giving them the benefit of his increased experience until that point at which he feels they are ready to compose dances for themselves? Will this latter method retard or will it encourage student creativity? These are questions for which the teacher must find answers.

Students can learn a great deal from performing in good dances that have been teacher choreographed. Not only does this experience help them to become aware of what constitutes good choreography, but it enables them to observe an efficient director in action. By seeing how a dance has been evolved and how the director works with the performers to achieve these desired ends, students are later able to apply this knowledge to their own choreographic efforts. Participating in a faculty directed dance can be made an increasingly valuable educational experience if the director permits the students to share in developing the dance idea through group discussion, and to assist in finding through their own exploratory efforts movements that will express the chosen concept. In such a way students can work creatively along with the directing teacher and can take pride in having contributed to the end result. Teacher choreographing is indefensible, however, if it is used only as a means of gratifying the instructor's own creative urges at the expense of the students' creative development.

Even when students have had sufficient compositional experience to do their own choreography, the teacher's guiding hand is needed. One of the most difficult tasks that the teacher faces is that of helping students to choose appropriate ideas to dance about. The daily routine of waking, getting up in the morning, dressing, passing the day in some fashion, undressing, and retiring at night, as a dance theme, seems to have some undeserved fascination for beginning students; but unless the performer is able to shed new light upon this common experience or is able to present it in some clever, original fashion the dance has little chance of succeeding. To attempt to dance about an atom bomb or about the creation of the world could overwhelm even a professional choreographer. But the innocent novitiate calmly entertains such ideas, anticipating none of their pitfalls. And again, although Rudyard Kipling's "If" may appeal greatly to students' idealistic values, an attempt to dance such a poem is doomed to failure because it simply does not lend itself to movement expression. To the harried dance teacher all student dance ideas seem to fall into one of three categories: the trite, the world-shaking, or the undanceable. But to respond with a flat-footed "no" to a student's cherished but ill-chosen idea might easily destroy what little confidence the student has in his own ability to create. If, on the other hand, by asking a few pertinent questions, the teacher can encourage the student to re-examine his idea in the light of certain essential criteria, the student will often decide for himself that he has made an unfortunate choice. Here are some questions that might help students to make valid evaluations of their dance ideas:

1. Can the idea be well expressed through movement, or is it better suited to some other art medium, such as sculpture, painting, or writing?

2. Is the idea one to which the dancer can bring some fresh interpretation or movement presentation instead of relying upon time-worn clichés?

3. Can the idea be made specific enough in concept so that the dancer can pin-point exactly what it is he wishes to communicate?

4. Is the subject within the range of the dancer's technical skill, intellectual understanding, and emotional experience?

5. Is the context of the idea simple enough that the meaning can be conveyed clearly without the aid of elaborate program notes?

6. Can the dance be completed and polished in the length of time allotted for the choreography?

With such considerations in mind, the student, with the help of the teacher, can sometimes re-orient his original idea, perhaps confining its scope, or giving it new direction. Helping students to grapple with their dance ideas and to distill from nebulous, undirected feeling-states specific concepts toward which they can channel their creative energies is a very important step in starting them off successfully.

When students are entirely lacking in dance ideas, the following sources might prove helpful in stimulating their creative thinking: titles of dances from dance programs performed elsewhere; words that suggest specific aspects of behavior such as "Frenzy," "Ritual," "Tantrum," or "Jubilee;" ballads and folk tunes; poetry that establishes a mood or suggests some kind of action response other than a mere pantomimic reiteration of the words; myths and legends (provided the story line is uncomplicated); historical happenings—frequently the human reaction to these events rather than a representation of the happenings themselves; episodes that are the outcome of human relationships; the use of objects such as ropes or bamboo poles that can be moved in interesting ways or that can suggest interesting movement to the dancer; and various sensory stimuli, especially music. Some individuals find it impossible to conceive a dance that has not been musically inspired, but it is important for students to learn to be free from overdependency upon another art form and to learn to seek within themselves the inspiration and the form of their dances.

When music is used as the basis for dance, it is often misused and poorly chosen. Here, the dance teacher must expect to take responsibility for upgrading the musical taste of his students and for developing their ability to use music in a way that will not offend those who know and love music for its own sake, avoiding, in particular, "cutting" music without concern for its musical structure, piecing together unrelated musical fragments, and radically changing the tempo of the music to accommodate the dancer. Students often tend to select popular music as dance accompaniment because it is familiar to them and because its obvious rhythmic beat convinces them that it will be easy to dance to. Quite the contrary, the monotonous, throbbing beat of dance band music is likely to be so compelling that it actually limits the dancer's rhythmic responses. The artistic merit of a dance can seldom be raised above the level of its accompaniment; and the choice of commonplace music generally results in commonplace choreography. There is much good music that will appeal to student tastes, but in order to enjoy listening to it and dancing to it, students first have to become familiar with it. A good record library of classical and semi-classical music appropriate for dance accompaniment can be of tremendous value in providing students with the means of enlarging their musical tastes. Short compositions for single instruments or small orchestra are generally the most suitable for dance. For a list of composers who have written music usable for dance accompaniment see Appendix II.

At first, when student acquaintance with music is limited, the teacher may find it advisable to choose a variety of musical compositions from which students may make selections. Later, when their musical tastes have been extended, students can be assigned to find music that they feel is appropriate for dance which the group as a whole can then listen to and evaluate. Sometimes nothing that a teacher can do or say can dissuade a student from making a poor musical choice. In such cases, the only solution is to let the student try to dance to the music he has chosen and to learn firsthand its limitations. Good taste cannot be imposed from without, but is developed gradually through repeated exposure to works of fine quality that students can understand. The wise teacher has long since learned that each group of students must make their own mistakes and learn from the consequences. Teacher guidance can go only so far; it can never become a substitute for experience.

Another area in which students often need assistance is that of learning to become effective student directors. To handle people competently without officiousness and to consider the ideas of others, while maintaining a leadership role are qualities of good directing that are learned through practice and extended effort. Likewise, appreciation by group members of when to make suggestions and when to accept direction without comment must be learned if successful results are to follow. In group projects where there are no appointed choreographers, the ability of individual students to share responsibility and to make compromises when necessary can make the difference between success and failure. Often, mature, impartial guidance is needed to enable students to learn how to work together effectively.

Students are inclined to be chronic time wasters when they work by themselves. With time at a premium, as it usually is, this tendency can be disastrous if allowed to flourish. Furthermore, ineffectual use of time can be extremely damaging to group morale. Here again, it is the teacher who must help the directing student to recognize his responsibility to the group to come to rehearsals with his ideas clarified, and whatever movements he wishes to teach worked out in advance. The student director should have his rehearsal plans organized in terms of a definite time schedule arranged to keep everybody busy, or should excuse in advance of the rehearsal those performers with whom he does not plan to work. When dance composition is being done by the group process, students can become so embroiled in talk that time is used to poor advantage, and they may need a gentle reminder of the obvious fact that dance movement can be found only by moving.

Once student compositions are underway, what then? Does the teacher fold his hands and hope for the best, or does he continue to prod and guide until the dances have been completed? Advice or criticism given a student choreographer after his dance is finished may come too late for him to take advantage of the suggestions without beginning over. Advice given at the strategic moment when changes can be made without entirely re-doing a dance is usually the most helpful. On the other hand, constant interference on the part of an instructor can frustrate a choreographer and undermine his confidence. Whatever suggestions are made should correlate with the *student's* concept rather than the teacher's concept of what the dance is about. It is therefore essential that the teacher understand completely the choreographer's intent before offering suggestions. And at all times, students should be encouraged to feel that they are free to accept or reject suggestions and that they are in no way pressured to act against the dictates of their own artistic integrity. Lack of experience often prevents students from detecting compositional errors and envisioning interesting choreographic possibilities. In order to enable students to learn from the results of their mistakes it is sometimes advisable to refrain from commenting altogether until after a composition is finished; but such a procedure is effective only if opportunity is provided for the students to attack the problem again to rectify the errors. Whatever method is used in giving suggestions, the critique should never be omitted altogether because it is by such means that students grow in artistic understanding and ability.

FOLK AND SQUARE DANCE FESTIVALS

Another worthwhile extracurricular activity is the folk or square dance festival designed to provide an opportunity for various dance groups to participate together in dances that are a part of their common experience. An audience is not required, for although a dance festival is usually interesting to watch, it is not intended primarily for the spectator. In large schools where an extensive curriculum of folk or square dance is offered, it is possible to hold successful dance festivals for students within the school itself, but often interest in the event is increased when dancers from other schools are invited to participate. Such a plan calls for advance preparation on the part of all participating schools, since all of the dancers will need to be made familiar with at least most of the repertory of dances to be included in the festival. Usually the dance teacher of the host school will take the initiative in calling together the teachers of other schools for such advance planning.

The theme of a folk festival could be centered around a particular culture, or it could be expanded to include dances of many nationalities. Other departments might also be encouraged to participate in the festival with the presentation of folk songs and displays of folk arts or costumes from the particular folk cultures. Exhibition folk or square dance groups from the different schools might be asked to present some of their dance specialities during the intermissions; or if there are foreign students or nationality groups within a city, they might be invited to perform or teach some of their dances to the festival group.

There will need to be a master of ceremonies who will see that the evening's program of events is effectuated smoothly. Because much of the success of a dance festival depends upon his leadership ability, the master of ceremonies needs to be chosen with care. Usually a dance or physical education teacher or recreation leader best fulfills this function, although in certain instances, particularly on the college level, there may be students with sufficient social skill and experience to carry out this responsibility. The job of the master of ceremonies includes getting the evening off to a spirited start, assisting shy students to find partners easily, encouraging those on the sidelines to join in the fun, controlling occasional obstreperous behavior, and keeping the tempo of the festivities from lagging, thus assuring a good time for all. The master of ceremonies will announce the dances, though it is also helpful either to post the order of the dances or to have a printed program available for each of the participants. Often students like to have access to the list of dances several days in advance of the festival so that they can review the dances they may have forgotten.

Another function of the master of ceremonies is to organize the dancers into couples (since folk festivals are often dateless affairs) or into whatever dance formation is desired. Line dances and circle dances that require no partners are often good activities with which to begin in order to get everyone out on the dance floor. Once the participants are dancing, it is usually a simple matter to get them into partners through the use of easy mixer dances or to organize them into groups of four, eight, or sixteen by means of a grand march. When some of the dancers have come with partners it is also important to remember to permit them to return to their original partners frequently during the evening. Normally, there is a tendency for students from different schools to congregate with the people they know; so additional thought must be given to ways of encouraging these groups to intermingle. Occasionally, even the spectators can be invited by the dancers to become their partners for some simple dance that can be learned easily.

For square dancing, an experienced caller is needed. While recordings with calls are available, the use of such recordings in place of a caller lacks the immediacy and spontaneity that gives zest to a square dance party. The caller for square dancing is usually the master of ceremonies who, in addition to his other duties, helps the dancers to organize their sets, gives assistance when possible to groups confused by the call, and in general, establishes a festive atmosphere.

Someone will also need to be in charge of the music. This responsibility can be handled by the master of ceremonies if necessary, although it may be advantageous to assign this task to someone else who can be free to move around the hall to check the volume of sound and the general acoustics. If a successful evening is to be assured, both the dance music and the announcements will need to be amplified sufficiently to be heard clearly, but without reverberating in the ears of the dancers. A speaker system more powerful than the type used for dance classes is frequently required.

Although live music is stimulating, it is seldom possible for local musicians to supply the variation in quality and instrumentation needed for folk dancing. For this reason recordings of authentic folk dance accompaniment are generally used in preference to live music. For efficiency's sake, it is usually advisable to tape the recordings in the order in which they are to be played and to have at hand a duplicate tape (or the records themselves, with the record player) in case of a mechanical emergency. When an old-time fiddler is available, his services can enliven an evening of square dancing, but there are also many excellent recordings (without calls) that will provide a satisfactory substitute.

BALLROOM DANCES

An appropriate culmination to any ballroom dance instruction is the opportunity to put such learning into practice outside of the classroom. Matinee dances at the close of school or at noontime can provide students with this much needed experience and add to their social enjoyment. High school dances will require faculty supervision, but student committees can do most of the planning. Rules of conduct to cover these occasions need to be formulated by a committee of faculty members and student representatives or by the student council. If social etiquette has been carefully taught in the dance classes there should be some degree of carry-over to these school dances. The choice of dance steps to be included will depend somewhat upon the steps that are currently popular and upon the social mores of the community.

Daytime dances, as well as informal evening dances following basketball games, can be dateless functions which all students can be encouraged to attend. If dateless dances are to be successful, however, some sort of leadership will be required to help the students find partners and exchange dances frequently. Members of the faculty are sometimes called upon to conduct mixers and to help with discipline, when necessary. Students can also be enlisted occasionally to teach new, popular steps to the rest of the group. Otherwise, matinee dances, being very informal, require little in the way of advance planning other than the dance music.

Evening dances, where dates are required, are more elaborate than matinee dances and necessitate the appointment of special committees to handle such matters as decorations, refreshments, music, program arrangements (including planning the intermission entertainment, if any, and arranging for printing of the dance programs) and (not to be forgotten) cleaning up the debris. When students come with dates, the problem of getting them to exchange partners is greatly increased. Discussion in ballroom dance classes of the values of social exchange is probably the best approach to this difficult situation. If mixers are used, they need to be cleverly devised to make them appealing to the students. Increased attention will also need to be given to the matter of chaperoning, with rules established regarding permission to leave the dance area while the dance is in progress.

Recordings are the usual accompaniment for daytime dances. While live music by local dance bands is sometimes used for high school evening affairs, it is often much too expensive except for very special occasions. The school should bear some of the responsibility for furnishing records for student dances, but the students may wish to augment this supply (which quickly becomes out-dated) by bringing their own recordings of the latest hit tunes. Not all musical arrangements are danceable. Care must be taken to choose recordings that have a definite beat and consistent tempo, and some thought must be given also to arranging them in a sequential order that will provide an alternation of fast and slow tempos. An advance check on the part of the music committee to see that the record player and public address systems are in good working condition will help to ensure a smooth-running party and thus contribute to everyone's enjoyment.

EXTRACURRICULAR ORGANIZATIONS

Because only a limited amount of school time can be set aside for dance activities, extracurricular organizations are often needed to enable students to further their study of dance and to work creatively. Membership qualifications for any extracurricular dance organization should be automatically determined by its purposes. If the club has been organized purely as a recreational group for the benefit of its participants only, then membership can be opened to all who are interested; but on the other hand, if the function of the club has been conceived as that of giving public perform-ances and of serving the needs of advanced students, then member-ship will need to be limited to those who are qualified to contribute to the group and to benefit from its activities. Standards will need to be set and tryout procedures organized. Tryout requirements should test those technical and creative proficiencies the club mem-bers feel an applicant must possess in order to be a contributing member. Acceptance or rejection of the auditioners is usually de-cided by the members of the group. Some high school administ-trators, however, prefer that a board of judges from outside the group be used to pass upon applicants in order that complete impartiality of judgment may be assured. Whatever procedure is followed, it is important to arrange the tryouts in such a way that each individual being tested can be observed by as many of the judges as possible. By having the evaluating members rotate periodically during the testing period so that they are responsible for observing different individuals during different sections of the audition, a reasonably fair judgment can be secured. It is usually wise to concentrate in the tryouts on activities that will reveal the individual's general skill as a performer (including basic techniques, rhythmic accuracy, style and projection) rather than to stress highly specialized skills in which only specifically trained individuals can excel. And for modern dance, simple creative problems that can be solved extemporaneously provide a good way of judging creative ingenuity.

In selecting new members, personality factors should be ruled out as much as possible and decisions made upon a purely objective basis. Occasionally, in extreme instances, inability to work cooperatively with others might become a debarring factor until the individual had demonstrated his desire to remedy this weakness. Many times, students (and even teachers) are sentimentally swayed in favor of an applicant who is eager to become a group member, and they want to accept him even though it is evident from the audition that the student is unqualified. To admit such a student is generally a mistake, not only because it lowers the standards of the group, but also because the person, himself, is sure to become discouraged by a belated discovery of his own inadequacies. Instead, such a student should be encouraged to overcome his deficiencies through participation in dance classes or extracurricular practice groups, and invited to try out again.

The functions of a club usually determine the complexity of its organization. Some groups may feel the need of very little formal organization. The election of a president or group chairman, and a secretary to notify the membership of special meetings and other events, the selection of a meeting time and place, and the adoption of a few simple rules and policies may suffice. Other groups may find it desirable to elect a body of officers and formulate a constitution—a procedure that provides excellent experience in interpreting and applying principles of democratic action. On the whole, however, it is wise to keep the organizational structure as simple as possible. Appendix I is an example of a fairly complex constitution for a modern dance group from which simple forms can easily be derived.

Of supreme importance to any organization is the matter of attendance. Halfhearted participation by a few members can seriously lower group morale. An organization will be strengthened by dropping a delinquent member after giving him adequate warning, regardless of his potential as a performer, rather than continuing to retain his name on the rolls. Absence from rehearsals is a particularly serious matter and needs to be dealt with severely. Regulations made by the group must be strictly adhered to, however; otherwise such rules have little value. Tardiness, also, can become a problem because it jeopardizes the efficiency of the group as a whole. While penalties can be imposed, it is mainly the pressure of group disapproval that provides the most effective means of control.

Normally, in most organizations, the year's activities are planned by the group members, themselves, at the beginning of the school year. General suggestions are made by the group as a whole, the officers, and the faculty advisor; and responsibility for planning and implementing details is delegated to the club officers. In some college situations, however, the *modern dance* club must serve both as a student organization and as a performing group for the dance major. Where this arrangement exists, the major department will need to share some of the responsibility in setting up the year's agenda in conjunction with the participating club members.

Folk, square, or ballroom dance club meetings are usually devoted in part to extending the dance repertory of the group members. New dances might be introduced to the participants by the faculty sponsor, by students members who have learned new dances elsewhere, by guest instructors from other schools, or by persons of foreign extraction who are intimately acquainted with folk dances from their native lands. Dances recently learned will also need to be reviewed if they are to be retained in the club repertory. When a group is preparing a dance performance, club meeting time will need to be set aside for polishing the exhibition dances, planning the costumes, and working out other details. Time may also be needed for planning folk dance festivals, preparing folk, square, or ballroom dance parties, or arranging other special events. Occasionally, meetings or portions of meetings might be devoted to the presentation of films or talks on the dances and customs of a particular people.

Most dance clubs also like to spend time dancing just for fun, and when the essential business of the club has been dispensed with, the remaining time can be spent in doing just that. An evening can be made especially enjoyable if students are permitted to request their dance favorites. The titles of specially requested dances can be written on a blackboard. However an orderly file of records will be essential if requests are to be handled expeditiously. Club members can perhaps take turns being in charge of the records during the club meetings so that no one individual will be deprived of the opportunity to dance. In addition to satisfying the needs of their own members, dance clubs may also wish to answer requests for dance leadership at other school functions, such as special parties and matinee dances. In so doing, the club members extend to others some of the pleasures of participating in dance that they, themselves, enjoy.

A modern dance club may wish to spend meeting time on the study of technique, which will contribute to their growth as dancers. Members of the dance faculty, guest teachers from outside the school, or even students who have had some special dance experiences that the group would like to share might be invited to instruct the group. Other meetings might be devoted to improvisation, using as points of departure special movement problems, dance ideas, or music and other stimuli for dance. Persons from related art fields might be invited to appear as guest speakers; or occasional joint meetings with dance clubs from other schools might be held to enable students to share ideas and to add variety to the program.

With most modern dance groups, however, a great deal of time will need to be spent in planning and rehearsing dances for public performance. A complete schedule of performance commitments should be made available to the planning committee at the beginning of the year so that adequate preparation time can be set aside. Additional rehearsal time outside of the scheduled club meetings must generally be anticipated, but the regular meetings should be utilized to the best possible advantage. Rehearsals need to be scheduled so that dances can be completed, ready for polishing, at least two weeks before performance time. When possible, it is often advantageous to have a private studio presentation of all student choreography at least a month before the program is to be given. At that time, the dances can be evaluated and selections made for public presentation. If such a procedure is followed, however, students need to be emotionally prepared for the possibility that their dances might not be chosen and be taught to accept such disappointments philosophically. Minor adjustments in casting may then need to be made in order to take care of students whose parts have been eliminated.

Performance times are times of tension. College students as well as high school students are likely to be guilty of immature behavior unless good leadership prevails. Students need to be encouraged as far as possible to feel the desirability of selecting dances and performers that will most effectively represent the group as a whole. They should strive to take pride in the achievements of the entire group rather than merely in their own accomplishments. Publicity that places undue attention upon individual accomplishment can do much to undermine a wholesome group spirit. But on the other hand, care should be taken to see that everyone is given some part to perform or some other responsibility in which he can take pride. The degree to which club members are able to work together in harmony depends a great deal upon faculty leadership. When problems do arise, students should be encouraged to discuss them openly with the entire group or with the officers and faculty advisor instead of airing their complaints in little private "gripe sessions." Student leaders themselves, through their own exemplary behavior, can be tremendously influential in establishing a healthy, working atmosphere. When harmony of action is fully realized, the pleasure and satisfaction that comes from cooperative effort and from sharing mutual achievement is immeasurable.

SELECTED BIBLIOGRAPHY

Hayes, Elizabeth R. *Dance Composition and Production.* New York: The Ronald Press Co., 1954. Chap. 10.

Kraus, Richard. *Folk Dancing.* New York: The Macmillan Co., 1962. Chap. 14.

Kraus, Richard. *Square Dances Today and How to Call Them.* New York: The Ronald Press Co., 1954. Chap. 8.

Turner, Margery J. *Modern Dance for High School and College.* Englewood Cliffs, N.J.: Prentice-Hall, Inc., 1957. Chap. VII.

CONCLUSION

In summary, no matter what type of dance it is—folk, square, ballroom, or modern—or what the teaching situation may be, there are educational values to be realized provided one appreciates these values and sets about intelligently to achieve them. Success in the accomplishment of educational goals necessitates careful planning and analysis of lesson material, wise selection of only a few objectives to be accomplished at any one time, and strong resistance to the temptation to cover too much material superficially. Dance as education implies the teaching of movement concepts rather than isolated movements as ends in themselves; it implies constant attention to the development of kinesthetic awareness, rhythmic understanding and accuracy of response, and sensitivity to the interacting elements of time, space, and energy as applied to movement. Dance as education is very much concerned with the development of technical proficiency while at the same time encouraging individual exploration of movement, creative expression, and social responsibility. The foregoing material has been intended to help the reader to succeed as a dance educator, but in the final analysis, there is no substitute for personal ingenuity.

And now it is time for the ship to drop the pilot vessel—for the teacher, as captain, to chart his own course according to his chosen destination. Fair sailing and occasional rough waters lie ahead—but adventure, always. Good luck, and pleasant voyaging!

Appendix I

CONSTITUTION FOR A MODERN DANCE CLUB

PREAMBLE

We, the members of ____(name of club)____ join together in this modern dance organization for a two-fold purpose:

1. To partake of the inner satisfaction and mutual stimulation that is received from working together and from participating in dance as a form of art expression;

2. To provide a favorable environment for the creation of dances by members of our group which may be performed for our own artistic growth and for the enjoyment and education of others.

ARTICLE I. MEMBERSHIP

SECTION I. MEMBERS

(a) Regular members are admitted through audition and acceptance by a two-thirds majority vote of those members in attendance.

(b) Regular members must be actively enrolled students at __(name of school)__ .

(c) Honorary membership may be extended to individuals by a two-thirds majority vote of the group. Such members do not pay dues and are not permitted to vote, but have all of the other rights and privileges of regular membership.

(d) Faculty advisors are ex-officio members of the group, but pay no dues and are not permitted to vote.

(e) A regular member, wishing to become inactive, must submit a formal request (stating his reasons) which is voted upon by the group. Such a member may not remain inactive for more than one semester (or two quarters), or he will be dropped from the group.

(f) In order to be reinstated, a former member who has been dropped from the group must audition and be voted upon again.

SECTION II. AUDITIONS

(a) Auditions shall be held at least once a year; further auditions may be scheduled according to the needs of the organization and the apparent readiness of auditioners. The primary audition shall be held in the fall, soon after the opening of school, during a regular club meeting. (When the majority of students are untrained and need preliminary training in an apprentice group, this primary audition will need to be scheduled later in the year.)

(b) Audition requirements shall be: (1) evidence of technical proficiency as indicated by the performance of certain designated skills (participants will be instructed during the audition regarding the exact skills to be performed); (2) evidence of creativity and of performing ability as indicated by: (a) the extemporized solution of several creative problems given during the audition and (b) the presentation of an original solo.

(c) A minimum of a fourth of the membership including at least one officer of the group must be present in the judging of an auditioner.

Section III. Initiation

(a) There shall be a formal initiation of new members, officiated by the president. This initiation shall be held as soon as possible after the primary audition in the fall.

(b) Auditioners who are accepted as members later in the year will be initiated the following year, but may participate as regular group members as soon as they have been notified of their acceptance.

(c) Special initiations may be held when so desired by the group.

Section IV. Attendance

(a) Active membership shall be maintained by regular participation in meetings and club activities and payment of dues.

(b) Roll call at regularly scheduled meetings will be taken by the secretary-treasurer at exactly the time the meeting is scheduled to commence. If a member enters the meeting after his name has been called, it is his responsibility to notify the secretary; otherwise, he will be marked absent.

(c) Excuses from meeting shall be written and submitted to a member of the executive board, if possible before the meeting from which the member must be absent. This procedure will enable the executive board to accept the excuse, or if its validity is doubtful, to bring the request before the membership for a vote at the regular meeting. No excuses are considered valid except those for illness, required school functions, and extreme emergencies.

(d) Four unexcused absences a year will be the basis for exclusion of a member from the group.

(e) After a member has had three unexcused absences, he shall be sent a warning notification by the secretary-treasurer; if a fourth absence occurs, he shall be notified and given two weeks to submit an excuse; if no excuse is presented, he shall be automatically dropped from the group.

ARTICLE II. EXECUTIVE ORGANIZATION

Section I. Officers

(a) The officers of _____ (name of club) _____ , elected annually, shall be president, vice-president, secretary-treasurer, publicity chairman, and historian.

(b) The president, vice-president, and secretary-treasurer, together with the faculty advisor, shall constitute the executive board.

Section II. Duties of the Officers

(a) The president shall be the executive in charge of the organization; he shall preside at all meetings of the group, and shall represent the organization on the Student Legislative Council.

(b) The vice-president shall assist the president in his executive duties, and shall officiate in his absence; he shall also be the student coordinator of (the apprentice group), working cooperatively with the faculty member in charge of that organization, and shall serve as audition chairman.

(c) The secretary-treasurer shall take roll; record minutes of the business meetings; collect and handle organizational dues, fines, and special assessments and disburse funds; he shall work with the faculty advisor and executive board on setting up a budget, and shall keep a financial record of income and expenditures; he shall be in charge of all official correspondence, including notification to successful candidates of their election to membership and notifications of membership lapses; he shall keep an accurate roll of names, addresses and telephone numbers of all active group members, and shall be in charge of a calling committee to notify the membership of unscheduled meetings and special events.

(d) The publicity chairman shall send notifications of auditions, initiation announcements, and publicity concerning the activities of the group to the student news organ and to local newspapers; he shall send to *Dance Magazine, Dance Observer*, and other appropriate journals accounts of the group activities which might be of general interest; and he shall be the student chairman in charge of all publicity for concerts given by the organization.

(e) The historian is responsible for maintaining in the scrapbook of the organization a record of the activities of the group during his term of office; the record shall include copies of all important newspaper and magazine articles pertaining to the group, and copies of concert programs; he shall also keep an up-to-date file of local alumni and their addresses.

SECTION III. DUTIES OF THE EXECUTIVE BOARD

(a) The executive board shall serve in an advisory capacity to the president; shall make recommendations to the organization as a whole concerning group policy and action; shall serve as a nominating committee; and shall act for the organization as a whole in emergencies or in situations where the course of action is self-evident.

(b) A minimum of three officers must be present during an executive board meeting.

(c) When it is impossible for a regular member of the executive board to attend a board meeting, the historian or publicity chairman may be asked to serve in his place.

ARTICLE III. ELECTIONS

SECTION I. PROCEDURE

(a) Elections shall be held at the end of the school year. The executive board shall present a slate of officers at the meeting prior to elections. The slate presented by the board shall consist of three nominations for president, and two nominations for all other offices except that of vice-president. The vice-president will be the person who receives the second highest vote for president.

(b) During the meeting in which elections are to be held, nominations from the floor shall be accepted.

(c) Voting shall be by secret ballot. Members shall vote for two candidates for president, and for one candidate for each of the other offices listed on the ballot. At least three-fourths of the membership must be represented in the voting. Candidates are elected to office by majority vote. Ballots shall be tallied by the secretary-treasurer.

Section II. Qualification of Candidates

(a) Candidates for office must have been a member of the organization for at least one semester (or two quarters).

ARTICLE IV. MEETINGS AND OTHER ACTIVITIES

Section I. Meetings

(a) There shall be one regular weekly meeting of the organization throughout the school year on a chosen day for a designated period of time (normally two hours).

(b) Special meetings may be called or regular meetings dispensed with according to the needs and wishes of the group as a whole.

(c) Members are expected to stay for the entire meeting unless excused by the president.

(d) A penalty of _____ shall be exacted for tardiness unless the latecomer is excused by the secretary-treasurer.

(e) The first part of each regular meeting shall be used as a business meeting; the remaining portion shall be devoted to activities in keeping with the purposes of the group as stated in the preamble.

(f) A suggested schedule of events shall be planned by the executive board, to be approved by the membership and arranged for by the president.

(g) One meeting during each semester (or quarter) will be designated as "studio night" at which time members may present dances for the group to evaluate. One "studio night" of the year will be designated as compulsory. At this time all of the members of the group will be expected to participate.

Section II. Other Activities

(a) The organization will present at least one concert or major production during the school year. Other performances may be arranged by the group.

(b) No member of the group may present a dance for public performance in the name of the group without official approval of the executive board or the group as a whole.

(c) Concert rehearsals are as important as club meetings. Absence from rehearsals is permissible only in the case of illness or extreme emergency and must be excused by the person in charge of the rehearsal. More than one absence without adequate reason may be considered just cause for dropping a person from the dance.

ARTICLE V. DUES

Section I. Dues

(a) An annual assessment of dues on the basis of _____ a semester (or quarter) shall be made at the first of the school year. New members will be assessed on the basis of the semester (or quarter) in which they enter.

ARTICLE VI. REVISION OF THE CONSTITUTION

Section I. Amendments

(a) The constitution may be amended by a two-thirds majority vote of the membership.

Appendix II

PIANO MUSIC AND RECORDINGS FOR DANCE

Piano Music for Modern Dance Techniques and Composition

Gilbert, Pia, and Lockhart, Aileene. *Music for the Modern Dance*. Dubuque, Iowa: W. C. Brown Company, 1961. For class work or dance program. Includes musical forms, folk and pre-classic forms; moderately difficult to play.

Hayes, Elizabeth R. *Dance Composition and Production*. New York: The Ronald Press Co., 1954. Music by Maurine Dewsnup includes a March in Three-Four, music for Studies in Colors, a Ground Bass, Theme and Variations, and a three-section piece called Jazz-Blues-Boogie Woogie; moderately difficult to play.

Hemmer, Eugene. *American Miniatures*. New York: Orchesis Publications. Short, provocative sketches, excellent for dance studies depicting various phases of Americana; easy to play.

Horst, Louis. *Comin' Round the Mountain*. New York: Orchesis Publications. A usable set of six contrasting settings of the traditional folk tune; easy to play.

Horst, Louis. *Three South American Dances*. New York: Orchesis Publications. A Latin American suite of gaiety and charm; The Andante is of a tango quality.

Jahn, Daniel. *Seven Pre-Classic Dances*. New York: Orchesis Publications. A modern treatment of pre-classic forms; short, easy to play.

Jahn, Daniel. *Eleven Choreographic Studies*. New York: Orchesis Publications. Based on Louis Horst's Modern Forms, these studies cover a variety of moods, styles and ideas; short, easy to play.

Johnston, Ben. *Celebration*. New York: Orchesis Publications. Exuberant, driving in quality; difficult to play, rhythmically complex. Excellent for concert dance.

Lloyd, Norman. *Accompaniments for Modern Dance*. New York: Orchesis Publications. Short, easy-to-play accompaniments for technique, fundamental steps, and movement qualities; includes Doris Humphrey's Seven-Seven-Ten Study and her variations, 7, 7, 7, 3.

Lloyd, Norman. *Five Pieces for Dance*. New York: Orchesis Publications. A collection of short pieces illustrating various forms and styles including

Blues, Dance Hall Study, Theme and Variations, Puritan Hymn from Martha Graham's Panorama, and Irish Dance; moderately difficult to play.

Lockhart, Aileene. *Modern Dance: Building and Teaching Lessons.* Dubuque, Iowa: W. C. Brown Company, 1957. Music by Jessie Flood. Short pieces for class techniques and problems in meter, form and quality. Also included are a Canon, a Resultant Rhythm, and a Theme and Variations; easy to play.

Miller, Freda. *Accompaniment for Dance Technique.* Northport, Long Island. Sixteen short accompaniments for class work; easy to play.

Miller, Freda. *Second Album for Dance.* Northport, Long Island. Four relatively long studies in different meters; easy to play.

Wessel, Mark. *Twenty Dance Studies.* Madison, Wisconsin: Department of Physical Education, University of Wisconsin. Good for dance studies involving movement qualities, unusual meters and rhythmic problems; moderately difficult to play.

Recordings for Modern Dance Techniques and Composition

Coleman, John. *Music for Contemporary Dance.* Supervised by Hanya Holm School of Dance, Oliver Kostock directing. Waldwick, New Jersey: Hoctor Records. For barre and center, walking, running, leaping, vibration, etc.

Gilbert, Pia. *Music for Dance.* Los Angeles, California: Children's Music Center. Designed for use as accompaniment for warm-ups and dance techniques, movement fundamentals and traditional dance steps. Included are a Study in Accumulative Rhythm, Ground Bass and a piece written for prepared piano entitled "Robot Sounds."

Lohoefer, Evelyn. *Music for Modern Dance,* vol. 1. Washington 7, D.C. This music may be freely adapted to any creative needs. Most of the selections are described only in terms of tempo and dynamics. Included also are Mood Piece, Piece with Decorations, and Strange Sounds, Fast and Slow.

Malament, Sarah. *Improvisations for Modern Dance,* series 1 and 2. New York. Sarah Malament. These records provide a comprehensive coverage of studio techniques and also include music for fundamental step combinations, grande and petit pliés, music with a Russian and a Spanish flavor, and a Blues.

Merrill, Kathleen. *Studies and Sketches for Modern Dance.* Miami, Florida: Kathleen Merrill. A collection of short pieces composed expressly for composition, technique and rhythm study; the studies are primarily for experience in unusual or varying meters, and exploration in movement qualities. The sketches, most of which are arranged in suites, include Frolic Suite, In a Jazz Idiom, In Latin American Idiom, and a Theme and Variations.

* Miller, Freda. *Accompaniment for Dance Technique.* Northport, Long Island: Freda Miller Records. Sixteen short pieces in different styles and tempos, with helpful suggestions for multiple uses of each piece; includes three pre-classic dance forms.

* Also available on tape.

* Miller, Freda. *Second Album for Dance*. Northport, Long Island: Freda Miller Records. This collection of four three-minute studies (The Two Beat, Three Beat, Four Beat and Off Beat) is also annotated with movement suggestions.

* Miller, Freda. *Third Album for Dance*. Northport, Long Island: Freda Miller Records. Recorded for two pianos, these ten "dancey" pieces may be used for program material. A Western Dance, Theme and Variations, and Two Antique Dances are included.

Nossen, Steffi, and Jess Meeker. *First Primer of Modern Dance*. New Haven 10, Connecticut: Dancers' Shop. This record includes music for Patterns in Triplets and Strides, Knee Bends and Balances, and Jump-Leap combinations.

Modern Composers Whose Music Is Often Good Accompaniment for Modern Dance

Antheil, George	Ginastera, Alberto	Phillips, Burrill
Barber, Samuel	Goeb, Roger	Porter, Quincy
Bartok, Bela	Goossens, Eugene	Poulenc, Francis
Bennett, Robert Russell	Gould, Morton	Prokofieff, Serge
Berg, Alban	Griffes, Elliot	Ravel, Maurice
Bergsma, William	Grofe, Ferde	Reigger, Wallingford
Berners, Lord	Guion, David	Rieti, Vittorio
Bernstein, Leonard	Haieff, Alexei	Rogers, Bernard
Bloch, Ernst	Hanson, Howard	Ruggles, Carl
Boulez, Pierre	Harris, Roy	Satie, Erik
Bowles, Paul	Hindemith, Paul	Schoenberg, Arnold
Brant, Henry	Hively, Wells	Schuman, William
Britten, Benjamin	Honnegger, Arthur	Scriabin, Alexander
Cage, John	Hovhaness, Alan	Sessions, Roger
Carter, Elliot	Ibert, Jacques	Shostakovich, Dmitri
Casella, Alfredo	Ives, Charles	Siegmeister, Elie
Cazden, Norman	Kay, Hershey	Sowerby, Leo
Chou-Wen, Chung	Khachaturian, Aram	Stravinsky, Igor
Copland, Aaron	Krenek, Ernst	Surinach, Carlos
Cowell, Henry	Lieberman, Rolf	Tansman, Alexander
Creston, Paul	Luening, Otto	Tcherepnin, Alexander
Debussy, Claude	McBride, Robert	Thomson, Virgil
Dello Joio, Norman	McDonald, Harl	Toch, Ernst
Diamond, David	Milhaud, Darius	Verese, Edgar
Fine, Irving	Mompou, Federico	Villa Lobos, Hector
Foss, Lukas	Moore, Douglas	Walton, William
Gershwin, George	Orff, Carl	Webern, Anton
Gillis, Don	Persichetti, Vincent	Williams, Ralph Vaughn

Recordings for Ballroom Dance

New popular music is constantly being produced that can be chosen appropriately for ballroom dance activities. The use of current favorites can create an impression of being up-to-the-minute

* Also available on tape.

in the mind of teen-age students. Nevertheless, many old standbys have certain timing and rhythmic qualities (depending upon the specific recording, of course) that make them especially satisfactory for ballroom dancing; among them are the following:

Cha Cha Cha:

La Dee Dah
Rockin' the Cha Cha
Tea for Two Cha Cha

Fox Trot

Amapola
Dancing in the Dark
Frenesi
How About You?
I May Be Wrong
In the Mood
Marie
Should I?
Side by Side
Star Dust
String of Pearls
Tea for Two

Lindy

China Boy
Dinah
Josephine
One o'Clock Jump
Opus No. 1
Sing, Sing, Sing
Sweet Georgia Brown
Tippin' In
When My Sugar Walks Down the Street

Mambo

Elmer's Tune Mambo
Fat Man Mambo
Mambo No. 5
Mambo Jambo
Mambo Riff

Rhumba:

Acerte Mas
Begin the Beguine
Besame Mucho
Frenesi
Green Eyes
My Shawl
Perfidia
Peanut Vendor
Querido
Siboney

Samba:

Brazil
Carioca
Caramba, it's the Samba!
Mama Quiero
Mañana
Samba Samba
Tico Tico

Tango

Adios, Muchachos
Blue Tango
El Choclo
Jalousie
La Comparsita
La Paloma
Midnight Tango
Orchids in the Moonlight

Waltz

Alice Blue Gown
Anniversary Waltz
Beautiful Ohio
Memories
Missouri Waltz
Naughty Waltz
Sleepy Lagoon
Three O'Clock in the Morning
Till We Meet Again
When I Grow Too Old to Dream
Wishing Well

Recordings for Folk Dance

Any list of recordings of available folk dance music is constantly having to be revised. Certain records become unavailable and new records are constantly being released. The two sources given below may be helpful to teachers in finding the records they need:

Folk Dance Federation of California Record List,
   Folk Dance Federation of California, San Francisco, California.
The Folk Dancer Catalog of Folk Dance Records and Books,
   Folk Dancer Record Service, Flushing, N.Y.

Some of the record companies that have released a large selection of good recordings for folk and square dance are the following:

Columbia
Decca
Folk Dancer
Folkraft
Imperial
Kismet
Kolo Festival

MacGregor
RCA Victor
Lloyd Shaw
Windsor
Methodist Publishing House (World
   of Fun)

Folk and square dance records may be ordered from the following companies if they are unavailable through local sources:

Folkraft Records, Newark, New Jersey.
Folk Dance House, New York, N.Y.
The Folk Dancers, Flushing, Long Island, N.Y.
The Folklore Center Inc., Seattle, Washington.
Sets in Order, Square Dance Square, Summerland, California.
Ed Kremers Record Shop, San Francisco, California.

Index